THE PHAGOCYTIC CELL IN HOST RESISTANCE

The Phagocytic Cell in Host Resistance

Edited by

Joseph A. Bellanti
Department of Pediatrics
Georgetown University Medical Center
Washington, D.C., U.S.A.

and

Delbert H. Dayton
Growth and Development Branch
National Institute of Child Health and Human Development
Bethesda, Maryland, U.S.A.

A Monograph of the National Institute of Child Health and Human Development
U.S. Department of Health, Education, and Welfare
Public Health Service
National Institutes of Health

Raven Press ■ New York

Made in the United States of America

International Standard Book Number 0–911216–90–1
Library of Congress Catalog Card Number 74–14147

ISBN outside North and South America only:
0–7204–7532–5

Program Planning Committee

Joseph A. Bellanti, M.D., Conference Co-Chairman
Department of Pediatrics
Georgetown University Medical Center
Washington, D.C.

Delbert H. Dayton, M.D., Conference Co-Chairman
Growth and Development Branch
National Institute of Child Health and Human Development
Bethesda, Maryland

Robert M. Blaese, M.D.
Metabolism Branch
National Cancer Institute
Bethesda, Maryland

Paul G. Quie, M.D.
Department of Pediatrics
University of Minnesota Hospital
Minneapolis, Minnesota

Peter A. Ward, M.D.
Department of Pathology
University of Connecticut Health Center
Farmington, Connecticut

Sheldon M. Wolff
Laboratory of Clinical Investigation
National Institute of Allergy and Infectious Diseases
Bethesda, Maryland

Preface

This work is intended for students of phagocytosis and clinicians concerned with the management of infections and disease entities involving defects in phagocytosis. Thus, it addresses those interested in the problem of host resistance to infections in its many aspects.

It sets forth the proceedings of the conference on *The Phagocytic Cell in Host Resistance* held in March 1974 at Winter Park, Florida, the seventh in a series on immunology, focusing on a developmental approach in exploring the human defense system. These conferences are sponsored by the National Institute of Child Health and Human Development.

A planning committee consisting of Drs. R. Blaese, P. Quie, P. Ward, and S. Wolff assisted us in establishing the excellent agenda for this meeting and worked hard before arriving at the final product. They deserve special thanks along with the participants who presented papers and enlivened the discussions with their thoughtful comments.

Recognition is also happily given to Ms. Christine Smith who contributed her organizational talents, typing skills, and assistance during the conference and the process of editing this material for publication. Ms. Christine Donnelly assisted in innumerable ways during the copyediting and proofreading by bringing the bibliographies up to date and persistently reviewing the material.

Joseph A. Bellanti
Delbert H. Dayton

Contents

List of Participants

Dr. Chester A. Alper
Department of Pediatrics
Children's Hospital Medical Center
Harvard Medical School
Boston, Massachusetts

Dr. Robert Baehner
Pediatric Oncology Division
Indiana University Medical Center
Indianapolis, Indiana

Dr. John Baum
Department of Medicine
University of Rochester School of Medicine
Rochester, New York

Dr. Elmer L. Becker
Department of Pathology
University of Connecticut Health Center
Farmington, Connecticut

Dr. Joseph A. Bellanti
Department of Pediatrics
Georgetown University Medical Center
Washington, D.C.

Dr. Michael Blaese
Metabolism Branch
National Cancer Institute
Bethesda, Maryland

Dr. Martin J. Cline
Departments of Medicine and Radiology
University of California San Francisco Medical Center
San Francisco, California

Dr. Zanvil A. Cohn
Rockefeller University
New York, New York

Dr. Delbert H. Dayton
Growth and Development Branch
National Institute of Child Health and Human Development
Bethesda, Maryland

Dr. John R. David
Department of Medicine
Robert B. Brigham Hospital
Harvard Medical School
Boston, Massachusetts

Dr. Michael M. Frank
Clinical Immunology Section
Laboratory of Clinical Investigation
National Institute of Allergy and Infectious Diseases
Bethesda, Maryland

Dr. John I. Gallin
Laboratory of Clinical Investigation
National Institute of Allergy and Infectious Diseases
Bethesda, Maryland

Dr. Harry R. Hill
Department of Pediatrics
University of Minnesota
Minneapolis, Minnesota

Dr. James G. Hirsch
Rockefeller University
New York, New York

Dr. Buelah Holmes-Gray
Department of Microbiology
University of Minnesota Medical School
Minneapolis, Minnesota

Dr. Richard B. Johnston, Jr.
Departments of Pediatrics and Microbiology
Department of Pediatrics
University of Alabama Medical Center
Birmingham, Alabama

Dr. Manfred L. Karnovsky
Department of Biological Chemistry
Harvard University Medical School
Boston, Massachusetts

Dr. Charles H. Kirkpatrick
Laboratory of Clinical Investigation
National Institute of Allergy and Infectious Diseases
Bethesda, Maryland

Dr. Seymour J. Klebanoff
Departments of Medicine and Microbiology
University of Washington
Seattle, Washington

Dr. Gerald L. Mandell
Department of Internal Medicine
University of Virginia School of Medicine
Charlottesville, Virginia

Dr. Michael E. Miller
Pediatric Research
Charles R. Drew Postgraduate Medical School
Los Angeles, California

Dr. Hans Müller-Eberhard
Department of Experimental Pathology
Scripps Clinic and Research Foundation
La Jolla, California

Dr. Byung H. Park
Department of Pediatrics
Harbor General Hospital
Torrance, California

Dr. Jacek Pietrzyk
Epidemiology Branch
National Institute of Child Health and Human Development
Bethesda, Maryland

Dr. Paul G. Quie
Department of Pediatrics
University of Minnesota Hospital
Minneapolis, Minnesota

Dr. Richard Root
Infectious Diseases Section
University of Pennsylvania
Philadelphia, Pennsylvania

Dr. Anthony J. Sbarra
Department of Pathology and Medical Research
St. Margaret's Hospital
Boston, Massachusetts

Dr. Ralph Snyderman
Departments of Medicine and Immunology
Duke University Medical Center
Durham, North Carolina

Dr. John K. Spitznagel
Departments of Bacteriology and Immunology
University of North Carolina School of Medicine
Chapel Hill, North Carolina

Dr. Thomas Stossel
Children's Hospital Medical Center
Boston, Massachusetts

Dr. Peter A. Ward
Department of Pathology
University of Connecticut
Farmington, Connecticut

Introduction

The long-intriguing phagocytic cell came into its own with the work of Metchnikoff a century ago. It was Metchnikoff who established that phagocytic cells serve a protective function, that they assist in resisting infection. This was in direct opposition to the current thought that the mobile phagocytes spread disease by circulating ingested organisms to other parts of the body.

Metchnikoff's work was contrary also to a belief that humoral factors played a greater role in natural resistance than cellular factors. In time, the vital importance of phagocytic cells for host resistance was recognized. Research is currently directed toward both the phagocytic cell and the humoral factors which together form a defense mechanism of great biological value. An appreciation of how this defense mechanism works is gradually being gained.

This publication describes the state of our understanding of the role of the phagocytic cell in host resistance. It testifies to a sophistication of research approach and a developing technology. It also testifies to the blind spots remaining and the concomitant research questions needing answers. The book was occasioned by a conference of leading scientists in both basic and clinical research. The current data were presented on chemotaxis and the phagocytic cell, endocytic events, biochemistry of phagocytic function, and bacteriocidal activity. The role of complement and the lymphokines was also considered to ensure coverage of the role of humoral factors in phagocytosis. One session was devoted to phagocytic defects to permit discussion of defined clinical entities, as well as the biochemical mechanisms involved and the current data on various chemotactic defects in both neutrophils and mononuclear leukocytes. Another session was devoted to maturational defects in leukocyte function, focusing on changes occurring during development in chemotaxis, macrophage antigen processing, and biochemistry of leukocytes.

This is the seventh in a series of publications released on developmental immunology by the National Institute of Child Health and Human Development to investigate the developmental events throughout the lifespan that contribute to effective host resistance. The effort continues to embrace a holistic approach to the development of immunologic competence to facilitate understanding of the totality of the mechanisms involved as well as time-dependent processes.

Delbert H. Dayton
Bethesda, Maryland

The Phagocytic Cell in Host Resistance, edited by Joseph A. Bellanti and Delbert H. Dayton. Raven Press, New York © 1975.

Enzyme Activation and the Mechanism of Polymorphonuclear Leukocyte Chemotaxis

Elmer L. Becker

Department of Pathology, University of Connecticut Health Center, Farmington, Connecticut 06032

There is general, although not universal agreement, that chemotaxis is a major, if not the major, mechanism by which polymorphonuclear leukocytes and other phagocytic cells are induced to move to the site of infection and thus function in host resistance. In addition, phagocytosis, chemotaxis, and lysosomal enzyme secretion are all manifestations of cell movement: either the movement of the whole cell, as in chemotaxis; movement of a part of the cell membrane and contiguous structures, as in phagocytosis; or the movement of an intracellular organelle from the interior of the cell to either a phagocytic vesicle or the plasma membrane, as in lysosomal enzyme secretion. There are numerous similarities as well as some differences in the mechanisms underlying these diverse functions of the leukocyte (reviewed in ref. 1), so that a consideration of the mechanism of one might be expected to throw light on the mechanisms of the others.

In what follows I shall review the present fragmentary state of our knowledge of the biochemistry of chemotaxis of the polymorphonuclear leukocyte, first paying particular attention to the involvement of the activation of a proesterase, proesterase 1, in the chemotactic process. Then I shall proceed to a very brief and incomplete overview of our knowledge of the other processes involved in the chemotactic response of these cells. (For a more complete review see refs. 1 and 2.) Finally, I shall present a rather diffident general hypothesis of the genesis of the chemotactic process in the polymorphonuclear leukocyte with some heretofore unpublished results of experiments suggested by this theory.

ACTIVATION OF PROESTERASE 1

Di-isopropyl phosphofluoridate and *p*-nitrophenyl ethyl phosphonates are relatively specific irreversible inactivators of a group of enzymes, the so-called serine esterases (serine esterases because they have serine in their active site). These organophosphorous inhibitors depress the chemotactic response of rabbit peritoneal neutrophils if they are present while the neutrophil is being acted upon by the chemotactic agent but not if they are used to pretreat the neutrophil or the chemotactic factor separately. This suggested that the chemotactic response involved the activation of a so-called "activatable esterase" which before contact of the cell with chemotactic factor existed in an enzymatically inert, phosphonate insusceptible form (3). The various series of *p*-nitrophenyl ethyl phosphonates yield structure-activity relationships, "inhibition profiles" which are characteristic of and serve to identify various serine esterases (4). The inhibition of the chemotactic response by the *p*-nitrophenyl ethyl phosphonates shows characteristic and specific inhibition profiles (3).

Leukocytes incubated with one of the complement-derived chemotactic factors C3a, C5a, or $C\overline{567}$ progressively lose their ability to respond chemotactically to any of the chemotactic factors (5, 6). They are desensitized or as we termed it "deactivated." The deactivation is prevented by the same phosphonates that inhibit chemotaxis and the inhibition profiles are the same for the two processes (5). This indicated that the same activatable esterase is involved in both chemotaxis and deactivation. However, not only phosphonate esters prevent deactivation and chemotaxis; aromatic amino acid derivatives rather specifically do the same. This suggested the hypothesis that the activatable esterase is the precursor of an esterase capable of hydrolyzing aromatic amino acid esters (5). The rabbit polymorphonuclear leukocyte was found to contain an enzyme, esterase 1, which hydrolyzed the aromatic amino acid ester acetyl DL phenylalanine β naphthyl ester, previously used as a substrate for chymotrypsin (7). When the *p*-nitrophenyl ethyl phosphonates were used to inactivate esterase 1, the enzyme gave the same inhibition profiles as found for the activatable esterase in both the inhibition of chemotaxis and the prevention of deactivation. From this, we concluded that esterase 1 was the activated form of the activatable esterase of chemotaxis (7). Esterase 1 is also found in an enzymatically inert, phosphonate insusceptible form which we termed proesterase 1 (8). When the chemotactic factors interact with the polymorphonuclear leukocyte, proesterase 1 is transformed into esterase 1, fully capable of being inhibited by the phosphonate esters and of hydrolyzing acetyl DL phenylalanine β naphthyl ester (8, 9). From this we concluded that proesterase 1 is the activatable esterase of chemotaxis (8).

Both the complement-derived factors $C\overline{567}$, C3a, C5a and a bacterial chemotactic factor activate proesterase 1, although with differing degrees of effectiveness (8, 9). Moreover, there is evidence suggesting that under several different circumstances the level of chemotactic activity attained is related to the degree of activation of proesterase 1 (9).

More recently, I have used the phosphonates to study whether activation of proesterase 1 is involved in the spontaneous motility of the rabbit polymorphonuclear leukocytes. The spontaneous motility of the leukocytes was measured as described previously (9). The rabbit peritoneal polymorphonuclear leukocytes were suspended in Hank's buffer in the top compartment of the modified Boyden chemotaxis chamber and Hank's buffer was placed in the bottom compartment. A 5-μm filter separated the two compartments. The chamber was incubated for 90 min at 37°C (rather than 3 hr as previously described) before counting the number of cells in 5 high-power fields (5 HPF) that penetrated the filter below the upper monolayer. The inhibition profiles were obtained by incubating the *p*-nitrophenyl ethyl alkylphosphonates and the *p*-nitrophenyl ethyl chloroalkylphosphonates with the cells at a final concentration of 0.33 mM. The inhibition profiles so obtained (Fig. 1) are the same as those found for the so-called chemotactic factor dependent inhibition of chemotaxis, for the prevention of deactivation, and for esterase 1. This suggests that the activation of proesterase 1 is also involved in the spontaneous motility of the leukocyte (see below).

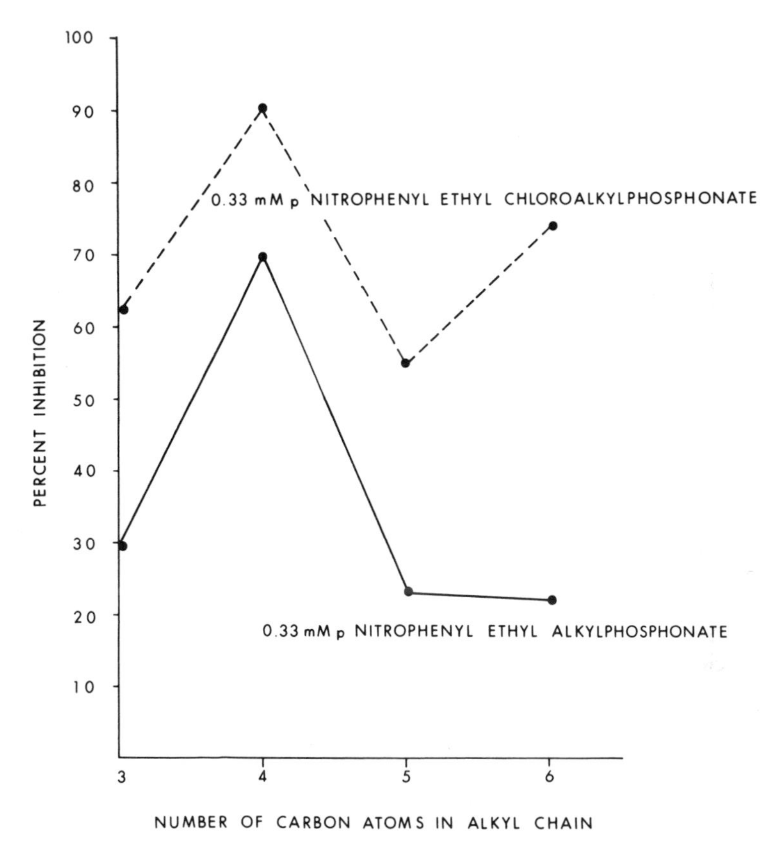

FIG. 1. The profiles of inhibition of spontaneous motility employing the *p*-nitrophenyl ethyl chloroalkylphosphonates and *p*-nitrophenyl ethyl alkylphosphonates.

Very little is known about the properties of proesterase 1. Its activation by C5a does not require divalent cations, implying that the step(s) dependent on divalent cations come after the proesterase activation (10). Dr. Peter Henson and I, on the basis of unpublished work, have estimated that there are at least 500 proesterase 1 molecules per rabbit blood polymorphonuclear leukocyte. We obtained this estimate using radioactively labeled DFP. In this study we first reacted the leukocytes with cold DFP to inactivate all the serine esterases present in an active form, washed the cells thoroughly, activated the proesterase with C5a, and then treated the cells with radio-labeled DFP. The amount of label taken up over and above that of control cells reacted with C5 was our measure of specific uptake attributable to the proesterase 1 that had been activated by C5a. The results are very preliminary and much more work has to be done, but I believe it does give us an order of magnitude as to the number of proesterase 1 molecules/cell.

We know little about the nature of esterase 1 and nothing concerning its function in the leukocyte. Esterase 1 is found predominately in the microsomal fraction of the neutrophil (unpublished work and 11). Efforts to isolate esterase 1 from the neutrophil have met with great difficulty and little success. This is in part due to the relatively small amount in the cell and its instability and ready breakdown, presumably by the proteolytic enzymes of the cell. When first isolated from cells lysed with Triton X-100, the enzyme has a molecular weight somewhat greater than 150,000. When acted upon by enzymes found in the cell, the activity becomes associated with a fraction of a molecular weight of 40,000 to 60,000.

OTHER ASPECTS OF THE MECHANISMS OF NEUTROPHIL CHEMOTAXIS

Ca^{2+} and Mg^{2+} are both required in the external medium for maximal chemotactic response (12, 13). Maximal spontaneous motility can be attained in the absence of Ca^{2+} by sufficiently increasing the concentration of Mg^{2+} alone, although Ca^{2+} reduces the concentration of Mg^{2+} required (9). However, the reverse is not true: increasing the concentration of Ca^{2+} in the absence of Mg^{2+} does not induce maximal spontaneous motility. Gallin and Rosenthal (13) showed that C5a enhances the efflux of $^{45}Ca^{2+}$ from the cell and it was the efflux which correlated with chemotactic responsiveness. Increasing the K^+ of the medium increases the chemotactic responsiveness; ouabain inhibits chemotaxis, the inhibition being reversed by K^+ (14).

The action of various inhibitors suggests that, as with phagocytosis or lysosomal enzyme secretion, anaerobic glycolysis is the major if not sole source of energy involved in cell motility and chemotaxis (reviewed in 1 and 2). Agents which increase intracellular cyclic AMP levels inhibit the motility of rabbit polymorphonuclear leukocytes and thus depress their chemotactic responsiveness (15). However, neither a bacterial chemotactic factor nor C5a has any effect on the intracellular concentrations of cyclic AMP suggesting that changes in the adenyl cyclase activity of the cell may modulate its motility and thus its chemotactic responsiveness but that adenyl cyclase is not itself a part of the direct biochemical sequence involved in chemotaxis or cell motility (15).

In contrast to β adrenergic agents that stimulate adenyl cyclase causing inhibition of cell motility and chemotaxis (15), cholinergic agents, such as acetylcholine, carbachol, or phorbal myristate acetate, that increase cellular cyclic 3′5′-guanosine monophosphate (cyclic GMP) enhance chemotactic activity (16). The chemotactic enhancement by acetylcholine and carbachol is inhibited by atropine. The effect of the cholinergic agents on spontaneous cell motility was not directly tested. The results, however, were considered as supporting the hypothesis that cyclic GMP promotes cellular events that are antagonistic to those considered to be mediated by cyclic AMP.

I have previously postulated that chemotaxis involves the contractile mechanism of the polymorphonuclear leukocyte (1, 17, 18). The microtubular disaggregating agents, colchicine (19, 20) and vincristine and vinblastine (18) at sufficiently high concentrations (10^{-4}M to 10^{-5}M), inhibit chemotaxis. At subinhibitory concentrations, and with the appropriate level of chemotactic stimulus, these same agents actually enhance chemotaxis and cell motility (21). Cytochalasin B, which is reported to depress microfilament function, reversibly inhibits chemotaxis and spontaneous motility at concentrations of 1 μg and above (22). However, below this level, cytochalasin B enhances the chemotactic response (22). In addition to these paradoxical findings there is accumulating evidence that the microtubular disaggregating agents as well as cytochalasin B have more than one mode of action (1). These findings indicate that more direct evidence than from the use of these inhibitors is necessary to demonstrate the involvement of the contractile elements of the cell.

Actomyosin-like proteins have been isolated from both horse (23) and guinea pig (24) neutrophils. Szent-Gyorgi more than 20 years ago demonstrated that muscle fibers extracted with glycerol contract on the addition of ATP. The ATP-induced contraction of glycerinated cells has been used as evidence for a contractile mechanism being present in a variety of isolated nonmuscle cells. Recently, we have shown that glycerinated rabbit neutrophils when exposed to ATP contract as observed microscopically and also decrease their volume (25). The characteristics of this ATP-induced decrease in volume strengthen the evidence that there exists in neutrophils a contractile system similar to actomyosin. However, the ATP-induced contraction of glycerinated cells does not correlate with the chemotactic responsiveness of the corresponding nonglycerinated cells (26). In fact, chemotactic factors induce an expansion of the volume of nonglycerinated cells (26, 27) and it is this which correlates with their chemotactic responsiveness (25). Thus, more direct and unequivocal evidence of the involvement of the contractile machinery of the cell in motility or any of the other functions of the neutrophil is still required.

AN HYPOTHESIS AS TO THE MECHANISM OF CHEMOTAXIS

Obviously, from the bits and pieces of information available to us, no detailed picture of the molecular mechanism of chemotaxis is possible. The best we can hope for is a generalized and tentative conceptual scheme which will serve as a framework for our present knowledge and a springboard for future experiment. (It should not pass unobserved that a framework may well prove to be a rather shaky springboard.)

Chemotaxis is cell movement directed along and by a gradient of chemical substance, i.e., the chemotactic factor. In this scheme I postulate that one or more molecules of chemotactic factor interact with some sort of receptor site or sites on the cell, resulting in activation of proesterase 1 to esterase 1. Esterase 1 in turn, probably by proteolytic action, although this is not material in the present context, triggers a complex series of reactions, the end result of which is movement of the neutrophil. The movement is in the direction of chemotactic factor and receptor site interaction and, in moving, fresh receptor(s) is exposed to chemotactic factor and more proesterase 1 is activated, triggering further movement. The net effect is a tendency of the cell to move in the direction of increasing concentrations of the chemotactic factor, that is, along the concentration gradient. However, the activating effect of the chemotactic factor in this scheme is not sufficient in itself to ensure movement along the concentration gradient. It is also required that once the stimulus has acted, the proesterase has been activated, and the subsequent events have been triggered that the site(s) will no longer be capable of being further fired off; it will be deactivated. Thus, the movement engendered by the chemotactic factor(s) acting at *a given site or set of sites* is self terminating and within the time scale in which the chemotactic response occurs is nonrenewable. This ensures that the direction of movement stimulated at one site (or set of sites) will not interfere with the direction of movement stimulated at subsequently reacting site(s).

According to this hypothesis, in the neutrophil, the events occurring in chemotaxis are essentially the same as those responsible for spontaneous cell movement; both are believed to be triggered by the activation of proesterase 1 (see Fig. 1). However, they differ in that the spontaneous movement of the cell is induced by either the spontaneous random activation of proesterase 1 or the activation of proesterase 1 by substances in the medium occurring without a concentration gradient. However, this theory does not preclude, and in fact envisages, that cell migration can occur if the reaction scheme is entered into subsequent to proesterase 1 activation or for that matter at a step or steps bypassing not only the activation step but the step or steps associated with deactivation (assuming the activation and deactivation steps are separable). Some of the implications of this putative ability to bypass the steps associated with deactivation will be dealt with below. In addition, this theory does not take into account the effects of substances released by the cells themselves (30), although this latter effect should be easily accommodated into the theory.

It is obvious from what I have just reviewed that the precise reactions triggered by the activation of proesterase 1 or their sequence is unknown. These reactions apparently involve divalent cations and energy source, and, in addition, one can visualize an ordered and compartmentalized activation and relaxation of the contractile mechanisms of the cell.

This generalized and indefinite scheme has certain implications: one of the first implications is that chemotactic agents should stimulate cell locomotion. Several studies have suggested that rates of movement, in fact, are not altered by a chemotactic stimulus (28, 29). However, as Zigmond and Hirsch (30) observed, in some of these studies the conditions were such that a possible stimulation of movement could have been masked. They considered in their investigation that some materials that stimulated chemotaxis also stimulated movement. Moreover, Keller and Sorkin (31) showed that cells incubated in the presence of a chemotactic agent increased their random motility.

Although the theory suggests that chemotactic agents increase cell movement, the theory also implies that not all agents that increase cell locomotion are chemotactic. This latter arises from the postulated necessity that a chemotactic agent not only triggers increased movement but that it also be capable of deactivating the sites at which it acts. Thus, substances that can stimulate movement by acting at a step or steps beyond the putative deactivating sequence would not be expected to be chemotactic.

Based on this last idea, and on the idea that, as in muscle, intracellular release of Ca^{2+} activates contraction in the leukocyte and thus presumably acts late in the sequence, I have studied the effects of the ionophore A23187 on spontaneous mobility and also tested it for its ability to serve as a chemotactic factor. A23187 is an antibiotic capable of transporting Ca^{2+} and, somewhat less effectively, Mg^{2+} into cells and isolated organelles such as mitochondria and inducing a release of their sequestered Ca^{2+} (32, 33).

THE ACTION OF A23187 ON THE MOVEMENT OF NEUTROPHILS

The first series of experiments was carried out using Hank's buffer containing the usual 1.7 mM Ca^{2+} and 0.7 mM Mg^{2+}. The techniques for measuring chemotaxis and spontaneous motility were as previously described (2, 9). Briefly, A23187 was tested for its effect on spontaneous motility by placing varying concentrations of the ionophore in the upper compartment with the cells and using only buffer in the lower compartment of the chemotaxis chamber with a filter of 5 or 8 μm average pore size separating the two compartments (10). When A23187 was tested for its possible chemotactic activity, it was placed in the bottom compartment of the chamber separated by a filter of 0.65 μm pore size from the cells in the upper chamber (3).

As seen in Table 1, the only effect of the ionophore was a pronounced inhibition of spontaneous movement at concentrations of 10^{-5} and 10^{-6} M. It had no chemotactic activity. I hypothesized that the reason for the inhibition of spontaneous motility was that in the presence of external Ca^{2+} the A23187 brought so much Ca^{2+} into the cell that the cell went into Ca^{2+} "rigor." In other words, the presence of a high concentration of unbound intracellular Ca^{2+} brought in by the ionophore led to a generalized activation of the contractile mechanism of the cell. Consonant with this interpretation was the microscopic observation that cells treated with concentrations of ionophore that inhibited spontaneous motility did not spread or spread incompletely and slowly on a microscope slide.

On this basis, the experiments were repeated using Hank's buffer containing no Ca^{2+} with the idea that the putative high influx of Ca^{2+} would be avoided and in its place there would be an intracellular influx of Mg^{2+}. Alternatively there could be an intracellular influx of A23187 alone. The Mg^{2+} (or A23187) could

TABLE 1. *Effect of A23187 on spontaneous movement and as a chemotactic agent in Hank's buffer (containing the usual 1.7 mM Ca^{2+} and 0.7 mM Mg^{2+}*

Concentration of A23187 (M)	Spontaneous motility [a] (cells/5 HPF)	Chemotaxis [b] (cells/5 HPF)
0	396	50
10^{-7}	438	79
10^{-6}	216	35
10^{-5}	180	50

[a] A23187 placed with 2 X 10^6 PMN's in upper compartment and Hank's buffer present in the lower compartment of chamber. Incubated for 1½ hr at 37°C. A Millipore filter of 8 μm pore size separated the upper and lower compartment (9).
[b] A23187 placed in lower compartment and 2 X 10^6 PMN's in upper compartment. Incubated for 1½ hr at 37°C. A Millipore filter of 0.65 μm pore size separated the lower from upper compartment (2).

then serve to free the sequestered intracellular Ca^{2+} with, as postulated above, an ordered compartmentalized activation and a corresponding relaxation of the contractile mechanisms of the cell and, thus, an enhancement of cellular movement. If, as indicated above, the effect of divalent cations is late in the sequence, one would expect their site(s) of action to be beyond the deactivation step or steps. Thus, the prediction followed that, in the absence of Ca^{2+}, A23187 should enhance spontaneous motility but not be chemotactic.

Table 2 shows that in a Mg^{2+}-containing, Ca^{2+}-free medium, concentrations of A23187 from 10^{-7} to 10^{-5} M progressively increased spontaneous motility to the level achieved in the presence of 1.7 mM added Ca^{2+}. Despite this distinct enhancing activity, it was not chemotactic.

I also tested the effect of the ionophore on chemotaxis induced by partially purified bacterial chemotactic factor. As expected, in the regular Hank's buffer containing Ca^{2+} and Mg^{2+}, 10^{-5} M ionophore in the upper compartment depressed chemotaxis, presumably through its inhibition of spontaneous motility. In Ca^{2+}-free Hank's buffer containing 0.7 mM Mg^{2+}, utilizing a maximal chemotactic stimulus (1 : 5,000 dilution), 10^{-7}M A23187 gave significant inhibition of chemotaxis. This increased progressively with the concentration of ionophore until at 10^{-5}M A23187 chemotaxis was inhibited more than 60%. However, at a 1 : 20,000 dilution of bacterial factor, giving approximately 20% of the chemotactic activity found with the 1 : 5,000 dilution, the effect of the ionophore varied with its concentration. At 10^{-7} and 10^{-6} M ionophore there was a significant enhancement of chemotactic activity, corresponding to the enhancement of spontaneous motility, but at 10^{-5} M A23187 the chemotactic activity was essentially the same as that of the control without ionophore. The decrease in chemotactic activity at the highest concentration of ionophore was reproducible. Its significance is obscure but suggests some form of interaction between the changes in distribution

TABLE 2. *Effect of A23187 on spontaneous movement and as a chemotactic agent in Ca^{2+}-free Hank's buffer with 0.7 mM Mg^{2+}*

Concentration of A23187 (M)	Spontaneous motility [a] (cells/5 HPF ± SE)	Chemotaxis [b] (cells/5 HPF)
0	302 ± 2	48
10^{-7}	341 ± 9	11
5×10^{-7}	418 ± 22	2
10^{-6}	431 ± 5	17
5×10^{-6}	456 ± 6	20
10^{-5}	466 ± 14	8
1.7 mM Ca^{2+}	452 ± 28	82

[a] A23187 placed with 2×10^6 PMN's in the upper compartment of chamber with Hank's buffer with no Ca^{2+} and 0.7 mM Mg^{2+} in lower compartment. Incubated for 1½ hr at 37°C. A Millipore filter of 5 μm pore size separated upper and lower compartment.
[b] A23187 placed in the lower compartment and 2×10^6 PMN's in upper compartment with Hank's buffer with no Ca^{2+} and 0.7 mM Mg. Incubated for 1½ hr at 37°C. A Millipore filter of 0.65 μm pore size separated lower from upper compartment.

of intracellular cation brought about by the chemotactic factor (13) and those presumably induced by the ionophore.

These experiments obviously have to be extended and, particularly, the shifts in intracellular cation must be directly measured. Nevertheless, they do demonstrate the primary thesis, that an agent can increase cellular locomotion without being chemotactic

SUMMARY

Chemotaxis of polymorphonuclear leukocytes involves a multistep, probably multibranched, sequence of reactions. These reactions require the activation of a proesterase by the chemotactic factor, a source of metabolic energy obtained mainly or wholly through anaerobic glycolysis, the presence of Ca^{2+} and Mg^{2+} in the external medium, and probably the activation of the contractile machinery of the cell.

I suggest that chemotaxis occurs through the activation of proesterase and the triggering of subsequent reactions, resulting in movement of the cell in the direction of the site(s) at which the proesterase was activated. Subsequent deactivation of the site ensures that movement triggered at a given site or sites is self terminating and nonrenewable. The same sort of mechanism triggered by the spontaneous and random activation of proesterase is envisaged as the trigger for spontaneous movement as well.

Among the consequences of this hypothesis is that chemotactic agents increase cell locomotion but not all agents increasing cell locomotion are chemotactic. The latter prediction was born out by the behavior of the ionophore A23187.

ACKNOWLEDGMENT

The work of this laboratory was supported by U.S. Public Health Service Grant No. A1–09648 from the National Institute of Allergy and Infectious Disease.

REFERENCES

1. Becker, E. L., and Henson, P. M.: *In vitro* studies of immunologically induced secretion of mediators from cells and related phenomena. *Adv. Immunol.* 17:93–193, 1973.
2. Wilkinson, P. C.: *Chemotaxis and Inflammation.* Churchill Livingstone, Edinburgh, 1974.
3. Ward, P. A., and Becker, E. L.: Mechanism of inhibition of chemotaxis by phosphonate esters. *J. Exp. Med.* 125:1001–1020, 1967.
4. Becker, E. L.: Nature and significance of antigen-antibody activated esterases. In Austen, K. F., and Becker, E. L. (eds): *Biochemistry of the Acute Allergic Reactions.* Blackwell, Oxford, pp. 199–213. 1968.
5. Ward, P. A., and Becker, E. L.: The deactivation of rabbit neutrophils by chemotactic factor and the nature of the activatable esterase. *J. Exp. Med.* 127:693–710, 1968.
6. Ward, P. A.: Complement-derived chemotactic factors and their interaction with neutrophilic granulocytes. In Ingraham, D. G. (ed.): *Proceedings of the International Symposium on the Biological Activities of Complement.* Karger, Basel, pp. 108–116. 1971.
7. Becker, E. L., and Ward, P. A.: Esterases of the polymorphonuclear leukocyte capable of hydrolyzing acetyl DL phenylalanine β naphthyl ester. Relationship to the activatable esterase of chemotaxis. *J. Exp. Med.* 129:569–589, 1969.
8. Ward, P. A., and Becker, E. L.: Biochemical demonstration of the activatable esterase of the rabbit neutrophil involved in the chemotactic response. *J. Immunol.* 105:1057–1067, 1970.
9. Becker, E. L.: The relationship of the chemotactic behavior of the complement derived factors C3a, C5a and $\overline{C567}$, and a bacterial chemotactic factor to their ability to activate the proesterase 1 of rabbit polymorphonuclear leukocytes. *J. Exp. Med.* 135:376–387, 1972.
10. Becker, E. L.: Enzyme activation and the mechanism of neutrophil chemotaxis. In Sorkin, E. (ed.): *Antibiot. Chemother.* 19:409–420, 1974.
11. Davies, P., Krakauer, K., and Weissmann, G.: Subcellular distribution of neutral proteases and peptidases in rabbit polymorphonuclear leukocytes. *Nature* 228:761–762, 1970.
12. Becker, E. L., and Showell, H. J.: Effects of Ca^{2+} and Mg^{2+} on the chemotactic responsiveness of rabbit polymorphonuclear leukocytes. *Z. Immunitaetsforsch.* 143:466–476, 1972.
13. Gallin, J. I., and Rosenthal, A. S.: Divalent cation requirements and calcium fluxes during human granulocyte chemotaxis. *Fed. Proc.* 32:819, 1973.
14. Ward, P. A., and Becker, E. L.: Potassium reversible inhibition of leukotaxis by ouabain. *Life Sci.* Part 2, 9:335–360, 1970.
15. Rivkin, I.: The possible role of cyclic AMP in the regulation of rabbit peritoneal neutrophil chemotaxis. Ph.D. Thesis. University of Connecticut, Storrs. 1973.
16. Estenson, R. D., Hill, H. R., Quie, P. G., Hogan, N., and Goldberg, N. D.: Cyclic GMP and cell movement. *Nature* 245:458–460, 1973.
17. Becker, E. L.: Phosphonate inhibition of the accumulation and retention of K^+ by rabbit neutrophils in relation to chemotaxis. *J. Immunol.* 106:689–697, 1971.
18. Becker, E. L.: Biochemical aspects of the polymorphonuclear response to chemotactic factors. In Austen, K. F., and Becker, E. L. (eds): *Biochemistry of the Acute Allergic Reactions. Second International Symposium.* Blackwell, Oxford, pp. 243–252. 1973.
19. Caner, J. E. Z.: Colchicine inhibition of chemotactic migration of human polymorphonuclear leukocytes. *Arthritis Rheum.* 7:297–302, 1964.
20. Ward, P. A.: Leukotactic factors in health and disease. *Am. J. Pathol.* 64:521–530, 1971.
21. Becker, E. L., and Showell, H. J.: The ability of chemotactic factors to induce lysosomal enzyme release II. The mechanism of release. *J. Immunol.* 112:2055, 1974.
22. Becker, E. L., Davis, A. T., Estenson, R. D., and Quie, P. G.: Cytochalasin B IV. Inhibition and stimulation of chemotaxis of rabbit and human polymorphonuclear leukocytes. *J. Immunol.* 108:396–402, 1972.

23. Senda, N., Shibata, N., Tatsumi, N., Kondo, K., and Hamada, K.: A contractile protein from leukocytes. Its extraction and some of its properties. *Biophys. Acta* 181:191–195, 1969.
24. Stossel, T. P., and Pollard, T. D.: Myosin in polymorphonuclear leukocytes. *J. Biol. Chem.* 218:8288–8294, 1973.
25. Hsu, L. S., Becker, E. L., and Weisel, A.: Contraction and lysosomal enzyme release induced by ATP in rabbit polymorphonuclear leukocytes (PMNs) treated with glycerol. *Fed. Proc.* 32:820, 1973.
26. Showell, H., Hsu, L. S., and Becker, E. L.: Chemotaxis, lysosomal enzyme release and volume expansion of rabbit polymorphonuclear leukocytes (PMN) induced by chemotactic factors. *Fed. Proc.* 32:973, 1973.
27. Hsu, L., and Becker, E. L.: Expansion and contraction of the cell volume of rabbit peritoneal neutrophils (PMN) induced by chemotactic factor in the presence and absence of cytochalasin B. *Fed. Proc. (in press).*
28. McCutcheon, M.: Chemotaxis in leukocytes. *Physiol. Rev.* 26:319–343, 1946.
29. Ramsey, W. S.: Analysis of individual leukocyte behavior during chemotaxis. *Exp. Cell Res.* 70:129–139, 1972.
30. Zigmond, S. H., and Hirsch, J. G.: Leukocyte locomotion and chemotaxis. New method for evaluation and demonstration of cell-derived chemotactic factor. *J. Exp. Med.* 137:387–410, 1973.
31. Keller, H. U., and Sorkin, E.: Studies in chemotaxis. IV. The influence of serum factors on granulocyte locomotion. *Immunology* 10:409–416, 1966.
32. Scarpa, A., Baldassare, J., and Inesi, G.: The effect of calcium ionophores on fragmented sarcoplasmic reticulum. *J. Gen Physiol.* 60:735–747, 1972.
33. Foreman, J. C., and Mongar, J. L., and Gomperts, B. D.: Calcium ionophores and movement of calcium ions following the physiological stimulus to a secretory process. *Nature* 245:249–251, 1973.

DISCUSSION

Snyderman: If I understand your hypothesis correctly you imply that, if the chemotactic factor hits a receptor site, you have an activation of proesterase, but essentially you describe a stable reaction on a point in the membrane. The way I visualize chemotaxis is by thinking of a fluid membrane with receptors actually moving toward the back of the cell as you will see if you look in phase-contrast microscopy. What are your thoughts on cell motility and the capping phenomenon?

Becker: I have no thoughts, or certainly no direct evidence, in regard to capping and cell movements in the neutrophil. But I know Emil Unanue et al. have very clear evidence that the capping phenomenon is not related to cell movement in the lymphocyte (*J. Exp. Med.* 139:295, 1974). On that basis, I would be willing to think that the capping phenomenon might not be related to the movement of the polymorphonuclear leukocytes either.

Cohn: Could you give us some idea of the location of this esterase?

Becker: We have no evidence as to the location of the proesterase although I think it is on the cell membrane. The DFP experiments that I mentioned, which are continuing with Peter Henson, will hopefully provide just such evidence. In corroboration of the work of Davies and Weissman et al., we find esterase 1 in the microsomal fraction. This is quite a heterogeneous fraction so we don't know what that means.

Cohn: How many esterases are we dealing with in terms of substrate specificity or separation on gels?

Becker: We have no direct evidence on this. We have some suggestive evidence, very minimal, very preliminary, that there is an esterase involved in lysosomal enzyme secretion, and this might differ from the esterase that is involved in the chemotactic response. We also have some tenuous evidence that there is an esterase involved in the erythrophagocytosis. We have already reported on this with Dave Pearlman and Pete Ward. And again there is a suggestion, but no more, that the esterase involved is different from the esterase of chemotaxis. But this is, I think, an extremely important point, and it is a point that we are starting to go back to to reinvestigate or investigate more thoroughly. I really can't answer at this time.

Spitznagel: Do you know whether this esterase on the cell surface might be related to *p*-nitrophenyl ethyl phosphatase?

Becker: No, but we are in the process of finding this out because we are studying, in another connection, this *p*-nitrophenyl ethyl phosphatase on the cell surface.

Hill: We have worked with the ionophore also and have tried to produce a chemotactic factor with it, but it has not been chemotactic under any circumstances. However, we found it does significantly enhance chemotaxis to the bacterial factor.

Becker: By varying the concentration of bacterial factor of the ionophore, the chemotactic activity of the cells is affected. The chemotactic factor at a 1-to-5,000 dilution gave a maximum chemotactic response; at a 1-to-20,000 dilution it gave distinctly less than a maximum response. When the chemotactic factor gave maximal stimulation, we got just inhibition of the chemotactic activity at all concentrations of ionophore. However, at less than maximal chemotactic stimulation, the chemotactic activity showed an increase at lower concentrations of ionophore, and then with higher concentrations of ionophore we obtained a decrease in chemotactic activity.

Stossel: In regard to experiments in which you occasionally see activity in the absence of divalent ions, have you ever seen this after washing the cells with EDTA, the idea being that the cells have many binding sites for calcium?

Becker: When we found these variable results, we did this. It was driving us crazy and it didn't make any difference. Those cells that were responsive to calcium and magnesium were still responsive after washing with EDTA.

Gallin: Regarding the last question, we found inhibition of chemotaxis with greater than 5 millimolar EDTA. However, from 0.5 to 1.0 millimolar EDTA, our results have been variable and we frequently get enhancement (Patten, E., Gallin, J. I., Clark, R. A., and Kimball, H. R.: Effects of cell concentration and various anticoagulants on neutrophil migration. *Blood* 41:711, 1973). Have you had similar observations?

Becker: We used either 1 millimolar EDTA or 5 millimolar EDTA and found inhibition in both instances, but have not varied the concentration of EDTA beyond those limits, up or down (*Z. Immunitaetsforsch.* 143:466, 1972).

Gallin: Have you varied the calcium concentration?

Becker: When we used EDTA, we employed no calcium or magnesium.

Gallin: Our experiments are in the presence of calcium.

Becker: We have also used magnesium EDTA and magnesium EGTA, and could show that with magnesium EGTA we got somewhat higher levels of responsiveness than we did with EDTA itself, but this was distinctly less than when we had both calcium and magnesium present.

Gallin: Our studies have suggested that a lowering of cytoplasmic calcium may be associated with the chemotactic response (Gallin, J. I., and Rosenthal, A. S.: Regulatory role of divalent cations in human granulocyte chemotaxis: Evidence for the association of calcium efflux with microtubule assembly. *J. Cell Biol., in press*). I gather from your theory of chemotaxis that you believe cellular contractile elements, which presumably are required for cell locomotion, may depend on the availability of ionized calcium for proper function and that the mobilization of calcium from intracellular compartments, such as mitochondria, may be essential for a normal response. I would like to extend these speculations and suggest that possibly two calcium regulated events may be associated with normal directed locomotion. A membrane associated microfilament system, which may contain actin-myosin like proteins may be associated with membrane ruffling and random locomotion; this system presumably is calcium dependent. In addition, the net vector of locomotion established during chemotaxis may be related to the polarized assembly of other cytoplasmic proteins (microtubules), as previously suggested by Allison et al. (Allison, A. C., Davies, P., and DePetris, S.: Role of contractile microfilaments in macrophage movement and endocytosis. *Nature New Biol.* 232:153, 1971). The *in vitro* assembly of isolated microtubules is regulated in part by ionized calcium with calcium inhibiting such assembly. Thus, if the microtubule system is required for a normal chemotactic response, one would predict that a lowered cytoplasmic calcium (which we have observed) would occur during chemotactic factor-neutrophil interaction. Associated with a decrease in cytoplasmic calcium might be increases in cytoplasmic-membrane calcium essential for microfilament function. Would you concur with the idea that such intracellular shifts of calcium may be necessary for a chemotactic response?

Becker: Certainly. I will join you in that speculation. With regard to relaxation and its relation to chemotactic response, we have been studying it as it occurs under a variety of circumstances. We started the work using the glycerinated cell model originally introduced by Szent-Gygörgi with muscle fibers in which he showed that, if he glycerinated his muscle fiber and added magnesium ATP, he got a contraction. This was taken up by Hoffman-Berling and others to show that this contraction occurred with a variety of nonmuscle cells, and recently we have been able to show the same with the polymorphonuclear leukocyte. What one obtains is not only a microscopically observable contraction, which is what others have demonstrated, but one can show, using the Coulter counter, that there is an actual decrease in volume under these circumstances, and that this decrease in volume is calcium-dependent as well as ATP-dependent. This has also led us to study volume changes under a variety of conditions, and we have shown that using nonglycerinated cells the chemotactic factors don't contract the volume of the cells; they actually expand it. This is an active process requiring energy apparently, but it does not require divalent cations. It appears to be a process that occurs before the cation-requiring steps in the cell. In addition and most importantly, this volume increase correlates with the chemotactic responsiveness of the cells. What we did here was to take cells from 16 rabbits and measure their volume expansion. We measured the ability of these cells to expand their volume in response to the chemotactic factor. We also measured their chemotactic activity and, in addition, measured their ability to secrete lysosomal enzymes in response to chemotactic factor. There was a very significant correlation between the chemotactic responsiveness of these cells and their ability to increase their volume. There was no correlation between the beta-glucuronidase or lysozyme release and the volume contraction under the same circumstances. What the nature of this volume expansion is I don't know. But it is part of my feeling that, in this process of cell movement and chemotaxis, one has to have not only contraction of cell but also expansion of the cell as well.

The Phagocytic Cell in Host Resistance, edited
by Joseph A. Bellanti and Delbert H. Dayton.
Raven Press, New York © 1975.

Recent Studies on the Physiology of Cultivated Macrophages

Zanvil A. Cohn

Rockefeller University, New York, New York 10021

In this chapter I review some selected observations concerning the *in vitro* responses of mouse macrophages—a system which we have been examining for some years. The background for this work can be found in two recent reviews. The first concerns the role of the macrophage as a tool in cell biology (1) and the second deals with its role in immunology, inflammation, and host defense (2).

ATTACHMENT AND SPREADING

Freshly harvested macrophages obtained from the unstimulated peritoneal cavity will adhere to and subsequently spread on a glass or plastic surface. Agents that modify this interaction have been defined by Rabinovitch and de Stefano (3). The spreading process was temperature dependent and required divalent cations. Of interest was the greater efficacy of Mg^{2+} than Ca^{2+}. The process was favored by slightly acidic hydrogen ion concentrations and inhibited by the presence of serum. Protease treatment of macrophages with trypsin, subtilisin, pronase, and papain but not chymotrypsin produced marked spreading of freshly attached cells. A similar high degree of spreading could be induced with dithiothreitol. In a subsequent study (4) manganese was found to be the most effective cation and could produce the spreading of cells plated on antigen-antibody complexes at micromolar concentrations.

In this form of rapidly induced spreading it is quite likely the preexisting membrane, in the form of folds and microprojections, is utilized. As pointed out by the authors, the underlying mechanisms may include modification of the membrane *per se,* an influence on the substrate, or alterations of the intracellular cytoskeleton.

THE STRUCTURAL ORGANIZATION OF MACROPHAGE CYTOPLASM

After completion of the attachment and spreading processes, macrophages often become highly oriented during subsequent *in vitro* cultivation. Long pseudopods are formed and these contain linearly oriented mitochondria as well as slips of rough endoplasmic reticulum. A well-defined centrosphere region appears and is the locus of secondary lysosomes and endocytic vesicles and vacuoles. The membrane shows continual ruffling although many of the initial microprojections are lost upon cultivation.

At this point, a system of microfilaments and microtubules is seen in transmission electron micrographs. The anatomy of this system has recently been defined by Reaven and Axline (5). The cell surface which is attached to the solid substrate illustrates this organization. Just beneath the plasma membrane a loose network of disoriented filaments is seen, which may represent actin molecules. Somewhat more proximal are oriented bands of 40 to 50 Å filaments which separate the cytoplasm from the subplasmalemmal region. Finally, microtubules may be seen penetrating the oriented filament network and some appear to be attached to the plasma membrane.

The majority of the microtubules are present in the central core of the cytosol in proximity to other cytoplasmic organelles. These structures radiate from the centrioles and course in a radial fashion to all portions of the cell periphery *(unpublished observations).* Pinocytic vesicles appear to be guided toward the centriolar region by the presence of microtubules and then congregate around the Golgi apparatus. The motive force that moves endocytic vesicles in a centripetal and saltatory fashion is presently unclear. However, it is possible that waves on the plasma membrane, moving from the periphery to the central cell body, and which are quite evident on time-lapse cinematography, are the propelling force. Such waves seem to require energy derived from oxidative pathways and are blocked by appropriate inhibitors.

The presence of both peripheral and centrally located microtubules markedly influences the polarity and structural organization of the cultivated macrophage. Colchicine, colcemid, and vinblastine when added to macrophages produce a rapid disappearance of peripheral microtubules, short stubs remaining attached to the centrioles. Within 30 min and associated with the disappearance of microtubules, cytoplasmic organelles such as mitochondria and endoplasmic reticulum are withdrawn from the cell periphery and are drawn into the central cell body, even though the plasma membrane remains attached to the substrate. Somewhat later the nucleus and Golgi apparatus are freed from their central position and often migrate into the subplasmalemmal region. Finally, as noted by others, the peripheral plasma membrane detaches from the substrate and the cell begins to exhibit random amoeboid motion. The fate of the oriented bundles of 40 to 50 Å microfilaments has not been examined under these conditions.

Microtubules therefore appear to increase the rigidity and polarity of the cell and maintain cytoplasmic organelles in the peripheral cytoplasm. Whether there are actual connecting links between microtubules and organelles such as mitochondria is unknown. In addition to the aforementioned alkaloids that depolymerize microtubules and lead to the retraction of organelles into the central cell body, a number of agents have similar effects which are reversible, however. Reduction of ambient temperature (4°C), fluoride at 2×10^{-2}M, and trypsin (200 μg/ml) all lead to the retraction of mitochondria, leaving a thin, empty veil of cytoplasm and a plasma membrane which remains attached to the glass surface.

Removal of these reagents leads to the prompt reappearance of microtubules and the migration of mitochondria into the peripheral pseudopods. In this regard, adenosine and its 5′-phosphates, agents which induce pinocytosis (6), accelerate the recovery of oriented cells and seem to yield larger numbers of apparent microtubules in the cell periphery and increase spreading. The role of cyclic nucleotides in the process is currently being investigated.

ENDOCYTOSIS AND THE SEGMENTAL RESPONSE OF THE MEMBRANE

The perturbations of the plasma membrane which lead to invagination and subsequent fusion are still unclear. Whether the stimulus activates large segments of the membrane or only localized areas is a topic recently approached by Griffin and Silverstein (7). Previous studies had demonstrated that the prior uptake of particles by both polymorphonuclear leucocytes (8) and macrophages (9) leads to the enhanced phagocytosis of a subsequent particle.

These studies required a method of firmly binding a particle to the macrophage membrane without inducing ingestion. Advantage was taken of the fact that mouse macrophages and erythrocytes share common surface antigens and that an antibody prepared against macrophages also reacts with mouse RBC's. The $F(ab')_2$ fragment of a rabbit anti-mouse macrophage antibody was used to treat mixtures of macrophages and erythrocytes. The two cells were then cross-linked with a sheep $F(ab')_2$ directed against rabbit $F(ab')_2$ and led to a stable association and the coating of the monolayer with syngeneic RBC's. Next, phagocytizable particles (polystyrene latex or opsonized pneumococci) were added and incubated with the cells. In such instances, only the latex or pneumococci were ingested and none of the attached RBC's was interiorized. Thus, ingestion of one particle does not trigger generalized membrane interiorization, but it triggers a localized and segmental response of the membrane. Similar techniques should be useful to evaluate smaller portions of the membrane by electron microscopic analysis.

MEMBRANE FUSIONS WITHIN THE VACUOLAR APPARATUS

The process of membrane fusion involves plasma membrane derived structures, such as, pinocytic and phagocytic vacuoles and those coming from the Golgi apparatus in the form of tiny vesicles. Such fusions exclude other cytoplasmic organelles, serve to constrict the activity of lysosomal hydrolases to within semi-permeable membranes, and lead to the association of exogenous pathogens with digestive enzymes and microbicidal agents derived from the granules of phagocytic cells. At present we are quite ignorant of the molecular mechanisms involved but it is an area of much interest in many laboratories.

Within the past few years a number of examples of defective membrane fusion between preexisting primary and secondary lysosomes and phagocytic vacuoles have been described. These have occured in protozoa (10) and mammalian macrophages (11,12). Virulent tubercle bacilli and viable toxoplasma when present within a phagosome inhibit fusion with lysosomes, a process which may influence their subsequent intracellular growth. Within the past year Paul J. Edelson has been conducting experiments that may shed some light on this interaction. Using the plant lectin concanavalin A (Con A) he noted that binding of the lectin to the macrophage plasma membrane stimulated pinocytosis and led to the formation of large clear vacuoles that remained free of acid phosphatase upon prolonged cultivation. These vacuoles contained Con A attached to the membrane, presumably the inner surface, and failed to fuse with preexisting lysosomes. When the fate of two exogenous proteins was examined in Con A–treated macrophages, their rate of digestion was markedly inhibited. Upon the addition of α-methyl mannoside, a specific inhibitor of Con A, the phase lucent vacuoles decreased in size and became typical dense granules. Furthermore, the presence of the competitive inhibitor accelerated the rate of protein degradation to control values. These experiments, which are still in progress, suggest that Con A is able to alter the membrane so that fusion with lysosomes is inhibited. Since it is presumably only on the inner surface of the vacuole, it may exert its influence by altering transmembranous receptor proteins. Other mechanisms are, of course, possible and deserve further exploration.

THE MACROPHAGE AS A SECRETORY CELL

Studies from this laboratory have delineated certain of the requirements for the accumulation of lysosomal acid hydrolases within cultured macrophages. In response to the uptake of digestible solutes or particles a variety of digestive enzymes increase in activity within the cell. Following phagocytosis of erythrocytes or polystyrene latex, these enzymes are redistributed among the phagosomes. In some cases when a large particle is employed lysosomal fusion may occur prior to the closure of the endocytic vacuole, and hydrolases appear in the extracellular medium. In the instances studied in this laboratory the extracellular release of enzymes does not exceed 15 to 20% of the total level and in most cases is less than 10%.

There are, however, two examples of enzymes which are biosynthesized by the macrophage but which do not conform to the above pattern. These have recently been investigated by Siamon Gordon. The first is the amino-polysaccharidase lysozyme or muramidase. Using a variety of rodent and human mononuclear phagocytes, it is apparent that these cells synthesize and secrete large amounts of lysozyme (13). At any given time 85 to 90% of the total lysozyme in a culture is extracellular and a small constant fraction remains within the cell. Once in culture, both monocytes and macrophages continue to secrete lysozyme at a constant rate for weeks and the product accumulates in the medium. This material has been characterized as lysozyme by immunochemical procedures and by its typical migration in polyacrylamide gels. Macrophages exposed to ^{14}C Algal hydrolysate secrete labeled lysozyme and this enzyme appears to be the major secretory product of the cell. Phagocytosis does not influence its production or secretion and exposure to its specific substrate does not induce higher levels. From these and other studies it appears that lysozyme is a constitutive enzyme in the macrophage. Furthermore, its production and secretion can be dissociated from the lysosomal enzymes and it presumably follows a different intracellular pathway.

A second secretory product has been investigated in collaboration with Edward Reich's laboratory at Rockefeller University in studies performed by Unkeless and Gordon (14). Reich and his colleagues have recently characterized a plasminogen activator which is released by virally transformed fibroblasts but is not found in their normal counterparts. Studies with cultivated macrophages have shown that a similar neutral protease is secreted by stimulated macrophages but not by unstimulated cells. The macrophage factor has a molecular weight of 48,000 and is a serine protease inhibitable by DFP, properties which are identical to the product of transformed fibroblasts. In addition, macrophages secrete another enzyme of 25,000 molecular weight in smaller quantities. Considerable amounts of the protease are released by thioglycolate-stimulated peritoneal macrophages, but normal macrophages and monocytes produce only trace amounts.

Analysis of the ^{14}C-labeled macromolecular products released by macrophages into their environment reveals a wide spectrum of products in addition to lysozyme and the plasminogen activator. Their nature is unknown but will be of interest to study in the future. These studies point out the variety of extracellular products and enzymes which can modify the environment of macrophages and possibly modify the function of neighboring cells. They may relate to the role of macrophages in supporting the viability of lymphoid cells, the release of colony-stimulating factors, the modification of complement, kinin, and clotting factors, and perhaps the extracellular destruction of microorganisms.

Studies are now in progress to define the triggers which turn on the release of these agents and their characterization.

THE FATE OF MEMBRANE FOLLOWING INTERIORIZATION

Following the ingestion of large numbers of particles, macrophages may interiorize as much as 50 to 60% of their plasma membrane in the form of phagosomes (15). These cells round up, cease both pinocytic and phagocytic activity, and maintain this conformation for 5 to 6 hr. They then respread on the substrate and gradually regain endocytic activity which reaches control ±10 hr after the meal. These morphological changes are correlated with biochemical events that suggest that new plasma membrane is synthesized. The amount of new membrane seems directly related to the amount initially interiorized. New membrane synthesis requires ongoing protein and RNA synthesis and the presence of cholesterol in the environment.

When membrane is interiorized, a plasma membrane marker 5′-nucleotidase is rapidly lost within the phagosome. The half-life of the interiorized enzyme is approximately 2 hr and suggests extensive modification of the membrane surface exposed to vacuole contents, presumably acid hydrolases. More recent studies have extended these observations employing mouse L cell fibroblasts. Employing the lactoperoxidase iodination system described by Hubbard and Cohn (16), Hubbard has iodinated L cells in suspension. The label has been localized to plasma membrane, and all iodine residues are in tyrosine groups of exteriorly disposed proteins as monoiodotyrosine. At least 15 polypeptides on the cell surface are iodinated by this procedure, when solubilized plasma membranes are analyzed on SDS slab gels. Iodinated L cells when exposed to polystyrene latex phagocytize these particles and interiorize approximately 30% of their plasma membrane. Latex-containing phagosomes were then isolated immediately after phagocytosis and at time intervals up to 19 hr. Shortly after ingestion, SDS gels revealed that 11 labeled plasma membrane polypeptides were present in the phagosomal membrane. However, with the passage of time, most of the labeled membrane proteins were degraded to the level of monoiodotyrosine and all but two labeled bands disappeared from the gels. In addition, an L cell plasma membrane marker, a phosphodiesterase, disappeared at a similar rate. The mechanism underlying this extensive membrane modification may reflect the presence of lysosomal hydrolases in the vacuole. Whether or not new proteins are inserted in the interiorized membrane, permeability properties are altered, or whether the cytosol side of the phagosome membrane is also altered are subjects for future study.

ACKNOWLEDGMENT

The work reported in this chapter was supported in part by National Institutes of Health grants AI 07012 and 01831.

REFERENCES

1. Gordon, S., and Cohn, Z. A.: The macrophage. *Int. Rev. Cytol.* 36:171, 1973.
2. Steinman, R. M., and Cohn, Z. A.: In Zweifach, B. W., Grant, L., and McCluskey, R. T. (eds): *The Inflammatory Process.* Academic Press, New York. *In press.*
3. Rabinovitch, M., and de Stefano, M. J.: Macrophage spreading *in vitro.* I. Inducers of spreading. *Exp. Cell Res.* 77:323, 1973.
4. Rabinovitch, M., and de Stefano, M. J.: Macrophage spreading *in vitro.* II. Manganese and other metals as inducers or as cofactors for induced spreading. *Exp. Cell Res.* 79:423, 1973.
5. Reaven, E. P., and Axline, S. G.: Subplasmalemmal microfilaments and microtubules in resting and phagocytizing cultivated macrophages. *J. Cell Biol.* 59:12, 1973.
6. Cohn, Z. A., and Parks, E.: The regulation of pinocytosis in mouse macrophages. III. The induction of vesicle formation by nucleosides and nucleotides. *J. Exp. Med.* 125:457, 1967.
7. Griffin, F. M., Jr., and Silverstein, S. C.: Segmental response of the macrophage plasma membrane to a phagocytic stimulus. *J. Exp. Med.* 139:323, 1974.
8. Cohn, Z. A., and Morse, S. I.: Functional and metabolic properties of polymorphonuclear leukocytes. I. Observations on the requirements and consequences of particle ingestion. *J. Exp. Med.* 111:667, 1960.
9. Rabinovitch, M., and Gary, P. P.: Effect of the uptake of staphylococci on the ingestion of glutaraldehyde-treated red cells attached to macrophages. *Exp. Cell Res.* 52:363, 1968.

10. Karakashian, M. W., and Karakashian, S. J.: Intracellular digestion and symbiosis in *Paramecium Bursaria. Exp. Cell Res.* 81:111, 1973.
11. Armstrong, J. A., and Hart, P. D.: Response of cultural macrophages to *Mycobacterium tuberculosis,* with observations on fusion of lysosomes with phagosomes. *J. Exp. Med.* 134:713, 1971.
12. Jones, T. C., and Hirsch, J. G.: The interaction of *Toxoplasma gondii* and mammalian cells. II. The absence of lysosomal fusion with phagocytic vacuoles containing living parasites. *J. Exp. Med.* 136:1173, 1972.
13. Gordon, S., Todd, J., and Cohn, Z. A.: *In vitro* synthesis and section of lysozyme by mononuclear phagocytes. *J. Exp. Med. (in press).*
14. Unkeless, J. C., Gordon, S., and Reich, E.: Secretion of plasminogen activator by stimulated macrophages. *J. Exp. Med. (in press).*
15. Werb, Z., and Cohn, Z. A.: Plasma membrane synthesis in the macrophage following phagocytosis of polystyrene latex particles. *J. Biol. Chem.* 247:2439, 1972.
16. Hubbard, A. L., and Cohn, Z. A.: The enzymatic iodination of the red cell membrane. *J. Cell Biol.* 55:390, 1972.

DISCUSSION

Ward: In the model of enzyme secretion and release, does this first require contact of the monocytes with, for instance, a glass surface, or will it occur if cells are kept in suspension? And can you modify the enzyme secretion by drugs that disassemble tubules?

Cohn: All of our studies have so far been done on cells which have been sitting on either glass or plastic. It is very difficult to keep these cells in suspension for long periods of time without extensive aggregation. We have done experiments with colchicine on the secretion of lysozyme. Unfortunately, colchicine decreases the production of lysozyme and it decreases its biosynthesis as well. So there is no real decrease in secretion, and we don't get any pileup of intracellular enzymes. We thought we might in terms of other systems. I forgot to mention that there are marked differences in the types of cells which will secrete plasminogen activator and those that will put out lysozyme. The cells we are looking at are those induced in the peritoneal cavity that actively put out plasminogen activator. We have some other hypotheses as to what will turn on the production and secretion of plasminogen activator, and it seems to be a rather complex situation in which there are two triggers, one, a preparative step accomplished by giving lipopolysaccharide endotoxin, harvesting these cells, and putting them in culture. These cells will not make plasminogen activator, but, when challenged with a phagocytizable particle, immediately begin its biosynthesis and secretion. There appear to be two separate triggers, and there is work going on concerning this point.

Klebanoff: With respect to the iodination data, could the loss of iodine with internalization of the plasma membrane be due to a deiodination reaction occurring within the vesicle without any major change in the primary structure of the protein? Also did you have the opportunity to look for the accumulation of chemotactic activity in the medium with the release of plasminogen activator?

Cohn: In terms of your first question, we can account for all the loss of label as monoiodotyrosine. We have not looked for chemotactic factor, but I think it is apparent that many of these secretory products may relate to the various functions of macrophages that have been reported in the literature, including trophic effects on lymphocytes, recently described extracellular killing factor, colony-stimulating factor, either directly or by a modification of the extracellular environment. These products may in themselves be stimulatory or may cleave extracellular molecules to other agents perhaps in a complement or clotting system and in turn have effects on other cells in the neighborhood of macrophages.

Karnovsky: I think Klebanoff is a little too gentle with you.

Cohn: Why is that?

Karnovsky: Because of the point you made about the appearance of monoiodotyrosine as the *sole* product after ingestion by the phagocyte. I wonder if that is sufficient evidence that the proteins are being chopped down completely. There could be some sort of transiodination phenomenon, and we don't know quite how much free tyrosine is kicking around. I would press for a little more evidence that the disappearance of those bands really means the digestion of the protein.

Cohn: First of all, we know that all the label is going into tyrosine groups on proteins. I think that is fairly certain. Number two, as I mentioned, if we get 50 percent release of it from the cell, we can account for it as monoiodotyrosine. If there is transiodination going on, we'd have to reevaluate this information.

Karnovsky: I am just suggesting that the question does need a little attention—the actual amount of iodinated product is very small.

Cohn: Immediately after the iodination step there is the release of small amounts of higher molecular weight material. We think this may be related to trauma during the iodination procedure, but after that it is all small molecular weight products.

Karnovsky: On the matter of the half-life of 5′ nucleotidase, I take it that the 5′ nucleotidase turns out to be totally latent, and that to measure it you have to break up the phagosomes.

Cohn: That is correct.

David: I have two questions: Is there an increase in lysozyme or plasminogen activator secreted by macrophages activated *in vivo* by BCG or *Listeria?* The second question is concerned with the effect of the phagocytic stimulus. If the macrophage which is obtained from the peritoneal cavity without irritant is challenged with a particle, will it show an increase in plasminogen activator secretion?

Cohn: The last question first—only a trace. It is only after this preparative step that we see this marked production and secretion. We have not looked carefully at all forms of activation. Certainly in the case of lysozyme production, so-called activated cells taken from the cavity produce more lysozyme per unit weight than unstimulated cells do. The situation with the plasminogen activator is currently under investigation and I can't give you any information on it.

Bellanti: Have you had an opportunity to examine for or compare the activities of the secretive enzymes in macrophages at different sites, such as alveolar versus peritoneal?

Cohn: We have only done preliminary studies. The alveolar macrophage is a different beast. It contains huge amounts of lysozyme and we think this is within granules which have the properties of lysosomes. And it is material I thought had been endocytized from respiratory secretions and was just packaged in these because of endocytosis. If we cultivate alveolar macrophages, first we have difficulty maintaining viability for long periods of time in culture, but we do get the release of lysozyme from such cells. We think the vast majority of this is not newly synthesized lysozyme but material just released from a preexisting pool within the alevolar macrophage.

Bellanti: Do you think this would be the logical place for this type of enzyme to exert its effect?

Cohn: Yes. We calculated the amount of lysozyme in alveolar macrophage from the BCG-stimulated animal. If you calculated how much lysozyme was in the lysosomes, using egg white lysozyme as a standard, it was approximately 10 percent of the particle, a huge amount.

Sbarra: I was interested in your ongoing studies in which you have stabilized your lysosomal membrane with Con A. Would you expect this to alter in any way the killing activity of the cell?

Cohn: It might. We are not at all certain whether this would take place.

Sbarra: Would this not be a logical assumption?

Cohn: Although we get nice stabilization of pinocytic vesicles, we get less clear-cut results when we put in a large particle. There is some fusion that takes place. The question at this point is whether it is as extensive a degree of fusion as occurs in the normal cell.

Sbarra: But any alteration could be very important.

Cohn: It might.

Baehner: My question relates to your studies of the selective phagocytosis of polystyrene by macrophages that have been rosetted with IgG-coated red cells. Have you looked at the effect of various sized latex spheres to be selectively phagocytized without simultaneous phagocytosis of the IgG-coated red cells?

Cohn: This has not been examined by Drs. Griffin and Silverstein.

Spitznagel: I think Mergenhagen's group has recently reported measurements of collagenase they thought was being synthesized by guinea pig macrophages. Have you looked at collagenase synthesis with mouse macrophages?

Cohn: No, this work is in progress now in England by Drs. Zena Werb and Saimon Gordon.

Spitznagel: One other question. Would you care to speculate, since you have mentioned the work with mycobacteria, the work of Jones and Hirsch, and your own work with Con A and methyl mannoside, has this any relation to the action of immunological adjuvants that usually contain mycobacteria?

Cohn: I think you are drawing me into a trap, because that assumes a role for macrophages in adjuvant action, which I question. And I don't see any direct correlation at this point.

Holmes-Gray: I remember some years ago there was an article by Wiener showing a large amount of esterase released to the culture medium by cultured macrophages. Is this a separate enzyme?

Cohn: It is a separate enzyme. Unfortunately, we have not been able to reproduce those results in our laboratory. Whether it is the strain of mice she was using . . . ?

Holmes-Gray: What was her substrate proesterase?

Cohn: The substrate she was using in these experiments was naphthyl acetate and the one for the plasminogen activator is iodinated fibrinogen. So I think they are separate.

The Phagocytic Cell in Host Resistance, edited
by Joseph A. Bellanti and Delbert H. Dayton.
Raven Press, New York © 1975.

Biochemical Aspects of the Functions of Polymorphonuclear and Mononuclear Leukocytes

Manfred L. Karnovsky

Department of Biological Chemistry, Harvard Medical School, Boston, Massachusetts 02115

Rather than present in a compendious fashion current understanding of the molecular events that govern or accompany the functional activity of polymorphonuclear or mononuclear leukocytic phagocytes, I have chosen, as potentially more provocative, to present an idiosyncratic view of the field. Data obtained by our own laboratory will be cited to exemplify points raised. The following topics will be covered:

1. The ingestion phase of phagocytosis, particularly its measurement.
2. The nature and properties of the cellular membrane of phagocytic cells.
3. The biochemical influences to which an internalized object is subjected, for example, exposure to some metabolites produced by the phagocytizing cell and to enzymes (and other proteins) released into the phagolysosome. In general, the fate of the internalized object may be determined by (a) the microbicidal mechanism and (b) the dismantling or digestion of the object.
4. Modification of the activities of various leukocytes, particularly the effect on functional behavior of the lymphocyte-mediated "activation" that results from infection with certain organisms. This is a phenomenon of some importance in the host-parasite field. The more general mode of modification of biochemical and functional activity of cells by hormones (here steroids and prostaglandins) will also be touched upon.
5. Comparisons between different cell types within the leukocytic phagocyte series, which will be made where possible.

THE INGESTION PHASE AND ITS MEASUREMENT

One of the critical deficiencies in the field up to recent times has been the lack of precise methods for measuring phagocytic ingestion *per se* with the degree of accuracy that pertains to the measurement of biochemical concomitants of phagocytosis. This is unfortunate, considering that the principal interest in the biochemistry of phagocytic leukocytes centers on their specific function. A welcome development was described by Roberts and Quastel in 1963 (1) when they introduced a method of determining the uptake of polystyrene spheres by extracting cells with dioxane after ingestion and applying absorptiometric measurements of the polystyrene. A more flexible approach was taken by Stossel and his colleagues (2) who incorporated mineral oil and Oil Red O into emulsions stabilized with albumin. The particles were of controllable size and could be exposed to leukocytes. This method offers great ease of measurement of the number of particles ingested, by extracting the oil from the cells and determining the amount colorimetrically. It also allows the preparation of many kinds of particles containing different substances, such as various proteins or other components of microorganisms, e.g., endotoxin and cell wall materials (3).

All measurements of phagocytosis require, of necessity, separation of cells from excess particles. When cell suspensions are used, this is usually accomplished by centrifugation, which introduces cumbersome maneuvers. For many purposes, cellular monolayers, which may be washed free of excess particles in a very simple fashion, provide advantages (4). Such methods can employ radioactively labeled particles of many different kinds, with considerable precision of measurement. A shortcoming of the monolayer method is that observation of the effects of some substances (e.g., colchicine) on the ingestion phase of phagocytosis is vitiated by the fact that they may cause cells to fall off the monolayers.

Our own monolayer method (4) has been applied to polymorphonuclear leukocytes (PMN) from guinea pig, rat, mouse, and man, elicited mononuclear phagocytes (i.e., elicited peritoneal macrophages—brought into the peritoneum with dilute caseinate or peptone—abbreviated MN or MC depending on conventions), as well as resident peritoneal macrophages from mouse and alveolar macrophages from mouse and guinea pig. The method allows one to measure with precision and accuracy the uptake of such particles as ^{14}C-labeled starch or ^{32}P- and ^{14}C-labeled bacteria of various kinds (*cf.* 5). When dead tubercle bacilli constituted the particles offered (6), elicited peritoneal macrophages were clearly superior to peritoneal macrophages or PMN with respect to the *maximal rate* of uptake and final *capacity*, two measures that should be considered in all such comparisons (4).

The use of precise methods that directly measure particle uptake on a linear scale and that can be employed to monitor uptake in short time periods may yield important new information on this bulk transport process (phagocytosis). In addition, the ability to follow cellular biochemical activities simultaneously with particle uptake in such systems is extremely helpful. Thus, for example, the kinetics of glucose oxidation (2, 4), the digestion of bacteria (5), and the iodination of ingested bacteria (7) may be correlated temporally with the kinetics of ingestion *per se*. Finally, in this methodological vein, extension of the type of technique represented by the monolayer method to kinetic measurement of bactericidal action and the possibility of considering the latter as an independent function (i.e., separately from ingestion) are potentially useful advances (see below).

LEUKOCYTE MEMBRANES AND INTERNALIZATION OF MEMBRANE DURING PHAGOCYTOSIS

Questions as to whether only specific portions of membrane are internalized during phagocytosis, how much membrane is taken in with the particle, and how much is newly synthesized are not yet completely resolved. Recently some advances have been made along these lines, among which is the demonstration by Tsan and Berlin (8) that, when (putatively) up to 50% of the membrane of rabbit PMN and alveolar macrophages was internalized during particle ingestion, the activities of five transport systems were undiminished, leading to the conclusion that different parts of the cellular membrane were involved in bulk transport (phagocytosis) and in specific molecular transport.

In an important more recent contribution, Berlin and collaborators (9) have used lectin-binding sites on the plasma membrane of PMN as markers for membrane movement during the ingestion phase of phagocytosis. Binding sites disappeared from the surface of the isolated membrane in parallel with particle uptake. This disappearance was prevented by colchicine.

In our own laboratory ectoenzymes have been used to follow the passage of plasmalemma into the cells during phagocytosis. Suspensions of intact PMN from guinea pigs hydrolyze ATP, AMP, and paranitrophenylphosphate under physiological conditions. The enzymatic activities are not due to artifacts, such as breakage of the cells during the incubation period, as determined by exclusion of trypan blue. It was, of course, necessary to establish the enzymatic markers as ectoenzymes, i.e., enzymes located on the cell membrane with their active sites directed externally.

Three kinds of experiments were performed. First, the activities of intact cells were compared to those of homogenates, sonicates, and cells treated with detergent. Disruption of cells resulted in an approximately twofold increase in maximal ATPase and *p*-nitrophenyl phosphatase activities, suggesting that the plasma membrane was acting as a permeability barrier to the substrates and that there might be both ectoenzymatic and intracellular activity. Disruption did not increase AMPase activity, leaving open the possibility that an ectoenzyme is the only protein in PMN capable of hydrolyzing AMP (10–12).

Second, the products of the enzymes of intact cells were localized by using substrates containing labeled phosphate. The concentration of labeled inorganic phosphate released was 18 to 100 times greater in the extracellular medium than in the intracellular milieu. This suggests that the substrates are cleaved outside the cells or that they are cleaved inside and the products transported out. The latter possibility was militated against by loading cells with inorganic phosphate-^{33}P, then allowing them to hydrolyze substrates labeled with ^{32}P. Almost all of the inorganic phosphate-^{32}P was found outside of the cells; 90% of the inorganic phosphate-^{33}P remained inside (11, 12).

Third, the cells were treated with the diazonium salt of sulfanilic acid, a reagent known not to penetrate into intact erythrocytes (13). This treatment rapidly and dramatically inhibited the intact-cell ATPase, AMPase, and *p*-nitrophenyl phosphatase, whereas lactate dehydrogenase, a soluble cytoplasmic enzyme, was unaffected (11, 12). Lactate dehydrogenase was as susceptible to the diazonium salt as the other three activities if the reagent was applied to already disrupted cells.

A search for other membrane markers indicated that all the neuraminidase-releasable sialate of the PMN is located on the outside of the plasma membrane. Neuraminidase was covalently attached to a sepharose particle with a diameter of 40 microns, i.e., too big to be internalized by the cells. This preparation removed all the sialidase-sensitive neuraminic acid from the cells. The effect was not due to release of the enzyme bound to the particle (11, 14).

The membrane AMPase and sialidase-sensitive sialic acid could thus be confidently employed to follow the passage of plasmalemma into the interior of cells during phagocytosis, since both are located exclusively on the membrane of PMN.

During phagocytosis of a number of particles that would theoretically account for internalization of the whole surface area of membrane on the cell (considered as a sphere) only 15 to 25% of the AMPase ectoenzyme disappeared from the outside. The possibility, of course, remained that "cryptoenzyme" is activated during the phagocytic event, but this has now been eliminated by measuring the AMPase present in the phagolysosome fraction after phagocytosis and determining recovery of enzyme. The phagolysosomes in guinea pig PMN and MN are rather easily isolated after the phagocytic event according to the method of Stossel and his colleagues (15). The enzyme that disappeared from the cell surface was found "latent" in the phagolysosomes and became manifest after sonication of this fraction, since internalization of cell-membrane produces an "inside-out" membrane-bound vesicle. Addition of colchicine (25μM) depressed phagocytosis by about 40% but more than doubled the AMPase internalized, calculated per particle ingested.

Further, we found that only 15 to 25% of the surface sialic acid was internalized during maximal phagocytosis, i.e., under conditions that were calculated as above to have caused the theoretical internalization of 100% of the cell surface area.

Our experimental results obviously have points of similarity with those of Berlin's group (8) and differences (e.g., effect of colchicine) (9). Many questions are raised about the flow of membrane, its topographic heterogeneity, and the role of "anchor" entities in endocytosis.

Experiments in this context, representing an important approach to membrane "utilization" and "replenishment," were reported by Werb and Cohn (16), who demonstrated that in the macrophage after phagocytosis there was a diminution of external membrane followed by the synthesis of new membrane after about 6 hr. This synthesis was dependent on the presence of exogenous cholesterol.

The phenomena indicated above should also be considered in conjunction with morphological observations made by several investigators (17, 18). Here multivalent molecules, such as ferritin or hemocyanin coupled to antibodies or lectins, were used to visualize the distribution of specific sites. The "capping" of the cells and the movement and final internalization of the cap, coupled perhaps with superimposed observations of phagocytosis, may help to provide important information on the mechanics of membrane invagination during ingestion.

THE FATE OF THE INTERNALIZED OBJECT

If the object is alive when ingested, e.g., a microbe, then (a) biochemical changes of the leukocyte that accompany phagocytosis may kill it. Furthermore, (b) digestion of the particle within the phagolysosome (19) may ensue. It is uncertain whether the killing action and the digestive action overlap, i.e., whether it is appropriate to separate them as definitively as above. In what follows, however, the microbicidal function linked to leukocyte metabolism will be reviewed first, followed by a few comments on lysosomal function.

Microbicidal Action

The mechanisms by which leukocytes kill bacteria and other microorganisms have been considerably clarified in recent years, especially in the case of PMN. The work of Klebanoff (20, 21) has made it quite evident that a system comprised of hydrogen peroxide, a halide, and myeloperoxidase is powerfully microbicidal and relevant to the neutrophilic granulocyte. The first mentioned component is known to be produced during the metabolic burst associated with phagocytosis (22), the second is known to be present as chloride ion in the intracellular milieu (although the participation of iodide cannot be entirely ruled out in these cells), and the third is known to be liberated into the phagolysosomes (23). There is some evidence that in such diseases as chronic granulomatous disease (CGD) of childhood, failure to produce hydrogen peroxide leads to at least partial failure of bactericidal action (24). This would seem to constitute ample grounds to believe that the peroxide-peroxidase-halide system is indeed operative in the normal bactericidal action of PMN. On the other hand, in another human dysfunction, myeloperoxidase deficiency, impairment of microbicidal action is less dramatic (25), suggesting that other microbicidal mechanisms may also pertain in the PMN (see Klebanoff, *this volume*).

Provocative recent information has been adduced concerning the role of superoxide (O_2^-) and perhaps of hydroxyl radical ($OH\cdot$) in bactericidal action. For example, Babior and his colleagues (26) have shown that during phagocytosis by PMN there is an increased production of superoxide. The work of Fridovich and his laboratory is of key significance in this context (27, 28). Evidence that this species is actually the antibacterial species is on far less firm ground than that for peroxide and is, in fact, rather insubstantial at this stage. Fridovich has presented some data that show that an *E. coli* depleted in periplasmic superoxide dismutase is indeed affected by O_2^-. Superoxide dismutase is present also in some mammalian cells and converts superoxide to hydrogen peroxide (29). It is possible that superoxide is simply a precursor of the true bactericidal agent, a position for which H_2O_2 seems currently best qualified. However, the whole matter requires resolution in terms of different microbial susceptibilities, the mechanisms of killing in different types of leukocyte (see below), and the actual mechanism of killing of ingested microorganisms at the level of the machinery of the organisms themselves.

In addition to the important model system explored by Klebanoff, at least one other is attractive in the context of the function of PMN. That is the system described by Miller (30) consisting of ascorbic acid and hydrogen peroxide. These substances together form an important antibacterial system especially with lysozyme. As will be seen later, we have found that the system (without lysozyme) *requires* copper or cobalt for full activity. Such systems should be considered seriously because PMN do contain high concentrations of ascorbate compared with the surrounding plasma.

The mechanisms by which macrophages kill ingested microorganisms are more obscure than those of the PMN. In the mouse, at least, these cells do not contain peroxidase (e.g., 7), and it is uncertain as to the quantities of hydrogen peroxide that may be generated during phagocytosis. Indeed, this applies also to the situation with respect to superoxide or the hydroxyl radical. It was believed that the lysosomes of macrophages also lacked lysozyme but this information has been revised very recently (31).

In order to evaluate the generality of, for example, the peroxidase-H_2O_2-mediated bactericidal system, it is important to compare various cell types for (a) their ability to kill microbes, (b) their ability to fix iodide (as an approximate measure of the Klebanoff system), and (c) for their content of enzymes appropriate to that system as well as their metabolic (particularly respiratory) behavior during phagocytosis.

Bactericidal Activity of Several Types of Leukocyte and the Relevance of the Peroxide-Halide System

Some efficiencies of killing, defined as the "percent of ingested bacteria killed," i.e., a function *independent* of the efficiency of actual ingestion (7), of various cells (PMN) and elicited macrophages from guinea pig and mouse, and resident mouse peritoneal macrophages, have been determined. Using radioactive live bacteria and the monolayer method described above, one can determine both the *total* number of bacteria ingested and, by plating out, the number of live intracellular bacteria, at any time (7). The kinetics of killing of intracellular microorganisms may thus be determined at short time intervals. The method sharpens the possibilities of comparing different cell types or cells in different stages of activation (see below). Whereas the mouse PMN are apparently superior bactericidal agents in the earlier period of the experiments (up to 1 hr), the mouse macrophage is roughly as competent as most of the other cell types, although it apparently does not kill by means of the peroxidase-mediated pathway since it lacks that enzyme

(7). At very high multiplicity (100:1), mouse macrophages are as successful as PMN in controlling the heavy live bacterial load; elicited macrophages are not able to manage the situation (7), even though they may be more efficient ingestors of particles (see above).

With radioactive $^{131}I^-$ in the medium and using the monolayer method, one may determine the rate of iodine fixation as a result of the intracellular activity of the system described by Klebanoff. Thus, one can measure the fixation of iodide simultaneously with uptake of particles and express it as a function of the number of particles phagocytized (7). Mouse macrophages, as expected, failed to iodinate internalized bacteria, and elicited macrophages were almost lacking in this ability, whereas PMN were at least an order of magnitude more efficient. Cells from humans with CGD were shown to have at least two orders of magnitude less ability to iodinate ingested bacteria than normal cells (7).

Studies of the metabolism of the five cell types indicated that the PMN and the elicited macrophages do indeed show a very considerable respiratory increase (6) during the ingestion phase, i.e., approximately doubling. Mouse peritoneal macrophages show only a very small increment, as previously noted for alveolar macrophages (6). Oxidation of glucose-1-^{14}C to $^{14}CO_2$ in the case of the PMN of guinea pigs and elicited macrophages of guinea pig and mouse increased six- to eightfold due to phagocytosis (6). In mouse PMN there was only about a doubling. Opinions vary as to whether the hexose-monophosphate pathway for glucose oxidation is driven by, or produces, H_2O_2 (summarized in 24). The oxidation of glucose-1-^{14}C to $^{14}CO_2$ must, for this and other compelling reasons, be taken only as a rough indicator.

Finally, a number of enzymes of each of these cells were selected for more intensive investigation (7). It was found that cyanide-insensitive NADH oxidase that is believed by some workers (24) to be, in the guinea pig or human granulocyte, the source of peroxide and of augmented oxygen consumption during particle ingestion was present in all cell types studied, leaving open the possibility that adequate peroxide might be available in all the cells when phagocytizing. On the other hand, the mouse cells were virtually completely deficient in catalase, and the mouse macrophages lacked peroxidase, as mentioned above (7).

Although the overall picture is one of as yet unresolved complexity, so that it is difficult to correlate bactericidal action and leukocyte metabolism, and although some of the correlations are obvious, it is, in my opinion, valuable and even necessary to try to construct a comprehensive picture and to question apparent failures in correlation, if the matter of the biochemical basis of bactericidal action by different cell types is to be solved.

The Ascorbate-Peroxide System

The system described by Miller (30) interested us, especially in view of observations with MPO deficiency in PMN, where killing was not totally impaired. The most successful model system we have used (apart from the myeloperoxidase system) consisted of ascorbate, metal, and peroxide, i.e., Miller's system modified to include metal ions. The most effective metals in this context were cobalt or copper. Manganese had no effect at concentrations as high as 1×10^{-1}M, and iron was itself rather toxic to bacteria at useful levels. Systems with cobalt at concentrations below 1×10^{-4}M were not appreciably bactericidal, whereas with copper even at concentrations as low as 5×10^{-6}M there was still some bactericidal activity in the presence of peroxide (1×10^{-3}M) and ascorbate (5×10^{-4}M). We noted that there was never complete killing of the entire bacterial population, in contrast to the situation with the Klebanoff system. The system used by Miller that contained only ascorbate and peroxide was in our hands not able to kill bacteria significantly, but the addition of traces of copper or of somewhat greater amounts of cobalt immediately established potent bactericidal activity. When the ascorbate was omitted from the most successful systems containing copper, there was a reduction in killing by three orders of magnitude. However, some bactericidal activity persisted. When dehydroascorbate replaced ascorbate, we noted that this substance, together with peroxide or alone, was not microbicidal. Cobalt at concentrations of about 1×10^{-2}M failed to enhance the activity. Copper at less than millimolar concentrations increased killing 10,000-fold over either the standard Miller system or the system described by Miller that included dehydroascorbate. The copper-dehydroascorbate system was, in fact, much more potent than the copper-ascorbate system.

When free-radical scavengers were added to the copper-ascorbate system, i.e., sodium thiosulfate and sodium metabisulfite, no protection resulted. The cobalt-ascorbate system, on the other hand, was almost totally inhibited. It is noteworthy that both these agents as well as hydroquinone block myeloperoxidase-mediated killing. What the active species is that induces the killing remains to be explored, but it is reasonable to suppose that in the copper system ascorbate is first converted to dehydroascorbate, or that both give rise to a third species. When radioactive iodide was included in the effective systems, iodination of bacteria did not occur. Preliminary studies so far have not implicated O_2^- or OH· in the ascorbate system above.

Superoxide Production by Various Leukocytes [1]

Since little is known of the mechanism(s) by which *macrophages* kill microbes, and since activated and elicited macrophages show so large a respiratory increment during phagocytosis (6), experiments have been initiated to explore superoxide production during phagocytosis by a variety of leukocytes other than PMN. The ingestion of *E. coli* does stimulate superoxide release from elicited guinea pig PMN [Babior, B., and Curnutte, J., *personal communication, cf.* human PMN and polystyrene spheres (26)]. Mouse macrophages appear to produce amounts of O_2^- comparable to PMN, when they phagocytize, even though they show

[1] These experiments were performed by Dr. David Drath.

minimal increases in respiration. Such agents as digitonin, traces of which have been shown to cause a mimicking of the metabolic behavior observed during phagocytosis, do produce a stimulation of superoxide production in PMN and peritoneal macrophages. Further, the presence of serum greatly increases superoxide production (by an order of magnitude). There is considerable dissociation between the size of the respiratory burst of phagocytosis and the amount of superoxide production (note above). The latter may range from 10 to 80% of the former, depending upon the particle ingested, and the type and state of the phagocytic cell.

Function of Granules and Digestion of the Internalized Object

With respect to the function of granules and digestion of the internalized object, this review will be even less comprehensive than on other matters. The classical papers on the origin of the granules of PMN remain those of Bainton and Farquhar (32). On the matter of granule function in phagocytosis, that of Cohn and Hirsch (19) was seminal. More recently, Bainton has given a picture of the sequential degranulation of the specific and azurophilic granules in PMN (33) and has correlated this with the temporal changes of pH in the phagolysosome (34). It may be recalled that Stähelin et al. (35) in 1956 gave indications of the release of ^{14}C-labeled bacterial material after phagocytosis by PMN, a digestive phenomenon more intensively explored by Cohn (36; *cf.* 5) in 1963. Finally, the presence of antibacterial cationic proteins in the granules that are released into the phagolysosome is still an important subject (37).

MODIFICATION OF THE ACTIVITIES OF LEUKOCYTES

Hormonal Mechanisms

A considerable amount of work has been done on the effect of steroids *in vitro* on blood leukocytes and their function. For example, Rauch et al. (38) observed, in confirmation of earlier studies, that there was a suppressive effect of cortisone on glucose utilization and lactate production without any effect on oxygen consumption. It might have been believed that the metabolic inhibitions noted would have been accompanied by suppression of phagocytosis itself, i.e., the ingestion phase. However, the methodology for measuring anything but massive depressions of particle uptake was not available at the time. Many conflicting conclusions have been reached in the literature as to whether the latter process is unaffected or inhibited by steroid hormones *in vitro*. The same situation is true of glucocorticoid treatment *in vivo* with subsequent measurements of phagocytosis *in vitro*. Some workers have claimed defective killing as a result of exposure of cells to glucocorticoids, whereas other workers have seen no impairment. Apart from the influence of corticosteroids on metabolism, affecting phagocytosis, there is considerable evidence of the effect of these substances directly on membranes, and thus on phagocytosis and ensuing events (release of lysosomal enzymes, etc.; e.g., 39, 40).

Another group of hormones whose effect on phagocytosis and leukocytes has been of particular interest is the prostaglandins. Weissmann et al. (41) have indicated that prostaglandin E_1 (PGE_1) reduces the release of lysosomal enzymes from phagocytes *in vitro.* Further, it may decrease the uptake and degradation of aggregated serum albumin by mouse macrophages (42). Bourne et al. (43) showed that preincubation of neutrophils with PGE_1 resulted in diminished phagocytosis and killing of yeasts. The prostaglandins probably act through the mediation of cyclic AMP (44). Data on the effects in this context of prostaglandins other than PGE_1 are surprisingly sparse.

The availability of more precise methods for assessing the ingestion phase of phagocytosis, and the kinetics of killing, may make it possible to reach more clear-cut decisions on the conditions that cause differences in the response of leukocytes to steroid hormones and to the prostaglandins, particularly with respect to establishing specifically the relationship of effects at the level of ingestion *per se,* and subsequent to that event (i.e., intracellularly).

Using the monolayer techniques mentioned above, hydrocortisone (at rather high concentrations, i.e., approximately millimolar) was shown to inhibit the ingestion of starch, *E. coli,* or polystyrene by approximately 50%. The effects were readily reversible when the cells were washed after exposure to the steroid. These concentrations of hydrocortisone appeared to interfere with *retention* of the particles undergoing ingestion. There was evidence that the phagocytic vesicles exhibited a failure of closure; for example, we noted that hydrogen peroxide leaked from the cells to a greater extent. Previous workers reported (45) that hydrocortisone inhibits the bactericidal activity of PMN. Using our simultaneous kinetic measurements of ingestion and killing, we came to the conclusion that this hormone inhibits killing by PMN only to the extent that the ingestion phase *per se* is depressed. A possibly paradoxical situation is, however, the fact that hydrocortisone inhibited the iodination of the ingested bacteria even though it did not seem to suppress the killing thereof.

Theophylline, dibutyryl-cyclic AMP and prostaglandins inhibited the phagocytosis of starch particles; PGE_1 was the most effective inhibitor. The effects of prostaglandins PGE_1, PGE_2, and $PGF_2\alpha$ were synergistic with that of theophylline. The effects of PGA_1 and PGA_2 were not (44). We have not examined these substances with respect to killing *per se,* as separated from ingestion.

Activation of Macrophages by Immunologically Linked Mechanisms

The second and extremely important mode of modification of the activity of leukocytes is represented by aspects of the phenomenon described by Mackaness (46–48) that produces the "activated" macrophage. Here there is an enhancement of macrophage function after infection of the animal with such organisms as *Listeria monocytogenes* or BCG, with an immunologic basis involving lymphocytes. Macrophages obtained from mice at a particular time after infection spread out more extensively on glass and appear to be more phagocytic than the normal cells. They have an enhanced bactericidal capacity that is effective in a nonspecific sense, i.e., is directed toward microorganisms not related antigenically to those that constituted the original infection, as well as to the activating organism. After this phenomenon has faded, recall is dependent on challenge with the original antigenic stimulus. The mechanisms of this activation are not yet clear, and, in fact, a full description of the "activated" macrophage is not yet at hand. Thus, for example, information on the metabolism of activated macrophages has only just begun to be available (49, 50). The oxidation of glucose, the ability to phagocytize tubercle bacilli, and bacteriostatic action are all increased (49, 50). The reason for enhanced antibacterial ability is not clear, and it is still a question as to whether the enhanced power to cope with bacteria is linked to the enhanced metabolism, whether it is simply (or to a degree) a reflection of the increased phagocytosis, or whether more specific factors are involved.

With respect to the way in which the activation is induced, one should take cognizance of such lymphokine substances as migration inhibitory factor (MIF). It has been demonstrated that macrophages from guinea pigs exposed to MIF for a number of days acquire an "activated" phagocytic ability and increased metabolic properties that are reminiscent of the macrophage activated *in vitro* (51). The observation tentatively suggests a linkage between cellular hypersensitivity and cellular immunity.

We have examined some metabolic activities of activated cells compared to normal cells and have carried out some experiments on the biochemical basis of the "activation" of macrophages. In the first context we have shown that several labeled glucose species are oxidized at markedly elevated rates, both at rest and during phagocytosis, by "activated" mouse macrophages compared with control cells (50). With respect to the oxidation of glucose, the increase in activity for "activated" macrophages appears to be dependent upon the virulence of the *Listeria* that were used to infect the mice (6). Furthermore, whereas control peritoneal macrophages of mice show a negligible respiratory increment during phagocytosis, the respiration of "activated" macrophages is markedly increased during that process. The differences are statistically significant ($p < 0.02$ to 0.05) when phagocytizing and resting cells are compared within each batch of mice (6). The "activated" cells are much better able to phagocytize dead tubercle bacilli than control cells are (with respect to both rate and capacity) but they are not superior in their ingestion of labeled starch (50).

In probing for the mechanism of activation of mouse macrophages, we have had recourse to a guinea pig model (51). The animals were sensitized with orthochlorobenzoyl bovine gamma globulin and 14 days later draining lymph nodes were taken, the lymphocytes cultured and challenged with the antigen. The culture fluid was fractionated and a preparation obtained, MIF, that also contained chemotactic factor and lymphotoxin. Macrophages elicited after intraperitoneal injection of 1% sodium caseinate were incubated with MIF or control medium for 3 days. It was noted that the cells cultured in the presence of the MIF-rich fractions had four times the capacity to oxidize glucose-carbon-1 to $^{14}CO_2$ than control cells. Furthermore, the uptake of tubercle bacilli was grossly enhanced whereas that for labeled starch was virtually unaffected in these "activated" cells (51). The picture observed was indeed similar to that of the mouse macrophages "activated" *in vivo* and tested *in vitro.*

A number of measurements have been made to compare elicited peritoneal macrophages, resident peritoneal macrophages, and activated peritoneal macrophages, all from mice. This stemmed from an observation that activated and elicited macrophages are "perturbable" in a respiratory sense during phagocytosis *in vitro* whereas resident peritoneal macrophages are not. Although the respiratory levels of all the cells are not significantly different at rest (ca. 15 μl/mg protein/hr), phagocytosis was accompanied, in the activated and elicited cells (but not the control resident peritoneal macrophages), by an increase of roughly 50 to 100% in oxygen consumption. Oxidation of glucose-carbon-1 to CO_2 was an order of magnitude greater in resting elicited or activated cells than in controls, and although phagocytosis did cause a marked increase in this function for all the cells, it was far greater (three- to fourfold) in the elicited and activated cells than in controls (6). These biochemical similarities and differences between activated and control cells—and cells obtained under various conditions—need to be explored much further before any conclusions can be reached. However, on the face of it, activated and elicited macrophages currently show a great deal of similarity in a metabolic sense.

On the other hand, they differ in at least one functional way. Elicited mouse peritoneal macrophages are superior to the resident macrophages in their ability to ingest *both* dead tubercle bacilli and starch granules. This represents a clear difference between elicited peritoneal macrophages and activated macrophages; the latter have been shown to phagocytize tubercle bacilli at increased rates and in greater amounts but not starch. The relevance of these observations must of course be monitored in terms of the cell populations studied, determined by microscopy. "Activation" of macrophages should, however, provide an important manipulative tool in defining the ways, qualitatively and quantitatively, by which macrophages exert their microbicidal activity.

CONCLUSION

This review of our own work and that of others covers only a fragment of the information already available and that yet to be gathered on the biochemical aspects of phagocytosis by leukocytes. One should obviously not apologize for not signaling future findings. However, it is with intense regret that one recognizes the omission of important and provocative existing observations. This chapter has not dealt, for example, with the general metabolism of leukocytes; with the biosynthesis of complex lipids—possibly membrane-related—during phagocytosis (52); with the recognition and possible role of respiratory enzymes during particle uptake (53); with such intriguing potential antibacterial agents as aldehydes derived from amino acids by peroxidase-mediated reactions (54); with the role of leukocytes in the metabolism of iodine-containing hormones (55); or with aspects of peroxide formation that involve, as potential substrates, bacterial components such as D-amino acids (56).

Enumerating these omissions is an autocatalytic process. The hope is that what *has* been included adequately stimulates recognition of all the contributions that are being made.

ACKNOWLEDGMENT

The work of this laboratory that is cited was supported by U.S. Public Health Service Grant No. AI 03260 from the National Institute of Allergy and Infectious Diseases.

REFERENCES

1. Roberts, J., and Quastel, J. H.: Particle uptake by polymorphonuclear leukocytes and Ehrlich ascites–carcinoma cells. *Biochem. J.* 89:150, 1963.
2. Stossel, T. P., Mason, R. J., Hartwig, J., and Vaughan, M.: Quantitative studies of phagocytosis by polymorphonuclear leukocytes. Use of paraffin oil emulsions to measure the rate of phagocytosis. *J. Clin. Invest.* 51:615, 1972.
3. Stossel, T. P., Alper, C. A., and Rosen, F. S.: Serum-dependent phagocytosis of paraffin oil emulsified with bacterial lipopolysaccharide. *J. Exp. Med.* 137:690, 1973.
4. Michell, R. H., Pancake, S. J., Noseworthy, J., and Karnovsky, M. L.: Measurement of rates of phagocytosis; The use of cellular monolayers. *J. Cell Biol.* 40:216, 1969.
5. Trippestad, A., and Midtvedt, T.: Phagocytosis of ^{32}P-labeled *E. coli* by rat peritoneal polymorphonuclear leukocytes. *Acta Pathol. Microbiol. Scand.* 74:259, 1968.
6. Karnovsky, M. L., Lazdins, J., and Simmons, S. R.: Metabolism of activated mononuclear phagocytes at rest and during phagocytosis. In van Furth, R., (ed.): *Metabolism of Macrophages, Vol. 2,* Blackwell Scientific Publications, Oxford and Edinburgh. *In press.*
7. Simmons, S. R., and Karnovsky, M. L.: Iodinating ability of various leukocytes and their bactericidal activity. *J. Exp. Med.* 138:44, 1973.
8. Tsan, M. F., and Berlin, R. D.: Effect of phagocytosis on membrane transport of non-electrolytes. *J. Exp. Med.* 134:1016, 1971.
9. Oliver, J. M., Ukena, T. E., and Berlin, R. D.: Effects of phagocytosis and colchicine on the distribution of lectin binding sites on cell surfaces. *Proc. Natl. Acad. Sci. (in press).*
10. DePierre, J., and Karnovsky, M. L.: Plasma membranes of mammalian cells. A review of methods for their characterization and isolation. *J. Cell Biol.* 56:275, 1973.
11. DePierre, J., and Karnovsky, M. L.: Ectoenzymes, sialic acid, and the internalization of cell membrane during phagocytosis. In Ward, P., and Lepow, I. (eds): *Inflammation,* Academic Press, Inc., New York, p. 55. 1972.
12. DePierre, J. W., and Karnovsky, M. L.: An ectoenzyme of granulocytes, 5′-nucleotidase. *Science* 183:1096, 1974.
13. Berg, H. C.: Sulfanilic acid diazonium salt; A label for the outside of the human erythrocyte membrane. *Biochim. Biophys. Acta* 183:65, 1969.
14. DePierre, J. W.: Steps toward the isolation of the plasma membrane of the guinea pig polymorphonuclear leukocyte. Ph.D. Thesis, Harvard University, 1972.
15. Stossel, T. P., Pollard, T. D., Mason, R. J., and Vaughn, M.: Isolation and properties of phagocytic vesicles from polymorphonuclear leukocytes. *J. Clin. Invest.* 50:1745, 1971.
16. Werb, Z., and Cohn, Z. A.: Plasma membrane synthesis in the macrophage following phagocytosis of polystyrene latex particles. *J. Biol. Chem.* 247:2439, 1972.

17. Rosenblith, J. Z., Ukena, T. E., Yin, H. H., Berlin, R. D., and Karnovsky, M. J.: A comparative evaluation of the distribution of concanavilin-A binding sites on the surfaces of normal, virally transformed, and protease-treated fibroblasts. *Proc. Natl. Acad. Sci.* 70: 1625, 1973.
18. Oseroff, A. R., Robbins, P. W., and Burger, M. M.: The cell surface membrane; Biochemical aspects and biophysical probes. *Annu. Rev. Biochem.* 42:647, 1973.
19. Cohn, Z. A., and Hirsch, J. G.: The influence of phagocytosis on the intracellular distribution of granule-associated components of polymorphonuclear leukocytes. *J. Exp. Med.* 112:1015, 1960.
20. Klebanoff, S. J.: Myeloperoxidase-halide-hydrogen peroxide antibacterial system. *J. Bacteriol.* 95:2131, 1968.
21. Klebanoff, S. J.: Intraleukocytic microbicidal defects. *Annu. Rev. Med.* 22:39, 1971.
22. Iyer, G. Y. N., Islam, D. F. M., and Quastel, J. H.: Biochemical aspects of phagocytosis. *Nature* 192:535, 1961.
23. Baehner, R. L., Karnovsky, M. J., and Karnovsky, M. L.: Degranulation of leukocytes in chronic granulomatous disease. *J. Clin. Invest.* 48:187, 1969.
24. Karnovsky, M. L.: Chronic granulomatous disease—Pieces of a cellular and molecular puzzle. *Fed. Proc.* 32:1527, 1973.
25. Lehrer, R. I., and Cline, M. J.: Leukocyte myeloperoxidase deficiency and disseminated candidiasis: The role of myeloperoxidase in resistance to candida infection. *J. Clin. Invest.* 48:1478, 1969.
26. Babior, B. M., Kipnes, R. S., and Curnutte, J. T.: Biological defense mechanisms. The production by leukocytes of superoxide, a potential bactericidal agent. *J. Clin. Invest.* 52:741, 1973.
27. Fridovich, I.: Superoxide radical and superoxide dismutase. *Account Chem. Res.* 5:321, 1972.
28. McCord, J. M., and Fridovich, I.: Superoxide dismutase. An enzyme function for erythrocuprein (hemocuprein). *J. Biol. Chem.* 244:6049, 1969.
29. Beauchamp, C., and Fridovich, I.: Superoxide dismutase: Improved assays and an assay applicable to acrylamide gels. *Anal. Biochem.* 44:276, 1971.
30. Miller, T. E.: Killing and lysis of Gram-negative bacteria through the synergistic effect of hydrogen peroxide, ascorbic acid and lysozyme. *J. Bacteriol.* 98:949, 1969.
31. Gordon, S., and Cohn, Z. A.: In van Furth, R., (ed.): *Mononuclear Phagocytes, Vol. 2,* Blackwell Scientific Publications, Oxford and Edinburgh. *In press.*
32. Bainton, D. F., and Farquhar, M. G.: Differences in enzyme content of azurophil and specific granules of polymorphonuclear leukocytes I and II. *J. Cell Biol.* 39:286, 299, 1968.
33. Bainton, D. F.: Sequential degranulation of the two types of polymorphonuclear leukocyte granules during phagocytosis of microorganisms. *J. Cell Biol.* 58:249, 1973.
34. Jensen, M. S., and Bainton, D. F.: Temporal changes in pH within the phagocytic vacuole of the polymorphonuclear neutrophilic leukocyte. *J. Cell Biol.* 56:379, 1973.
35. Stähelin, H., Karnovsky, M. L., and Suter, E.: Studies on the interaction between phagocytes and tubercle bacilli. III. The action of phagocytes upon C^{14}-labeled tubercle bacilli. *J. Exp. Med.* 104:137, 1956.
36. Cohn, Z. A.: The fate of bacteria within phagocytic cells. I. The degradation of isotopically labeled bacteria by polymorphonuclear leukocytes and macrophages. *J. Exp. Med.* 117:27, 1963.
37. Zeya, H. I., and Spitznagel, J. K.: Arginine-rich proteins of polymorphonuclear leukocyte lysosomes. Antimicrobial specificity and biochemical heterogeneity. *J. Exp. Med.* 127:927, 1968.
38. Rauch, H. C., Loomis, M. E., Johnson, M. E., and Favour, C. B.: *In vitro* suppression of polymorphonuclear leukocyte and lymphocyte glycolysis by cortisol. *Endocrinology* 68:375, 1961.
39. White, A.: Hormonal steroids, biochemistry, pharmacology and therapeutics. *Proceedings of the First International Congress of Hormonal Steroids, Vol. 1,* Academic Press, New York, p. 571, 1964.
40. DeDuve, C., Wattiaux, R., and Wibo, M.: Effects of fat-soluble compounds on lysosomes *in vitro. Biochem. Pharmacol.* 9:97, 1962.
41. Weissmann, G., Dukor, P., and Zurier, R. B.: Effect of cyclic AMP on release of lysosomal enzymes from phagocytes. *Nature* [*New Biol.*] 231:131, 1971.
42. Weissmann, G., Dukor, P., and Sessa, G.: Studies on lysosomes: Mechanisms of enzyme release from endocytic cells and a model for latency *in vitro.* In Forscher, B. K., and Houck, J. C. (eds): *Immunology of Inflammation,* Excerpta Medica Foundation, Amsterdam, p. 107. 1971.
43. Bourne, H. R., Lehrer, R. I., Cline, M. J., and Melmon, K. L.: Cyclic 3′, 5′-adenosine monophos-

phate in the human leukocyte: Synthesis degradation, and effects on neutrophil candidacidal activity. *J. Clin. Invest.* 50:920, 1971.
44. Cox, J. P., and Karnovsky, M. L.: The depression of phagocytosis by exogenous cyclic nucleotides, prostaglandins, and theophylline. *J. Cell Biol.* 59:480, 1973.
45. Mandell, G. L., Rubin, W., and Hook, E. W.: The effect of an NADH oxidase inhibitor (hydrocortisone) on polymorphonuclear leukocyte bactericidal activity. *J. Clin. Invest.* 49:1381, 1970.
46. Mackaness, G. B.: The immunological basis of acquired cellular resistance. *J. Exp. Med.* 120:105, 1964.
47. Mackaness, G. B.: The influence of immunologically committed lymphoid cells on macrophage activity *in vivo. J. Exp. Med.* 129:973, 1969.
48. Mackaness, G. B.: In Mudd, S. (ed.): *Infectious Agents and Host Reactions,* W. B. Saunders, Philadelphia, p. 62. 1970.
49. Ratzan, K. R., Musher, D. M., Keusch, G. T., and Weinstein, L.: Correlation of increased metabolic activity, resistance to infection, enhanced phagocytosis, and inhibition of bacterial growth by macrophages from Listeria—and BCG-infected mice. *Infect. Immun.* 5:499, 1972.
50. Stubbs, M., Kühner, A. V., Glass, E. A., David, J. R., and Karnovsky, M. L.: Metabolic and functional studies on activated mouse macrophages. *J. Exp. Med.* 137:537, 1973.
51. Nathan, C. F., Karnovsky, M. L., and David, J. R.: Alterations of macrophage functions by mediators from lymphocytes. *J. Exp. Med.* 133:1356, 1971.
52. Elsbach, P., Zucker-Franklin, D., and Sansaricq, C.: Increased lecithin synthesis during phagocytosis by normal leukocytes and by leukocytes of a patient with chronic granulomatous disease. *N. Engl. J. Med.* 280:1319, 1969.
53. Patriarca, P., Cramer, R., Dri, P., Fant, L., Basford, R. E., and Rossi, F.: NADPH-oxidizing activity in rabbit polymorphonuclear leukocytes; localization in azurophilic granules. *Biochem. Biophys. Res. Commun.* 53:830, 1973.
54. Paul, B. B., Jacobs, R. R., and Sbarra, A. J.: The role of the phagocyte in host-parasite interactions XXIV. Aldehyde generation by the myeloperoxidase-H_2O_2-chloride antimicrobial system: A possible *in vivo* mechanism of action. *Infect. Immun.* 2:414, 1970.
55. Stolc, V.: Regulation of iodine metabolism in human leukocytes by adenosine 3′, 5′-monophosphate. *Biochim. Biophys. Acta* 264:285, 1972.
56. Cline, M. J., and Lehrer, R. I.: D-Amino acid oxidase in leukocytes: A possible D-amino acid linked antimicrobial system. *Proc. Natl. Acad. Sci.* 62:756, 1969.

DISCUSSION

Hirsch: In the ascorbate model, did iron have any effect like that of copper?

Karnovsky: I don't believe it did. We tried iron and my recollection is that it is rather toxic on its own.

Hirsch: How about the affinity of lactoferrin for copper? Does anybody know?

Spitznagel: Masson has shown that lactoferrin has marked affinity for copper.

Sbarra: I am confused about the ascorbate effect. What does ascorbate do to killing by intact white cells? It seems to me that it has been reported.

Karnovsky: I don't know what was reported because I don't know much about the role of ascorbate, in mechanistic terms, in killing in the intact cells. I think there are data on ascorbate in terms of ascorbate-deficient animals and so on, but they are very complicated. This is purely a model system. We have no idea what the mechanism is at the level of the killed bacteria, and all I can report is that ascorbate and peroxide without metal ions really don't have any significant effect. Immediately after you add 10^{-5} molar copper, you begin to kill by three or four or more orders of magnitude.

Sbarra: I think the people at Bowman-Gray reported the effect of ascorbate on killing, and I think they have shown that killing is inhibited with ascorbate.

Klebanoff: Ascorbate was found to have no effect on the microbicidal activity of intact leukocytes although it did inhibit iodination by intact cells.

Sbarra: That is the point I want to make. I think in that work they were comparing ravioli with manicotti instead of manicotti with manicotti, and you can't really do that. They were studying iodination and decarboxylation by purified MPO preparations and killing by intact cells. Ascorbate did not effect killing by intact cells, but it did inhibit iodination and decarboxylation. We have studied decarboxylation and killing by an MPO preparation and ascorbate inhibits both decarboxylation and killing *(unpublished results).*

Klebanoff: Not in intact cells.

Sbarra: That is right.

Holmes-Gray: When you add ascorbate to the system, aren't you competing for peroxide?

Klebanoff: You are either competing for peroxide or reducing the oxidized product of the peroxidase reaction back to its original form.

Karnovsky: I tried to be quite clear that this is a model system and it *may* have relevance—I suspect it does. But wherever you get involved with ascorbate, as you and Linus Pauling know, there is a very complex situation.

Klebanoff: Table 1 demonstrates the bactericidal effect of ascorbic acid alone at relatively high concentrations on *E. coli* in lactate buffer pH 5.0. The involvement of a trace metal is indicated by the inhibitory effect of EDTA and by the prevention of this inhibition by the addition of an equimolar concentration of cupric sulfate. This antimicrobial effect of ascorbic acid is also inhibited by catalase, suggesting the involvement of H_2O_2 which is known to be formed during the copper-catalyzed autoxidation of ascorbic acid. When the ascorbic acid concentration was decreased to a level at which it had no bactericidal effect alone, the addition of iodide resulted in a return of toxicity. As with high concentrations of ascorbic acid alone, the ascorbic acid–iodide system was inhibited by EDTA and this was reversed by the addition of copper. The microbicidal activity of intact leukocytes is inhibited by azide and, to a lesser degree, cyanide presumably

TABLE 1. *Stimulation of the bactericidal activity of the ascorbic acid system by iodide*

Supplements	*E. coli* (organisms/ml)
None	4.7×10^6 [a]
AA (10^{-2}M)	0
AA (10^{-2}M) + EDTA (10^{-4}M)	3.7×10^6
AA (10^{-2}M) + EDTA (10^{-4}M) + Cu^{++} (10^{-4}M)	0
AA (10^{-4}M)	3.6×10^6
AA (10^{-4}M) + I^- (10^{-2}M)	0
AA (10^{-4}M) + I^- (10^{-2}M) + EDTA (10^{-4}M)	4.8×10^6
AA (10^{-4}M) + I^- (10^{-2}M) + EDTA (10^{-4}M) + Cu^{++} (10^{-4}M)	0

[a] Viable cell count following 60-min incubation.

due to the inhibition of the peroxidase system. Azide had no effect on the ascorbic acid system under our experimental conditions; however, cyanide was inhibitory presumably due to its chelating properties.

Karnovsky: This is without adding peroxide, of course.

Klebanoff: No peroxide was added.

Karnovsky: It certainly is true that ascorbic acid under certain conditions, particularly in the presence of traces of metals and particularly transitional metals, will produce peroxide. I wonder whether the experiment in which 10^{-4} molar ascorbic acid and iodide give complete killing in your system isn't due to the production of a small amount of peroxide which you are blocking when you add the EDTA.

Klebanoff: That is what we assume the mechanism is because we can get further potentiate with peroxide and because the system is inhibited by catalase as well as by EDTA.

Cohn: Have you looked at dehydroascorbate in the system?

Klebanoff: No.

Karnovsky: The dehydroascorbate is a little more active in our copper-mediated system but not in the cobalt-mediated system.

Alper: What is known about the distribution and concentration of copper and similar elements in phagocytic cells?

Karnovsky: I asked Bert Vallee this question the other day because he and others have done so much on the distribution of zinc in these cells, and offhand he didn't have data on copper or cobalt. I suppose it is possible that, if there is a metallo protein that is involved in a reaction that concerns ascorbate and peroxide, it might not be a copper enzyme. It might be an iron enzyme or a zinc enzyme.

Alper: Has the microprobe been used for this purpose? It would seem to be admirably suited to the task.

Karnovsky: Morris Karnovsky and I have talked about getting that going but have not tried it yet.

Spitznagel: Have you tried vitamin B_{12}?

Karnovsky: No.

Cohn: You talked about a polymorph taking in 100 percent of the membrane. What is this based upon, what type of calculation?

Karnovsky: You know as well as I do what sort of rough calculation it's based upon. It's based on the radius of the particle and the number of particles that you get in—and they are reasonably spherical—and it's based on the radius of the cell and the assumption that the cell is a sphere, which is pretty poor. That is all you can do at the moment, until somebody can tell us exactly what the total surface area of these cells is likely to be. And I am sure it is much, much greater than that of a sphere of the same diameter. However, there is a limit to the number of particles you can get the cells to phagocytize. We are pushing that limit. It is the maximum phagocytosis we can get without having the cells burst.

Cohn: Actually, this has been approached recently by Ralph Steinman in our lab, using certain fibroblasts that are grown in suspension, as more or less round cells, and then using morphometric studies on electron micrographs to calculate the actual area of the surface membrane. If you compare these figures to what you'd expect with a simple sphere, you find the surface area is at least three times greater in such a cell in suspension, which might fit very well with the amount of nucleotidase you interiorize.

Karnovsky: Except when cells are growing as real spheres, as you describe, we have no idea what relevance the surface area has to that of the phagocytic, active cell. Are these cells nonphagocytic?

Cohn: These are phagocytic.

Karnovsky: Really phagocytic?

Cohn: Fifty percent, for polystyrene latex.

Karnovsky: That much? Really, a factor of threefold wouldn't frighten me too much.

Hirsch: Another technical difficulty encountered in this kind of study is the difficulty of establishing whether particles are on or in.

Karnovsky: On or in?

Hirsch: Yes. How do you distinguish the two?

Karnovsky: That was a topic that was discussed by Haeckel in 1862. At that time he worried about exactly the same problem, but I don't think there has been a great deal of advance on what Haeckel originally did. He put the cells gently between two cover glasses and rolled them around a bit to see if any of the particles came off; they didn't so he assumed the particles were internalized. We make electron micrograms as often as we can to make sure we are not seeing too many particles just clumping around outside of the cell. Adequate washing does remove most of the external particles. And, if you look at the cells under electron microscopy, you see that most of the particles you believe to be inside by chemical measurements are really in.

Hirsch: I think it's a difficult question to answer. Especially as the cell begins to run out of membrane or run short on membrane, you may have a large number of particles in phagocytic crypts in which the vacuole has not really closed.

Karnovsky: That we do look for. We once reported peroxidase coming out of those semiclosed vesicles. I have pictures here showing the "secretion," if you will, of peroxidase from those semiclosed crypts. Although we looked for that particularly, it represents an awfully small amount compared with the number of particles that, as far as you can see in a single section, are really internalized.

Becker: As a possible answer to that, you might try erythrophagocytosis in which one can lyse the red cell which adheres but is not internalized.

Bellanti: I was intrigued by your figures on the amount of superoxide production by alveolar macrophages following phagocytosis. I wonder if you'd comment on this as a function of the metabolic behavior of the cell.

Karnovsky: The alveolar macrophage has a high respiratory rate, about 20. This is very high if you consider that liver is about 10. It is tightly coupled respiration. This cell shows a very small respiratory increase during phagocytosis, perhaps

10 percent, but really quite small compared with its base line respiration, most of which is cyanide-sensitive and cytochrome-linked. You can come to the conclusion that this is an efficient cell which by increasing its respiration just a little bit provides the energy to do the job—if you accept that energy is needed for phagocytosis. If the value is 40 percent for superoxide production upon oxygen consumption, I won't be too amazed, but, if it goes up to 80 percent as was true in the normal peritoneal macrophage, I will be quite surprised.

Snyderman: I was interested in the superoxide production from different sources, and I wondered how much that varies and how you correct for that.

Karnovsky: That is a very tough problem. In laboratories that have tried to measure it on whole cells you have a choice, either break up the cells and deproteinize to get at the superoxide, which is painful to contemplate because you are going to lose it anyway, or take simply what is to be found in the external medium. One accepts two things: one, that a good deal of the superoxide might have remained intracellularly, and two, there is superoxide dismutase kicking around in the cell and we are only getting that part of the superoxide that escaped. There is some information on superoxide dismutase in some of these cells, particularly the polymorphonuclear leukocyte. If anybody here has any information it would be very important.

Stossel: Concerning the question about paraffin oil particles sticking nonspecifically to cells, the paraffin oil particles and cells are undergoing different centrifugal forces leading to efficient separation. If at the end of a washing procedure, you trypsinize so that the albumin falls apart and the extracellular emulsion breaks, you don't lose any of the cell-associated particles.

Karnovsky: Under conditions in which you recover the phagosomes and compare the phagosomes that you try to recover as quantitatively as possible with the cells on which you have measured the phagocytosis, i.e., the same batch of cells, we seem to get a very good agreement as to the number of particles ingested. One could argue that when we break up the cells we break up the particles that are on the outside and we get the dye immediately released—giving high results. One also does a gradient centrifugation and extracts the dye after isolating the phagosomes according to Dr. Stossel's methodology. I think this takes care of the problem.

Cohn: You'd have to assume all those particles that flow to the gradient are membrane-bounded.

Johnston: We have looked very hard at the location of superoxide dismutase in polys that are as pure as we can get them. Most of the enzyme appears to be present in the cytosol in the form of a copper-zinc protein. There is also a mitochondrial enzyme.

Karnovsky: But probably none of that, considering the state of the mitochondria in the polymorphonuclear leukocyte.

Johnston: That is right; its concentration appears very small.

The Phagocytic Cell in Host Resistance, edited
by Joseph A. Bellanti and Delbert H. Dayton.
Raven Press, New York © 1975.

Antimicrobial Systems of the Polymorphonuclear Leukocyte

S. J. Klebanoff

Departments of Medicine and Microbiology, University of Washington School of Medicine, Seattle, Washington 98195

The neutrophilic polymorphonuclear leukocyte (PMN) is a highly specialized cell whose primary function is to ingest and kill microorganisms and it does this extremely well. The striking morphologic and metabolic consequences of phagocytosis initiate a massive and varied attack on the ingested organisms from which few survive. Some aspects of this attack will be considered here, using the classification shown in Table 1.

TABLE 1. *Antimicrobial systems of the PMN*

Oxygen-dependent antimicrobial systems
MPO-mediated
MPO-independent
H_2O_2
Superoxide anion (O_2^-)
Hydroxyl radical ($OH\cdot$)
Singlet oxygen
Oxygen-independent antimicrobial systems
Acid
Lysozyme
Lactoferrin
Granular cationic proteins

OXYGEN-DEPENDENT ANTIMICROBIAL SYSTEMS

The capacity of PMN's to kill certain ingested organisms is decreased by anaerobiosis (1–5) indicating a requirement for oxygen for optimal microbicidal activity. The oxygen-dependent antimicrobial systems are divided here into those that require myeloperoxidase (MPO) and those that do not.

MPO-Mediated Antimicrobial Systems

MPO in highly purified form has marked antimicrobial activity when combined with H_2O_2 and an appropriate oxidizable cofactor. This was demonstrated first with thiocyanate (6, 7) and subsequently with iodide, bromide, or chloride as the cofactor (8,9). The MPO-mediated antimicrobial system has potent bactericidal

(5–10), fungicidal (11,12), virucidal (13), and mycoplasmacidal (14) activity. It is also toxic to certain mammalian cells (15–17).

Recently evidence for the involvement of the MPO-mediated antimicrobial system in the microbicidal activity of the PMN was reviewed (4) and I will not consider it in detail here. The accumulated evidence strongly supports an important role for this system in the microbicidal activity of the cell. Consideration will be limited here to the possible role of the superoxide anion and singlet oxygen in the MPO-mediated antimicrobial system.

Superoxide Anion

The superoxide anion ($0_2^{\cdot}$) is a highly reactive radical which is formed by the univalent reduction of oxygen (18). It can act either as a reductant (e.g., in the reduction of ferricytochrome C) or as an oxidant (e.g., in the oxidation of epinephrine), and when two radicals interact, one is oxidized and the other is reduced as follows:

$$0_2^{\cdot} + 0_2^{\cdot} + 2H^+ \rightarrow 0_2 + H_2O_2$$

This dismutation occurs spontaneously; it is also catalyzed by the enzyme superoxide dismutase. Superoxide dismutase inhibits reactions dependent on the superoxide anion; indeed, the demonstration of such an inhibition is used as evidence for the presence of this oxygen radical.

The formation of the superoxide anion by intact PMN's is suggested by the reduction of ferricytochrome C by human leukocytes and the inhibition of this reduction by added superoxide dismutase (19). The formation of the superoxide anion as measured in this way is increased by phagocytosis (19) and is low in the leukocytes of patients with chronic granulomatous disease (CGD) (20). Two questions are posed by this observation. Is the superoxide anion an intermediate in H_2O_2 formation by the PMN and thus indirectly involved in the MPO-mediated antimicrobial system? Is the superoxide anion toxic to ingested organisms and thus directly involved in the microbicidal activity of the cell? The first question will be considered here and the second in a later section of this chapter.

Xanthine, xanthine oxidase, chloride, and MPO have a marked microbicidal effect on *E. coli* (Table 2), which is abolished by deletion of any of the components of the system (21). Iodide or bromide, at 1mM concentration, cannot substitute for chloride as the halide component under these conditions; indeed, iodide and bromide inhibit the chloride-dependent system (Table 2). Xanthine and xanthine oxidase generate both the superoxide anion and H_2O_2 (22). The requirement for H_2O_2 in the chloride- and MPO-dependent microbicidal system is indicated by the inhibitory effect of catalase and by the replacement of xanthine and xanthine oxidase by reagent H_2O_2 (Table 2). The superoxide anion, however, is an intermediate in H_2O_2 formation and its involvement in the antimicrobial system is

TABLE 2. *Role of the superoxide anion in the xanthine-xanthine oxidase-chloride-MPO system*

Supplements	*E. coli* (organisms/ml $\times 10^{-6}$)
None	6.6
Complete system	0.00009
Chloride omitted, iodide (1 mM) added	7.3
Chloride omitted, bromide (1 mM) added	7.4
Iodide added	7.5
Bromide added	5.0
Catalase (6 μg/ml) added	5.8
Xanthine and xanthine oxidase omitted, H_2O_2 (0.1 mM) added	0
Cytochrome C (70 μg/ml) added	2.8
Cytochrome C and superoxide dismutase (4.4 μg/ml) added	0.04
Cytochrome C, superoxide dismutase and catalase added	7.5

The complete system consisted of 0.06 M sodium phosphate buffer pH 7.0, 1×10^{-4}M EDTA, 5×10^{6} *E. coli*, 1×10^{-5} M sodium xanthine, 0.5 μg xanthine oxidase, 0.1 M sodium chloride, and 30 *o*-dianisidine units MPO. Final volume 0.5 ml. Incubation 60 min at 37°C.

indicated by the inhibitory effect of cytochrome C and the partial reversal of this inhibition by superoxide dismutase. Catalase inhibited microbicidal activity in the presence of cytochrome C and superoxide dismutase as it did in their absence. These studies can be best explained by an inhibition of H_2O_2 formation by cytochrome C due to its reaction with the superoxide anion and the reversal of this inhibition by superoxide dismutase (21).

The superoxide anion therefore can serve as an intermediate in the formation of the H_2O_2 needed for the isolated MPO-mediated antimicrobial system. If a similar relationship exists in the intact cell, then the interaction of superoxide dismutase and scavengers of the superoxide anion offers a mechanism for the control of microbicidal activity through the control of H_2O_2 formation.

Singlet Oxygen

Singlet molecular oxygen is an electronically excited state of oxygen which emits light (chemiluminescence) when it reverts to the triplet ground state. Chemiluminescence is observed when normal leukocytes are incubated with particles (23), whereas CGD leukocytes are unresponsive in this regard (24). Although chemiluminescence can result from reactions other than those dependent on singlet oxygen, these studies nevertheless have focused attention on electronic excitation states in the PMN.

One possible source of singlet oxygen is the MPO-mediated antimicrobial system. When hypochlorite is added to an excess of H_2O_2, oxygen is released in an amount nearly equivalent to the amount of hypochlorite added as follows:

$$H_2O_2 + OCl^- \rightarrow O_2 + Cl^- + H_2O$$

A weak red chemiluminescence accompanies this reaction and it has been proposed that the metastable intermediate responsible for this emission is singlet molecular oxygen (25). Since hypochlorite is the presumed product of the oxidation of chloride by MPO and H_2O_2, its reaction with excess H_2O_2 to form singlet oxygen might be expected and, indeed, chemiluminescence is observed when MPO is mixed with H_2O_2 and chloride (26). Singlet molecular oxygen is also formed during the dismutation of $0_2^{\overline{\cdot}}$ (25).

Singlet oxygen can dissipate its excess energy not only by the emission of light as it reverts to the ground state but also by reaction with certain chemical groups, particularly double bonds. Substituted dioxetanes are formed

$$>C{=}C< \;\rightarrow\; \begin{array}{c} 0{-}0 \\ |\quad\;| \\ >C{-}C< \end{array}$$

which are generally labile, dissociating to electronically excited carbonyl groups, which also revert to the ground state with chemiluminescence. It was proposed by Allen et al.(23) that reactions of this type may be toxic to microorganisms and thus responsible, in part or totally, for the microbicidal effect of the peroxidase system. That singlet oxygen is microbicidal is suggested by the toxicity of certain dyes in the presence of both light and oxygen, a reaction which may be mediated by singlet oxygen (for review see 27). This photodynamic action of eosin on *E. coli* is shown in Table 3. Maximum toxicity to the organisms under the

TABLE 3. *Photodynamic effect of eosin on E. coli*

Supplements	Viable cell count (organisms/ml $\times 10^{-6}$)
Eosin + light + oxygen	0.11
Oxygen omitted	4.08
Light omitted	4.79
Eosin omitted	4.56

The complete system contained 0.1 M sodium acetate buffer pH 5.0, 5.0 $\times 10^6$ *E. coli*, and 5 $\times 10^{-5}$ M eosin. Oxygen was deleted by gassing the mixture with prepurified nitrogen in the dark for 5 min prior to and 5 min following the addition of the bacteria and eosin. The tubes were then exposed to light to initiate the reaction. Light was omitted by incubation in darkened tubes. Final volume 0.5 ml. Incubation 60 min at 37°C.

conditions employed required both light and oxygen. If singlet oxygen is the reactive species responsible for the photodynamic effect of eosin under these conditions, then it is certainly bactericidal. Table 4 demonstrates the effect of the singlet oxygen quencher DABCO [1,4-diazobicyclo (2,2,2) octane] (28) on the photodynamic effect of eosin and on the MPO-mediated antimicrobial system

TABLE 4. *Inhibitory effect of DABCO*

DABCO (M)	Viable cell count (organisms/ml X 10^{-6})		
	Eosin	$MPO + I + H_2O_2$	$MPO + Cl + H_2O_2$
—	0.14	0.013	0.007
1×10^{-2}	2.37	4.47	5.28
1×10^{-3}	0.49	0.08	4.91
1×10^{-4}	0.21	0.03	5.13
1×10^{-5}	0.12		3.30
1×10^{-6}			0.05
1×10^{-7}			0.01

The complete system contained 0.06 M sodium lactate buffer pH 4.6, 5.0×10^6 *E. coli,* DABCO [1,4-diazobicyclo (2,2,2) octane] as indicated and either (a) 2×10^{-4} M eosin, (b) 30 units of MPO, 2×10^{-7} M sodium iodide and 1×10^{-5} M H_2O_2, or (c) 30 units of MPO, 1×10^{-5} M sodium chloride and 1×10^{-5} M H_2O_2. Final volume 0.5 ml. Incubation 60 min at 37°C.

using either iodide or chloride as the cofactor. DABCO was found to inhibit all three systems; however, the MPO-H_2O_2-chloride system was considerably more sensitive to this inhibitor than were the other two systems. It should be emphasized that the action of DABCO on the microbicidal systems may not be due solely to the quenching of singlet oxygen. The question remains as to whether singlet oxygen is formed in adequate amounts by intact leukocytes to produce a significant antimicrobial effect.

MPO-Independent but Oxygen-Dependent Antimicrobial Systems

The microbicidal activity of PMN's with no detectable peroxidase, although decreased, is not abolished (29–31), indicating that MPO-independent antimicrobial systems also are present in the cell. The MPO-independent systems are, in part, dependent on oxygen. Thus the microbicidal defect in the leukocytes of patients with hereditary MPO-deficiency is not as severe as in CGD leukocytes, suggesting the retention of a microbicidal system or systems in cells that lack peroxidase which is not present in cells deficient in oxidative metabolism. The inhibition of the staphylocidal activity of MPO-deficient leukocytes by anaerobiosis (4) is further evidence that at least one of the antimicrobial systems in these cells is oxygen-dependent. Increased oxygen consumption (4), glucose C-1 oxidation (32), and formate oxidation (32) by MPO-deficient leukocytes is compatible with the formation of potentially toxic oxygen radicals and H_2O_2 in these cells in amounts that are greater than normal. Their microbicidal activity in the absence of MPO is considered here.

H_2O_2

H_2O_2 at relatively high concentration has antimicrobial activity in the absence of myeloperoxidase. The toxicity of H_2O_2 is increased by certain low molecular weight substances such as iodide (8, 33) or ascorbic acid (34–36). Catalase can substitute for myeloperoxidase as the catalyst of the antimicrobial system at acid pH in the presence of iodide and a H_2O_2-generating system (33, 37). Catalase, however, has been localized in the cytosol of the guinea pig PMN (38–40) and is not transferred into the phagocytic vacuole following phagocytosis (40). Peroxidase (or catalase) of microbial origin could theoretically substitute for MPO as the catalyst of the microbicidal system.

Superoxide Anion

A possible role for the superoxide anion as an intermediate in H_2O_2 formation in the leukocyte has been considered above. This highly reactive radical may, in addition, exert a direct toxic effect on certain ingested organisms.

The toxicity of the superoxide anion is affected by the level and location of superoxide dismutase in the microorganism. Organisms that require oxygen as a terminal electron acceptor contain relatively high levels of this enzyme; organisms which tolerate but do not require oxygen have intermediate levels; and obligate anaerobes have none (41). This suggests that microorganisms exposed to oxygen may be protected from the toxic effect of the superoxide anion by superoxide dismutase (41, 42). Support for this thesis has come from the studies of Gregory et al. (43). *E. coli* B grown in an iron-rich medium contain relatively high levels of an iron superoxide dismutase in the periplasmic space and are resistant to exogenous superoxide anion. In contrast, organisms grown in an iron-deficient medium contain low levels of this enzyme and are killed by superoxide anion generated either enzymatically or photochemically. Similarly, our studies (Table 2) (21) suggest that the toxic effect of the superoxide anion on *E. coli, Staphylococcus aureus,* and *C. tropicalis* grown in complete medium is weak when compared to that of the H_2O_2 formed from it, when supplemented with chloride and MPO. It should be emphasized that other organisms low in superoxide dismutase (e.g., obligate or aerotolerant anaerobes) may be more susceptible to the superoxide anion.

Other oxygen derivatives, e.g., hydroxyl radicals (44, 45) or singlet oxygen also may be microbicidal in the absence of MPO. Further studies are needed to properly evaluate their role.

OXYGEN-INDEPENDENT ANTIMICROBIAL SYSTEMS

The microbicidal activity of PMN's is not abolished by anaerobic conditions (1–5, 31), suggesting that oxygen-independent antimicrobial systems are also present in the cell.

Some caution should be exercised in the interpretation of data based on the production of anaerobiosis by gassing with nitrogen since: it may be difficult to remove the last trace of oxygen sequestered in intracellular compartments; a pool of preformed H_2O_2 or other product of oxidative metabolism may persist; and the retention of microbicidal activity under anaerobic conditions does not necessarily indicate that oxygen-independent systems are responsible for the death of the organisms under aerobic conditions, only that a system is available when oxygen is removed which can kill the organism. This may be a back-up system which is not needed when oxygen is present. However, the accumulated evidence obtained not only from studies of the effect of anaerobiosis on microbicidal activity but also from the isolation of antimicrobial agents from leukocytes that are active in the absence of oxygen supports the presence of oxygen-independent antimicrobial systems in the intact cell. They include acid, lysozyme, lactoferrin, and granular cationic proteins.

Acid

There is abundant evidence that the pH within the phagocytic vacuole is distinctly acid. In a recent study, Jensen and Bainton (46) reported that in rat cells the pH falls to approximately 6.5 in 3 min and reaches a level of about 4.0 in 7 to 15 min. A fall in intravacuolar pH in human neutrophils to 6.0 to 6.5 has been reported (47). The pH level attained in the vacuole may be microbicidal for certain acid-sensitive organisms and microbiostatic for others.

Lysozyme

There is strong evidence that lysozyme-sensitive bacteria can be killed by this enzyme in the phagocytic vacuole (48, 49). The organisms lysed by lysozyme under the usual conditions of testing, however, are limited to a small number of saprophytic bacteria (these organisms may be saprophytic in part *because* of their sensitivity to lysozyme). Most organisms are resistant to the lytic action of lysozyme unless damaged in some way [e.g., by complement + antibody (50), ascorbic acid + H_2O_2 (35) or chelating agents (51).] Although a synergistic relationship may exist between lysozyme and other antimicrobial systems in the leukocyte, it is probable that lysozyme serves a digestive rather than a microbicidal function for most organisms.

Lactoferrin

Lactoferrin is an iron-binding protein which has microbiostatic properties when not fully saturated with iron, due to the chelation of the iron required for the growth of the organisms (52–54). Since lactoferrin is present in leukocyte granules (55, 56), it may serve this function in the phagocytic vacuole.

Granular Cationic Proteins

The description of phagocytin (57) and leukin (58) in 1956 aroused intense interest in the antimicrobial agents that can be extracted from intact leukocytes or leukocyte granules by dilute acid. These agents are heat stable, resistant to strong acid (0.2N H_2SO_4), and strongly cationic. They have been divided into a number of fractions by electrophoretic techniques, and differences in the antimicrobial specificity of the various fractions have been detected (59,60). Some of the cationic proteins of human PMN granules have been isolated in highly purified form (61). They have been detected by cytochemical techniques in the phagocytic vacuole bound to the ingested organism (62). These studies strongly suggest that granular cationic proteins are among the antimicrobial systems of the PMN. Their contribution to the total antimicrobial activity of the cell, however, is not known. Neutrophil dysfunction associated with a specific defect in cationic proteins has not yet been detected.

MPO as well as granular cationic proteins are extracted from PMN's by dilute acid. A comparison of the antimicrobial activity of an acid extract of human leukocytes either alone or supplemented with chloride and H_2O_2 is shown in Table 5. The extract alone produced a small (approximately 30%) but statistically significant fall in viable cell count at a dilution of 1:5 and 1:50 with *E. coli* as the test organism. This effect was markedly increased when the extract was supplemented with H_2O_2 and chloride. A greater than 3 log fall in viable cell count was produced by the supplemented system at an extract dilution of 1:5,000. A similar difference in the bactericidal activity of the supplemented and nonsupplemented extract was observed with *S. aureus* 502A as the test organism or when the extract was prepared from isolated human leukocyte granules. The bactericidal effect of the supplemented cell extract was not observed at the highest extract concentration employed due to the presence of inhibitors of the MPO-

TABLE 5. *Bactericidal activity of an acid extract of intact leukocytes*

Extract (E)			Bactericidal activity (viable cell count $\times 10^{-6}$)		
Dilution	Protein (μg)	Peroxidase activity (U)	E alone	$E + H_2O_2 + Cl^-$	$E + H_2O_2 + Cl^- + MPO$
—	—	—	—	9.9 [a]	0 [a,b]
1:50,000	.045	0.24	9.1	9.1	0 [b]
1:5,000	0.45	2.4	8.9	0.002 [b]	0 [b]
1:500	4.5	24	8.3	0 [b]	0 [b]
1:50	45	240	6.3 [c]	0.002 [b]	0.0006 [b]
1:5	450	2,400	6.1 [c]	6.6	7.4

Human leukocytes were isolated by dextran sedimentation and ammonium chloride lysis and suspended in 0.01 M citric acid at a concentration of 1×10^8 PMN's per ml. The preparation was homogenized with a Potter-Elvehjehm homogenizer and the supernatant collected by centrifugation. The extract (E) was added in the amounts indicated to 9×10^6 *E. coli* in 0.06 M sodium lactate buffer pH 5.0. The mixture was incubated for 60 min at 37°C with (1) no other additions, (2) H_2O_2 (10^{-4} M) and chloride (0.1 M), or (3) H_2O_2 (10^{-4} M) + chloride (0.1 M) + MPO (30 *o*-dianisidine U) and the viable cell count determined. Final volume 0.5 ml. Results are the mean of three experiments.

[a] E not added.

[b] $p < 0.001$ experimental vs. control viable cell count.

[c] $p < 0.05$ experimental vs. control viable cell count.

H_2O_2-chloride system. The inhibitors were almost entirely removed by dialysis, indicating that they are largely of low molecular weight. They presumably consist mainly of low molecular weight reducing agents present in the cytosol of the cells, since extracts prepared from isolated granules contained considerably lower levels of the inhibitors. The presence of these inhibitors in the phagocytic vacuole and their influence on the activity of the peroxidase system are not known.

The small antimicrobial effect of the extract alone may reflect the particular test organisms used. Further, the measure of toxicity employed (i.e., fall in viable cell count) is not particularly sensitive and would not detect a milder injury leading to a decreased rate of growth. The findings do emphasize, however, that the antimicrobial activity of the leukocyte extract is increased many orders of magnitude by the addition of H_2O_2 and a halide, suggesting that the microbicidal potential of the MPO-mediated antimicrobial system is considerably greater than that of cationic proteins extracted under the same conditions. It cannot be assumed that the MPO-mediated antimicrobial system is not operative when extract is employed in the absence of added H_2O_2 or chloride since some organisms generate H_2O_2, and the amount of chloride (or other cofactor) present in the extract or organism may be adequate. The two systems can be differentiated under these conditions by the sensitivity of MPO to heat and to certain inhibitors, e.g., azide and cyanide.

In conclusion, it can be assumed that a number of systems contribute to the antimicrobial activity of the PMN. Their relative role would be expected to vary with the source of the leukocytes, the availability of oxygen, and the type of microorganism ingested. For example, chicken leukocytes do not contain MPO (63), bovine leukocytes do not contain lysozyme (64), and rabbit heterophils are particularly rich in cationic proteins (65). Some microorganisms contribute to their own destruction through the formation of H_2O_2 or acid, whereas others are protected from cellular antimicrobial systems by catalase or superoxide dismutase or by the nature of their cell wall material (66). Particular organisms may be susceptible to more than one antimicrobial system in the PMN and thus are effectively handled despite the loss of one of these systems. Completely effective back-up systems appear to be unavailable for other organisms, e.g., those organisms found in the lesions in CGD.

ACKNOWLEDGMENT

This work was supported in part by U.S. Public Health Service grants AI 07763 and HD 02266.

REFERENCES

1. Selvaraj, R. J., and Sbarra, A. J.: Relationship of glycolytic and oxidative metabolism to particle entry and destruction in phagocytosing cells. *Nature* 211:1272–1276, 1966.
2. McRipley, R. J., and Sbarra, A. J.: Role of the phagocyte in host-parasite interactions. XI. Relationship between stimulated oxidative metabolism and hydrogen peroxide formation, and intracellular killing. *J. Bacteriol.* 94:1417–1424, 1967.
3. Holmes, B., Page, A. R., Windhorst, D. B., Quie, P. G., White, J. G., and Good, R. A.: The

metabolic pattern and phagocytic function of leukocytes from children with chronic granulomatous disease. *Ann. N.Y. Acad. Sci.* 155:888–901, 1968.
4. Klebanoff, S. J., and Hamon, C. B.: Role of myeloperoxidase-mediated antimicrobial systems in intact leukocytes. *J. Reticuloendothel. Soc.* 12:170–196, 1972.
5. Mandell, G. L.: Bactericidal activity of aerobic and anaerobic polymorphonuclear neutrophils. *Infect. Immun.* 9:337–341, 1974.
6. Klebanoff, S. J., and Luebke, R. G.: The antilactobacillus system of saliva. Role of salivary peroxidase. *Proc. Soc. Exp. Biol. Med.* 118:483–486, 1965.
7. Klebanoff, S. J., Clem, W. H., and Luebke, R. G.: The peroxidase-thiocyanate-hydrogen peroxide antimicrobial system. *Biochim. Biophys. Acta* 117:63–72, 1966.
8. Klebanoff, S. J.: Iodination of bacteria: A bactericidal mechanism. *J. Exp. Med.* 126:1063–1078, 1967.
9. Klebanoff, S. J.: Myeloperoxidase-halide-hydrogen peroxide antibacterial system. *J. Bacteriol.* 95:2131–2138, 1968.
10. McRipley, R. J., and Sbarra, A. J.: Role of the phagocyte in host-parasite interactions. XII. Hydrogen peroxide-myeloperoxidase bactericidal system in the phagocyte. *J. Bacteriol.* 94:1425–1430, 1967.
11. Lehrer, R. I.: Antifungal effects of peroxidase systems. *J. Bacteriol.* 99:361–365, 1969.
12. Klebanoff, S. J.: Myeloperoxidase-mediated antimicrobial systems and their role in leukocyte function. In Schultz, J. (ed.): *Biochemistry of the Phagocytic Process: Localization and the Role of Myeloperoxidase and the Mechanism of the Halogenation Reaction.* North-Holland Publ. Co., Amsterdam, pp. 89–110. 1970.
13. Belding, M. E., Klebanoff, S. J., and Ray, C. G.: Peroxidase-mediated virucidal systems. *Science* 167:195–196, 1970.
14. Jacobs, A. A., Low, I. E., Paul, B. B., Strauss, R. R., and Sbarra, A. J.: Mycoplasmacidal activity of peroxidase-H_2O_2-halide systems. *Infect. Immun.* 5:127–131, 1972.
15. Smith, D. C., and Klebanoff, S. J.: A uterine fluid-mediated sperm-inhibitory system. *Biol. Reprod.* 3:229–235, 1970.
16. Edelson, P. J., and Cohn, Z. A.: Peroxidase-mediated mammalian cell cytotoxicity. *J. Exp. Med.* 138:318–323, 1973.
17. Philpott, G. W., Bower, R. J., and Parker, C. W.: Selective iodination and cytotoxicity of tumor cells with an antibody-enzyme conjugate. *Surgery* 74:51–58, 1973.
18. Fridovich, I.: Superoxide radical and superoxide dismutase. *Accts. Chem. Res.* 5:321–326, 1972.
19. Babior, B. M., Kipnes, R. S., and Curnutte, J. T.: Biological defense mechanisms. The production by leukocytes of superoxide, a potential bactericidal agent. *J. Clin. Invest.* 52:741–744, 1973.
20. Curnutte, J. T., Whitten, D. M., and Babior, B. M.: Defective leukocyte superoxide production in chronic granulomatous disease. *N. Engl. J. Med.* 290:593–597, 1974.
21. Klebanoff, S. J.: Role of the superoxide anion in the myeloperoxidase-mediated antimicrobial system. *J. Biol. Chem.* 249:3724–3728, 1974.
22. Fridovich, I.: Quantitative aspects of the production of superoxide anion radical by milk xanthine oxidase. *J. Biol. Chem.* 245:4053–4057, 1970.
23. Allen, R. C., Stjernholm, R. L., and Steele, R. H.: Evidence for the generation of an electronic excitation state(s) in human polymorphonuclear leukocytes and its participation in bactericidal activity. *Biochem. Biophys. Res. Commun.* 47:679–684, 1972.
24. Stjernholm, R. L., Allen, R. C., Steele, R. H., Waring, W. W., and Harris, J. A.: Impaired chemiluminescence during phagocytosis of opsonized bacteria. *Infect. Immun.* 7:313–314, 1973.
25. Kasha, M., and Khan, A. U.: The physics, chemistry and biology of singlet molecular oxygen. *Ann. N.Y. Acad. Sci.* 171:5–23, 1970.
26. Allen, R. C., and Steele, R. H.: The functional generation of electronic excitation states by myeloperoxidase. *Fed. Proc.* 32:478, 1973.
27. Spikes, J. D., and Straight, R.: Sensitized photochemical processes in biological systems. *Ann. Rev. Phys. Chem.* 18:409–436, 1967.
28. Foote, C. S., Denny, R. W., Weaver, L., Chang, Y., and Peters, J.: Quenching of singlet oxygen. *Ann. N.Y. Acad. Sci.* 171:139–145, 1971.
29. Lehrer, R. I., Hanifin, J., and Cline, M. J.: Defective bactericidal activity in myeloperoxidase-deficient human neutrophils. *Nature* 223:78–79, 1969.
30. Klebanoff, S. J.: Myeloperoxidase: Contribution to the microbicidal activity of intact leukocytes. *Science* 169:1095–1097, 1970.

31. Lehrer, R. I.: Functional aspects of a second mechanism of candidacidal activity of human neutrophils. *J. Clin. Invest.* 51:2566–2572, 1972.
32. Klebanoff, S. J., and Pincus, S. H.: Hydrogen peroxide utilization in myeloperoxidase-deficient leukocytes: A possible microbicidal control mechanism. *J. Clin. Invest.* 50:2226–2229, 1971.
33. Klebanoff, S. J., and Hamon, C. B.: Antimicrobial systems of mononuclear phagocytes. In van Furth, R. (ed.): *Mononuclear Phagocytes in Immunity, Infection and Pathology (in press).*
34. Ericsson, Y., and Lundbeck, H.: Antimicrobial effect *in vitro* of the ascorbic acid oxidation. 1. Effect on bacteria, fungi and viruses in pure culture. *Acta Pathol. Microbiol. Scand.* 37:493–506, 1955.
35. Miller, T. E.: Killing and lysis of Gram-negative bacteria through the synergistic effect of hydrogen peroxide, ascorbic acid and lysozyme. *J. Bacteriol.* 98:949–955, 1969.
36. DeChatelet, L. R., Cooper, M. R., and McCall, C. E.: Stimulation of the hexose monophosphate shunt in human neutrophils by ascorbic acid: Mechanism of action. *Ant. Ag. Chemotherap.* 1:12–16, 1972.
37. Klebanoff, S. J.: Antimicrobial activity of catalase at acid pH. *Proc. Soc. Exp. Biol. Med.* 132:571–574, 1969.
38. Evans, W. H., and Rechcigl, M., Jr.: Factors influencing myeloperoxidase and catalase activities in polymorphonuclear leukocytes. *Biochim. Biophys. Acta* 148:243–250, 1967.
39. Michell, R. H., Karnovsky, M. J., and Karnovsky, M. L.: The distribution of some granule-associated enzymes in guinea pig polymorphonuclear leucocytes. *Biochem. J.* 116: 207–216, 1970.
40. Stossel, T. P., Pollard, T. D., Mason, R. J., and Vaughn, M.: Isolation and properties of phagocytic vesicles from polymorphonuclear leukocytes. *J. Clin., Invest.* 50:1745–1757, 1971.
41. McCord, J. M., Keele, B. B., Jr., and Fridovich, I.: An enzyme-based theory of obligate anaerobiosis: The physiological function of superoxide dismutase. *Proc. Natl. Acad. Sci.* 68:1024–1027, 1971.
42. Gregory, E. M., and Fridovich, I.: Oxygen toxicity and the superoxide dismutase. *J. Bacteriol.* 114:1193–1197, 1973.
43. Gregory, E. M., Yost, F. J., Jr., and Fridovich, I.: Superoxide dismutase of *Escherichia coli:* Intracellular localization and functions. *J. Bacteriol.* 115:987–991, 1973.
44. Johnston, R. B., Jr., Keele, B., Webb, L., Kessler, D., and Rajagopalan, K. V.: Inhibition of phagocytic bactericidal activity by superoxide dismutase: A possible role for superoxide anion in the killing of phagocytized bacteria. *J. Clin. Invest.* 52:44a, 1973.
45. Gregory, E. M., and Fridovich, I.: Oxygen metabolism in *Lactobacillus plantarum. J. Bacteriol.* 117:166–169, 1974.
46. Jensen, M. S., and Bainton, D. F.: Temporal changes in pH within the phagocytic vacuole of the polymorphonuclear neutrophilic leukocyte. *J. Cell Biol.* 56:379–388, 1973.
47. Mandell, G. L.: Intraphagosomal pH of human polymorphonuclear neutrophils. *Proc. Soc. Exp. Biol. Med.* 134:447–449, 1970.
48. Brumfitt, W., and Glynn, A. A.: Intracellular killing of *Micrococcus lysodeikticus* by macrophages and polymorphonuclear leucocytes: A comparative study. *Br. J. Exp. Pathol.* 42:408–423, 1961.
49. Glynn, A. A., Brumfitt, W., and Salton, M. R. J.: The specific activity and specific inhibition of intracellular lysozyme. *Br. J. Exp. Pathol.* 47:331–336, 1966.
50. Muschel, L. H.: Immune bactericidal and bacteriolytic reactions. In Wolstenholme, G. E. W., and Knight, J. (eds): *Ciba Foundation Symposium on Complement.* Little Brown & Co., Inc., Boston, pp. 155–169. 1965.
51. Repaske, R.: Lysis of Gram-negative organisms and the role of versene. *Biochim. Biophys. Acta* 30:225–232, 1958.
52. Kirkpatrick, C. H., Green, I., Rich, R. R., and Schade, A. L.: Inhibition of growth of *Candida albicans* by iron-unsaturated lactoferrin: Relation to host-defense mechanisms in chronic mucocutaneous candidiasis. *J. Infect. Dis.* 124:539–544, 1971.
53. Masson, P. L., and Heremans, J. F.: Studies on lactoferrin, the iron-binding protein of secretions. *Protides Biol. Fluids* 14:115–124, 1966.
54. Oram, J. D., and Reiter, B.: Inhibition of bacteria by lactoferrin and other iron-chelating agents. *Biochim. Biophys. Acta* 170:351–365, 1968.
55. Masson, P. L., Heremans, J. F., and Schonne, E.: Lactoferrin, an iron-binding protein in neutrophilic leukocytes. *J. Exp. Med.* 130:643–658, 1969.
56. Baggiolini, M., deDuve, C., Masson, P. L., and Heremans, J. F.: Association of lactoferrin with specific granules in rabbit heterophil leukocytes. *J. Exp. Med.* 131:559–570, 1970.

57. Hirsch, J. G.: Phagocytin: A bactericidal substance from polymorphonuclear leucocytes. *J. Exp. Med.* 103:589–611, 1956.
58. Skarnes, R. C., and Watson, D. W.: Characterization of leukin: An antibacterial factor from leucocytes active against Gram-positive pathogens. *J. Exp. Med.* 104:829–845, 1956.
59. Zeya, H. I., and Spitznagel, J. K.: Arginine-rich proteins of polymorphonuclear leukocyte lysosomes. Antimicrobial specificity and biochemical heterogeneity. *J. Exp. Med.* 127:927–941, 1968.
60. Lehrer, R. I.: The bactericidal components of human neutrophil (PMN) granules. *Clin. Res.* 21:560, 1973.
61. Olsson, I., and Venge, P.: Cationic proteins of human granulocytes. I. Isolation of the cationic proteins from the granules of leukaemic myeloid cells. *Scand. J. Haematol.* 9:204–214, 1972.
62. Spitznagel, J. K., and Chi, H.-Y.: Cationic proteins and antibacterial properties of infected tissues and leukocytes. *Am. J. Pathol.* 43:697–711, 1963.
63. Brune, K., Leffell, M. S., and Spitznagel, J. K.: Microbicidal activity of peroxidaseless chicken heterophile leukocytes. *Infect. Immun.* 5:283–287, 1972.
64. Padgett, G. A., and Hirsch, J. G.: Lysozyme: Its absence in tears and leukocytes of cattle. *Aust. J. Exp. Biol. Med. Sci.* 45:569–570, 1967.
65. Zeya, H. I., and Spitznagel, J. K.: Characterization of cationic protein-bearing granules of polymorphonuclear leukocytes. *Lab. Invest.* 24:229–236, 1971.
66. Tagesson, C., and Stendahl, O.: Influence of the cell surface lipopolysaccharide structure of *Salmonella typhimurium* on resistance to intracellular bactericidal systems. *Acta Pathol. Microbiol. Scand.* 81:473–480, 1973.

DISCUSSION

Hirsch: In your last two tables what is your test medium for comparing two bactericidal systems? I think the results are going to very much depend on the test system.

Klebanoff: We extracted the granules or cells with 0.01 molar citric acid, and the extract was incubated with the organisms in lactate buffer pH 5 for 1 hour. The viable cell count was then determined by the pour plate method.

Cohn: Have you done that with rabbit cells rather than human cells because there appear to be differences in cationic protein content?

Klebanoff: It is true that there is less cationic protein in human cells than in rabbit cells and the results might be different if rabbit cells were employed. We have not performed this experiment with rabbit cells. Also the antibacterial activity of the cationic proteins may be more readily apparent with a different assay system since the assay system we employed could not detect a decrease in the rate of growth of the organisms if the same number of colonies were present at 24 hours. The results emphasize the difference in the bactericidal activity of the two systems for the test organisms employed rather than give any absolute measure of the antibacterial activity of the cationic proteins.

Spitznagel: I think it is important not just to emphasize that there are differences in the response of different bacterial species, but the way you do the test makes a great deal of difference in the outcome. Moreover, it really isn't fair to call a citric acid extract cationic protein. It is actually a heterogeneous mixture of all sorts of things. It is interesting, for example, that you didn't see an inhibitor for the citric acid extract as well as for the H_2O_2-dependent system. We find there are probably one or more potent inhibitors for the nonoxygen-dependent system.

Bellanti: Have you looked for this inhibitor in leukocyte homogenates of other cells?

Klebanoff: The inhibitors are largely from the cytosol since extracts from whole cells have greater inhibitory activity than extracts from isolated granules. Many low molecular weight reducing agents present in tissues inhibit the peroxidase system.

Karnovsky: Just to comment on the xanthine-xanthine oxidase system: we had pretty much the same experience although not as extensive. I wonder if anybody has considered superoxide as a transport form. If you look at the nature of the chemistry of superoxide, you would expect it to be quite soluble in membranes. I have wondered whether it was perhaps involved in the cell as a transport form in getting into the phagosome. I must confess I have always had a lot of trouble correlating what goes on enzymatically in the cytoplasm with what is going to hit the bacteria in the phagosome, with respect especially to H_2O_2.

Did I understand that the singlet oxygen would oxidize, in the old sense, lipid double bonds and give you peroxides of lipid substances and maybe hydroperoxides? Those would then cleave and this could be a very damaging phenomenon at the level of the bacterial membrane. Finally, is DABCO usable with intact polys? I mean, can you incubate polys in the presence of DABCO and diminish killing?

Klebanoff: Singlet oxygen can enter into many kinds of oxygenation reactions. It can introduce oxygen into heterocyclic compounds, or form organic peroxides of many kinds. The formation of fatty acid peroxides is an interesting possibility.

Karnovsky: Let me interject that ascorbate has long been known to promote just that sort of activity at the level of fatty acids of membranes, oddly enough.

Klebanoff: With respect to your question regarding the effect of DABCO on intact cells, this is of course what we are building up to. We have some preliminary data, which I hesitate to even mention, that DABCO does inhibit bactericidal activity at high concentrations, but under conditions in which there is extensive cytotoxicity to the neutrophils. I cannot say at this point whether these agents will produce an effect on the intact cell without a corresponding cytotoxic effect.

Holmes-Gray: Is this xanthine-xanthine oxidase system, which is potentiated by chloride, inhibited by iodide? Will iodide substitute at all in the system?

Klebanoff: Iodide did not substitute for chloride at neutral pH although it can be employed at acid pH. However, at acid pH, xanthine oxidase is very weak due to its alkaline pH optimum. Superoxide dismutase partially reversed the inhibition of the chloride-dependent microbicidal system by iodide. The inhibition thus may be a function of the reaction of iodide with certain radicals formed by the xanthine oxidase system which are not formed by the glucose oxidase system.

Holmes-Gray: Can you think of any way superoxide anion or singlet oxygen could be involved as intermediates in iodide binding? I ask this because we have done studies using your quantitative procedure for iodination with alveolar macrophages, and they don't iodinate at all.

Klebanoff: We also have been unable to detect iodination by rabbit alveolar macrophages. These cells do not contain myeloperoxide.

Holmes-Gray: True. But, if superoxide were formed, do you think that it could participate in an iodination reaction?

Johnston: How about through hydroxyl radical?

Klebanoff: The reaction $I^- + OH\cdot \rightarrow I\cdot + OH^-$ is known to occur with great speed, and iodide may be reacting with hydroxyl radicals under our experimental conditions. In fact, we are coming to the view that the reaction of hydroxyl radicals to form hydrogen peroxide ($OH\cdot + OH\cdot \rightarrow H_2O_2$) may be a significant pathway for hydrogen peroxide formation. If this is the case then reaction with hydroxyl radicals may well inhibit total activity of the peroxidase system.

Holmes-Gray: One more thing about the alveolar macrophage and iodide binding. We have introduced agarose beads with horse radish peroxidase bound to their surface, along with zymosan particles, and the alveolar macrophage still will not bind iodide.

Sbarra: I have two comments to make, but before I do I would like to suggest a possible reason why Dr. Holmes-Gray could not get her alveolar macrophages to iodinate. There are at least two laboratories that I know of that have reported that the alveolar macrophage does have peroxidase activity if assayed under "optimal conditions" (i.e., assay in absence of sucrose, at 37°C, and at higher H_2O_2 concentrations). Perhaps she would have noted iodination by the alveolar macrophage if the reaction was carried out under "optimal conditions." The peroxidase activity noted appears to be different than myeloperoxidase. Specifically, the antimicrobial activity of alveolar macrophage granular peroxidase is observed only with iodide. This peroxidase does not participate in killing or decarboxylation when chloride is the halide. In this sense it resembles horse radish peroxidase.

Klebanoff: Catalase that can act as a peroxidase has antimicrobial activity at acid pH with iodide but not chloride (*Proc. Soc. Exp. Biol. Med.* 132:571, 1969).

Sbarra: I think there is evidence suggesting that this fraction has peroxidase activity and that it is involved in antimicrobial activity (*Science* 181:849, 1973; *J. Reticuloendothelial Soc.* 13:399, 1973). It has been suggested that hypochlorous acid is involved in the antimicrobial system, and, as far as I know, this is only a postulation. Zgliczynski was unable to find it and, as far as we know, no one else has been able to either. Further, we have two experiments suggesting that hypochlorous acid is not an intermediate. One of the experiments was designed in this way: bacteria and MPO were separated by placing one in a dialysis bag with added chloride and H_2O_2 equilibrated. Under these conditions, bacteria were not killed. That is, MPO–H_2O_2–Cl did not appear to form a dialyzable product (i.e., HOCl) that could kill the bacteria. From this experiment it would appear that the MPO–H_2O_2–Cl antimicrobial system had to be in direct contact with the microbe to be operational (*Infect. Immun.* 2:414–418, 1970). In a further experiment, we took some hypochlorous acid in the form of Chlorox and placed *E. coli* on one side of a dialysis bag and HOCl on the other side. *E. coli* was effectively killed. This, of course, suggested that HOCl could get through the membrane. I recognize that the half-life of hypochlorous acid is such that it could be destroyed before it gets to the *E. coli.* From the above and from what is in the literature HOCl is probably not an intermediate.

Finally, may I ask you a question. Would it be possible that iodination has nothing to do with killing and that the killing mode by the MPO–H_2O_2–I_2 antimicrobial system is not due to iodination but to the production of a more oxidized and/or reactive form of iodine?

Klebanoff: Certainly. Iodination is a measure under certain conditions of the reaction of the peroxidase system within the cell and is not necessarily the mechanism of toxicity. One should think of a pool of co-factors in which iodide, either absorbed as such, or released by deiodination of thyroid hormones, chloride, and possible other agents contributes to the antimicrobial effect. Even though iodide is considerably more active than chloride on a molar basis, chloride is present in such high concentrations that it may be the major contributor to this pool.

Sbarra: I think it's a happy circumstance. To use it as an indication of killing may be very courageous.

Baehner: This question is related to Dr. Sbarra's question. What is the presumed biochemical mechanism involved in the bactericidal response? Does the cell membrane of the bacteria demonstrate any morphologic or biochemical alterations? In other words, how do they die?

Klebanoff: This is a question which hasn't been resolved. Lysis of the organisms does not occur. In the early days when we were interested in the thiocyanate system we did some studies using nonmetabolizable amino acids (and sugars) and found that the uptake of the nonmetabolizable amino acid was inhibited. If one allowed the organism to take up the amino acid prior to exposure to the system, such that the level increased to a plateau, then the addition of the system resulted in a discharge of the radioactive metabolite to the exterior of the cell. We assume that the thiocyanate system affects the transport of metabolites across the cell membrane. We do not know whether the same sort of mechanism is operative with chloride or iodide.

Root: Did you look at a variety of organisms? Presumably there are going to be different sensitivities in different species as suggested by Spitznagel's work.

Klebanoff: I would certainly anticipate that organisms would vary in their sensitivity to the cationic proteins and to the peroxidase system.

Baehner: Do you have any information relating to requirement of the bacteria to be in active cell cycle in order to be killed? Are the bacteria in your system in log phase growth?

Klebanoff: We have routinely used bacteria in the stationary phase of their growth. We grow them overnight. But we have looked at cells during the logarithmic phase and they are killed by the peroxidase system.

Mandell: We have looked at the killing of certain organisms by anaerobic white blood cells and there is a group of organisms killed very well by anaerobic cells.

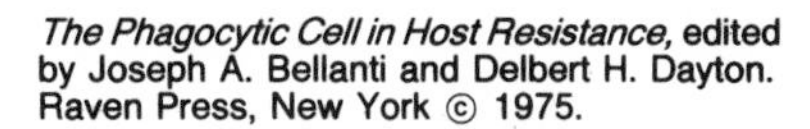
The Phagocytic Cell in Host Resistance, edited
by Joseph A. Bellanti and Delbert H. Dayton.
Raven Press, New York © 1975.

Superoxide Anion Generation and Phagocytic Bactericidal Activity

Richard B. Johnston, Jr., Bernard B. Keele, Jr., Hara P. Misra,
Lawrence S. Webb, Joyce E. Lehmeyer, and K. V. Rajagopalan

Departments of Pediatrics and Microbiology and the Institute of Dental Research, University of Alabama, Birmingham, Birmingham, Alabama 35233, and Department of Biochemistry, Duke University Medical Center, Durham, North Carolina 27710

Recognition that superoxide anion ($O_2^{\bar{\cdot}}$), a free radical form of oxygen, can be generated in biological systems has emerged primarily from study of the aerobic oxidation of xanthine by the enzyme xanthine oxidase (1), according to the reaction

$$\text{xanthine} + H_2O + O_2 \xrightarrow{\text{xanthine oxidase}} \text{uric acid} + O_2^{\bar{\cdot}}$$

The radical can be detected by its capacity to reduce compounds such as ferricytochrome *c* or nitroblue tetrazolium (NBT) (2–4), or to oxidize epinephrine to adrenochrome (5). Auto-oxidative processes and enzymes capable of generating this highly reactive anion have been identified in various mammalian tissues, bacteria, and fungi (reviewed in ref. 1). However, it has not been clear whether or not this free radical serves a useful biological purpose. On the contrary, its presence should pose a potential threat to those cells in which it is elaborated, and a possible role for $O_2^{\bar{\cdot}}$ in the process of aging has been suggested (1).

Greater understanding of the physiological control of $O_2^{\bar{\cdot}}$ developed after the demonstration by McCord and Fridovich (6) of enzymic activity which catalyzes the dismutation of superoxide anions in the reaction

$$O_2^{\bar{\cdot}} + O_2^{\bar{\cdot}} + 2H^+ \rightarrow O_2 + H_2O_2$$

The enzyme superoxide dismutase is now known to be identical to "cuprein," the copper protein previously isolated without known function from mammalian erythrocytes, liver, brain, and other tissues (6). The presence of superoxide dismutase in aerobic bacteria and its absence from strict anaerobes has suggested that this enzyme serves to protect oxygen-metabolizing bacteria, and presumably other cells, from the potentially detrimental effects of $O_2^{\bar{\cdot}}$ (7).

INHIBITION OF PHAGOCYTIC NBT REDUCTION BY SUPEROXIDE DISMUTASE

The apparent ubiquity of $O_2^{\bar{}}$ production in biological systems, the potent reactivity of this agent, and its ability to reduce NBT in chemical systems, a capacity exhibited by normal phagocytes (8), suggested to us the possibility that this free radical might be generated by leukocytes and involved in the killing of bacteria by these cells. We began our experiments by looking for evidence that $O_2^{\bar{}}$ is generated by phagocytes, the report of Babior et al. (9) not having been published at that time. Since the demonstration by Rajagopalan and Handler that $O_2^{\bar{}}$ can reduce NBT to formazan (3), inhibition of NBT reduction by superoxide dismutase has become a standard means of determining $O_2^{\bar{}}$ formation *in vitro* (4). Therefore, in initial experiments we looked for inhibition by superoxide dismutase of the NBT reduction accompanying phagocytosis, using opsonized zymosan particles in a modification of a previously developed technique (10).

The superoxide dismutase used in these experiments was purified from bovine erythrocytes (6). A portion of each preparation was denatured by autoclaving for 30 min; apoenzyme was prepared from another portion by dialysis for 40 hr against acetate-EDTA buffer, which removed the copper (6). The autoclaved enzyme lost all inhibitory activity in the aerobic xanthine oxidase system (2); the apoenzyme lost approximately 90% of its original activity. Bovine serum albumin (BSA) was purchased. All three superoxide dismutase preparations and the BSA were suspended in 0.15 M NaCl to a concentration of 1 mg/ml.

The results are summarized in Table 1. Although there was some variation from experiment to experiment in the extent of NBT reduction achieved by the enzyme preparations and BSA control, the inhibition by active enzyme was constant at approximately one-third of the total dye reduction. In three recent experiments we achieved inhibition by superoxide dismutase of about 60% of phagocytosis-associated NBT reduction using latex as the ingestate (see also Baehner, *this volume*). The enzyme adheres much better to latex than to zymosan (Johnston, R. B., Jr., *unpublished observations*) and thus makes its way into the phagocytic vacuole more effectively in that system. In any event, it would seem clear that $O_2^{\bar{}}$ is responsible for at least one-third of the NBT reduction accomplished by phagocytizing leukocytes and, accordingly, that $O_2^{\bar{}}$ is generated by these cells.

TABLE 1. *Inhibition of phagocytic NBT reduction by superoxide dismutase*

Protein added (200 μg/ml)	OD_{515} [a]	Inhibition (%)
BSA	0.230 ± 0.025 (7)	
Superoxide dismutase	0.158 ± 0.021 (7)	31 (25–46) [b]
Superoxide dismutase, denatured	0.227 ± 0.021 (2)	
Superoxide dismutase, apoenzyme	0.228 ± 0.041 (3)	

[a] Mean ± SEM of optical density of reduced NBT. Number of experiments is given in parentheses.
[b] Mean (range).

In further attempts to demonstrate that phagocytes have the capacity to generate superoxide anion, the particulate fraction (containing cell membranes and nuclei) from an homogenate of purified leukocytes was sonicated, cleared by centrifugation (12,000 × *g* for 30 min), and studied for its ability to reduce NBT in the presence or absence of superoxide dismutase. Reduced nicotinamide dinucleotide (NADH) was added as substrate for the reaction. As shown in Fig. 1, the rate of NBT reduction in this system was rapid, but in the presence of superoxide dismutase this rate was inhibited by 60 to 70%. The results shown here were achieved at pH 10.2; at physiologic pH the rates achieved with and without the enzyme were slower, but the inhibitory effect of the enzyme was similar.

Thus it would appear that $O_2^{\overline{\cdot}}$ was generated by constituents of the leukocyte lysate, presumably through transfer of electrons from NADH to oxygen. Homogenates from two patients with chronic granulomatous disease reduced NBT

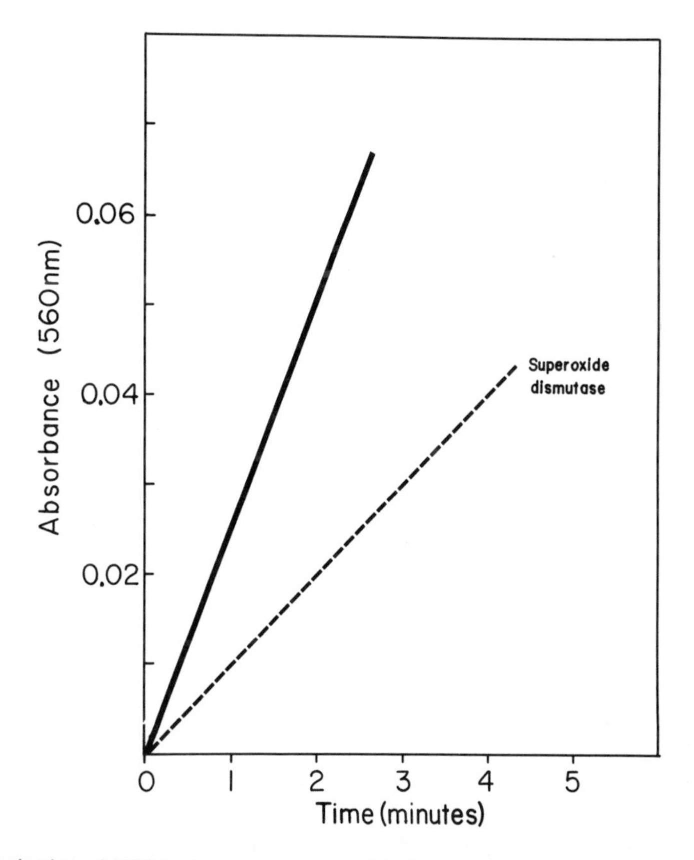

FIG. 1. Reduction of NBT to formazan by material obtained from an homogenate of human leukocytes (see text). Formazan generation was monitored continuously as absorbance at 560 nm, using a Gilford recording spectrophotometer.

at approximately 70% of the normal rate. However, only about 25% of this reduction was inhibited by superoxide dismutase, in agreement with the concept that leukocytes from these patients may be deficient in NADH oxidase activity (11) and with the finding that these cells do not generate $O_2^{\overline{\cdot}}$ normally (12, and Johnston, R. B., Jr., Keele, B. B., Jr., and Baehner, R. L., *unpublished studies*).

INHIBITION OF PHAGOCYTIC BACTERICIDAL ACTIVITY BY SUPEROXIDE DISMUTASE

Our efforts were next directed toward determining whether or not $O_2^{\overline{\cdot}}$ is involved in the killing of phagocytized bacteria (13). We began by simply adding

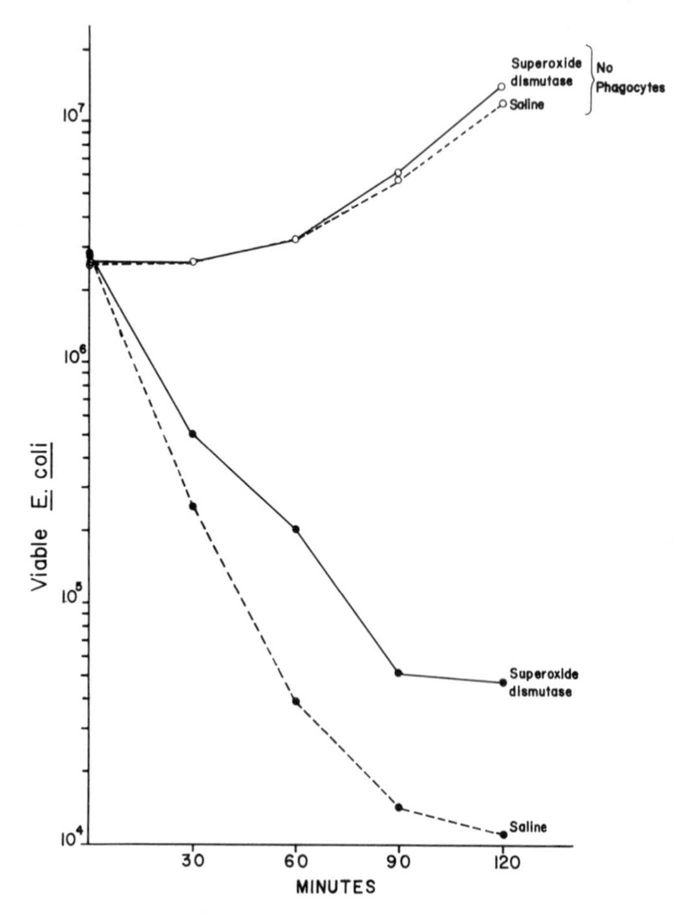

FIG. 2. Inhibition of phagocytic bactericidal activity by superoxide dismutase (200 μg/ml). The number of viable *E. coli* in the 1 ml reaction mixture is plotted as a function of the time at which the mixture was sampled; 2.5 X 10^6 phagocytes were used in all bactericidal assays.

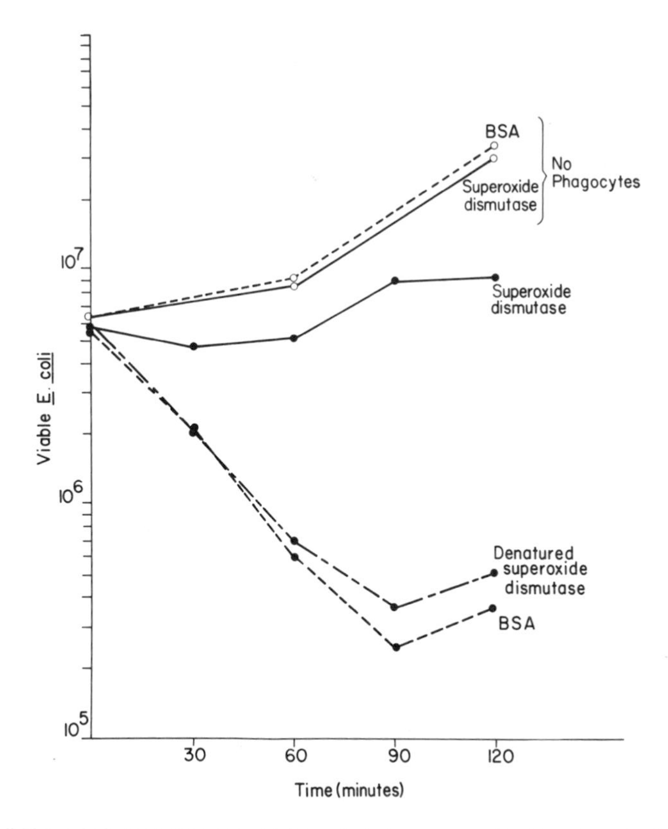

FIG. 3. Inhibition of phagocytic bactericidal activity by superoxide dismutase in the presence of latex particles. BSA stands for bovine serum albumin. In the experiment represented here, 200 μg of either BSA, superoxide dismutase, or denatured superoxide dismutase was present in an individual assay tube.

superoxide dismutase to the assay system used to study phagocytic bactericidal activity [that of Maaløe, modified by Hirsch, Quie, and ourselves (14)]. Strains of bacteria obtained from infected humans were employed. The inhibition achieved was modest, at best; results of one of the better experiments are illustrated in Fig. 2. However, the effect was reproducible in that some inhibition was achieved in nine consecutive experiments with either *E. coli* or *Staphylococcus aureus*.

It occurred to us that the inhibitory effect might be greater if the enzyme were delivered more effectively to the phagocytic vacuole. Therefore, in an attempt to facilitate entry of superoxide dismutase into the vacuole, various concentrations of the enzyme or its controls were fixed to latex particles by preincubation in the reaction tube with 0.1 ml of the particles (15). Approximately 20% of the total enzyme activity in the 200 μg of preparation incubated with the latex was associated with the particles when they were separated by centrifugation; 5% of

TABLE 2. *Uptake of ¹⁴C-labeled bacteria by phagocytes in the presence of superoxide dismutase or control preparations*

	latex	*E. coli*[a]	*S. aureus*[a]
Superoxide dismutase	—	1,632 ± 126	2,352 ± 531
Saline	—	1,702 ± 222	2,307 ± 268
Superoxide dismutase	+	1,134 ± 210	1,013 ± 79
Superoxide dismutase, denatured	+	1,180 ± 160	1,049 ± 112
Superoxide dismutase, apoenzyme	+		1,079 ± 51

[a] Mean ± SD of cpm from five to 15 replicates. Square root transformations of enzyme and control values were not significantly different ($p > 0.2$) by analysis of variance.

the total activity remained after one wash with water. Electron micrographs[1] made of this system after 20 min of phagocytosis indicated that particles and bacteria could be commonly found together within the same vacuole.

In the presence of superoxide dismutase and latex particles there was consistent, marked inhibition of the killing of bacteria by normal human leukocytes, as illustrated in Fig. 3 for one experiment with *E. coli.* Heat denaturation of superoxide dismutase or removal of its copper atoms eliminated its ability to suppress bacterial killing. The enzyme had no effect on bacterial growth in the absence of phagocytes. Identical results were obtained when *S. aureus* or *S. viridans* was used instead of *E. coli.* Supeoxide dismutase did not inhibit the ingestion of *E. coli* or *S. aureus* whether or not latex particles were present, as determined by counting the number of phagocytized bacteria on stained smears or measuring the uptake of radiolabeled bacteria by phagocytes after incubation for 30 min (16) (Table 2). The reaction mixture used in the uptake experiments was that of the phagocytic bactericidal assay.

INHIBITION OF PHAGOCYTIC BACTERICIDAL ACTIVITY BY CATALASE AND BENZOATE

Evidence that hydrogen peroxide is involved in the killing of phagocytized bacteria is well documented. In order, then, to determine the role of peroxide in the bactericidal activity demonstrated by this assay system, we tested the ability of catalase to inhibit phagocytic killing. Bovine liver catalase was purchased, made free of superoxide dismutase activity by gel filtration (17), and suspended in saline. As shown in Fig. 4, catalase inhibited the killing of *E. coli* as effectively as did superoxide dismutase. The killing of staphylococci was similarly inhibited. There was no enhancement of bacterial growth in the presence of the enzyme when leukocytes were omitted.

The results of these studies suggested that peripheral blood phagocytic cells must generate both superoxide anion and hydrogen peroxide in order to efficiently kill ingested bacteria. Since bactericidal activity was markedly inhibited by enzymes that removed one or the other of these agents, we considered the possibil-

[1] Kindly performed by Dr. A. W. Atkinson, Jr., University of Alabama Medical Center.

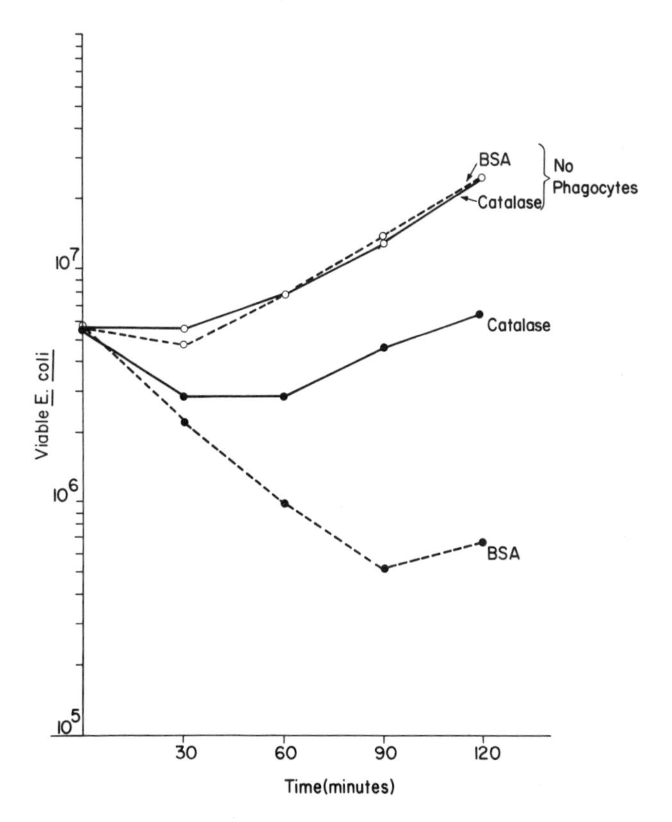

FIG. 4. Inhibition of phagocytic bactericidal activity by catalase (200 μg/ml) in the presence of latex particles. An equal concentration of BSA was used as control.

ity that optimal killing required the combined effect of both agents. Interaction of $O_2^{\overline{\cdot}}$ and H_2O_2 has been shown to occur *in vitro* and to lead to production of the potent oxidizing agent hydroxyl radical (OH·) (18), as represented by the reaction

$$O_2^{\overline{\cdot}} + H_2O_2 \rightarrow OH\cdot + OH^- + O_2$$

In order to test the possibility that OH· is generated by phagocytizing leukocytes and that this strongly oxidizing radical is required for the bactericidal event, we performed the phagocytic bactericidal assay in the presence of sodium benzoate, a scavenger of hydroxyl radicals (19). As shown in Fig. 5, there was modest but definite inhibition of phagocytic killing by benzoate concentrations that had no direct effect on the bacteria. The same result was achieved with staphylococci. There was no inhibition of the uptake of radiolabeled organisms by catalase or benzoate, as summarized in Table 3. Since the activity of benzoate upon phagocytes may not be limited to its removal of hydroxyl radicals, it must be stated

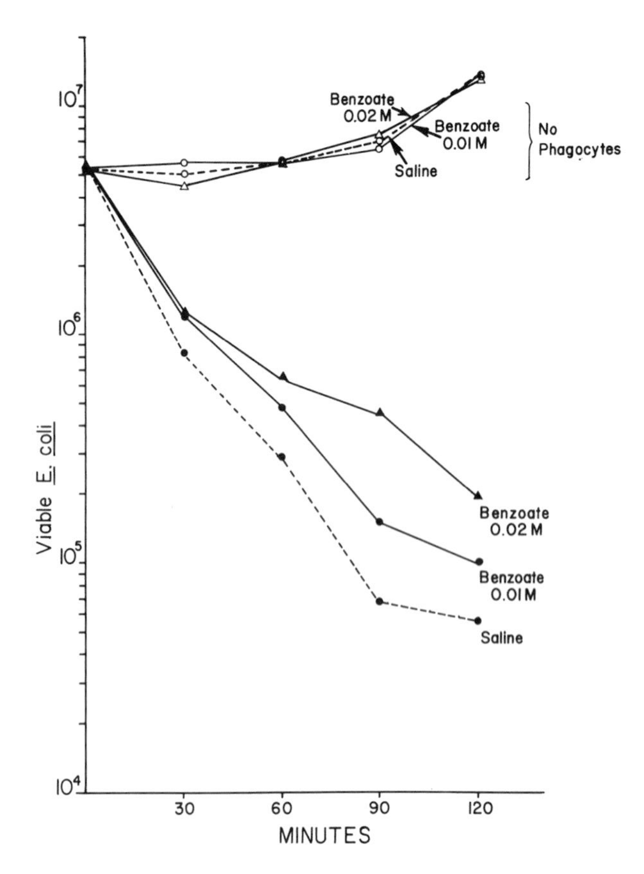

FIG. 5. Inhibition of phagocytic bactericidal activity by sodium benzoate at a final concentration of 0.01 M or 0.02 M (50 or 100 μl of 0.2 M benzoate was present in the 1 ml reaction mixture); 0.15 M NaCl was used as control. Latex particles were not present.

TABLE 3. *Uptake of ¹⁴C-labeled bacteria by phagocytes in the presence of catalase, benzoate, or their controls*

	latex	*E. coli*[a]	*S. aureus*[a]
Catalase	—	1,553 ± 56	
BSA	—	1,225 ± 81	
Catalase	+	878 ± 105	1,465 ± 704
BSA	+	796 ± 175	1,387 ± 670
Benzoate, 0.01 M	+	1,020 ± 165	
Benzoate, 0.02 M	+	1,089 ± 185	
Saline	+	966 ± 114	

[a] Mean ± SD of cpm from five to 10 replicates. Square root transformations of catalase and benzoate values were not significantly different from those of their controls ($p > 0.2$) by analysis of variance.

that its antibacterial effect is compatible with but does not prove our hypothesis that the hydroxyl radical is important in phagocytic killing.

SUPEROXIDE ANION GENERATION AND CHEMILUMINESCENCE

During the process of phagocytosis, human leukocytes emit a burst of luminescence that can be quantitated in a liquid scintillation spectrometer (20). In order to obtain further evidence that O_2^- is generated by phagocytizing leukocytes and to determine if O_2^- plays a part in phagocytosis-associated chemiluminescence, we tested the capacity of superoxide dismutase to inhibit this phenomenon (17). In the presence of BSA as control, the luminescence rose rapidly from a background level of approximately 8×10^3 counts per min (cpm) at time 0 to a maximum of more than 2×10^5 cpm after 14 min (Fig. 6). When BSA was replaced by an equal concentration of superoxide dismutase (100 μg/ml), peak luminescence was reduced by 71% (Fig. 6). In 11 experiments, superoxide dismu-

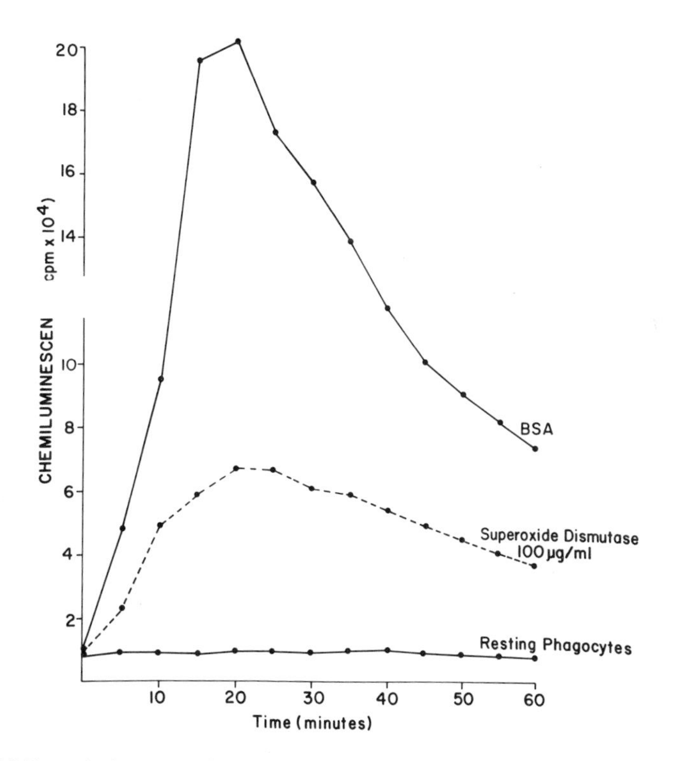

FIG. 6. Inhibition of phagocytosis-associated chemiluminescence by superoxide dismutase (100 μg/ml). The extent of chemiluminescence (number of counts per minute) is plotted as a function of the time at which the vial was counted. BSA at a concentration of 100 μg/ml was used as control. "Resting phagocytes" were not given particles for ingestion; 1×10^7 phagocytes were present in each vial; the particle : cell ratio was approximately 44 : 1.

tase at a concentration of 100 μg/ml inhibited peak luminescence by 65 to 76% (mean 70%). Superoxide dismutase did not inhibit ingestion of the particles used (opsonized zymosan), as determined by counting numbers of ingested particles on smears and by comparing the uptake of ^{125}I-labeled zymosan in the presence of BSA or the enzyme (17). In confirmation of the report of Stjernholm and colleagues (21), we have found that leukocytes from patients with chronic granulomatous disease do not emit luminescence in this system.

It should be stated clearly that we have no proof that O_2^- is the actual luminescing agent. Allen et al. (19) believe singlet oxygen ($^1O_2$) to be that agent. The presence of this excited form of oxygen has not been clearly demonstrated in biological systems, but it appears reasonably well established that this species participates in ordinary chemical reactions involving molecular oxygen (22).

Several laboratories have shown that the aerobic xanthine-xanthine oxidase reaction, which generates O_2^-, can generate chemiluminescence (e.g., see refs. 23 and 24). Inhibition of this luminescence by superoxide dismutase has also been shown (23–25). Thus two O_2^- radicals might produce a molecule of oxygen in the excited singlet state according to the reaction (26)

$$O_2^- + O_2^- \rightarrow O_2^{2-} + {}^1O_2$$
$$\downarrow 2H^+$$
$$H_2O_2$$

The enzyme-catalyzed dismutation does not give rise to $^1O_2$ (24, 25), which could explain the inhibition of chemiluminescence by superoxide dismutase.

GRANULOCYTE SUPEROXIDE DISMUTASE

Superoxide dismutase as originally purified from mammalian tissues contains two atoms each of copper and zinc per molecule (6). It is now clear that this protein is located in the cytosol of eukaryotic cells, which also possess smaller amounts of a manganese-superoxide dismutase in their mitochondria (27). Aerobic bacteria contain an intracellular manganese-containing enzyme (28) as well as a periplasmic iron-containing enzyme (29).

Beckman and colleagues have analyzed various human tissues for their content of the copper- and manganese-containing isoenzymes, utilizing polyacrylamide gel electrophoresis (30). This technique depends upon the capacity of superoxide dismutase to prevent the reduction of NBT which is incorporated into the polyacrylamide along with a photoreduction system after electrophoresis of the cell homogenate (4). They found superoxide dismutase with the electrophoretic mobility of cupric enzyme in all cells except peripheral blood granulocytes, which apparently contained only the mitochondrial enzyme (30). On the other hand, DeChatelet and co-workers have found considerable superoxide dismutase activity in the cytosol fraction (supernatant fluid after centrifugation at 105,000 X *g* for 60 min) of purified granulocyte and macrophage preparations (31). Activity of the mitochondrial enzyme cytochrome oxidase was not present in this fraction. In our experiments, lysates of 96 to 98% pure neutrophils from defibrinated blood of normals and patients with chronic myelogenous leukemia have consistently shown two distinct bands on electrophoresis in polyacrylamide. A minor, slower band corresponds in position to electrophoresed manganese-containing superoxide dismutase, purified from *E. coli;* the major band corresponds in electrophoretic mobility to purified cupric enzyme. The major band—but not the minor one—is removed by prior cyanide treatment of the lysate, a result expected with cupric enzyme. We have been unable to reproduce the negative results of Beckman et al., and at the moment cannot explain the contradictory findings.

Establishing the intraphagocytic location of superoxide dismutase is of some importance to currently developing concepts of granulocyte physiology. Since these cells elaborate O_2^- on ingesting particles, enzymic protection of their cytoplasm from this radical would promote their survival after phagocytosis and, thus, their functional capacity. This would not necessarily diminish the intraphagocytic antibacterial activity of O_2^-. If O_2^- is generated in the proximity of the phagocytic vacuole, which seems likely, then O_2^- and H_2O_2 could accumulate within the vacuole with little interference from cytosol enzyme. Inside the vacuole these agents would be free to act on the captured microorganisms or to interact to generate other oxidants such as hydroxyl radical or singlet oxygen. There is a precedent for such an arrangement in that catalase, which removes H_2O_2, resides in neutrophil cytosol, and cannot be detected in the phagocytic vacuole after ingestion (32). The release of lysosomal hydrolytic enzymes only into the phagocytic vacuole or, under special circumstances, to the outside of the cell illustrates the same principle.

CONCLUSIONS

On the basis of experiments reported here and those of other investigators it would seem clear that the respiratory burst coincident with granulocyte phagocytosis is associated with significant production of O_2^-. Through this process the oxygen molecule is literally charged with new energy. The inhibition of phagocytic bactericidal activity, as well as chemiluminescence, by superoxide dismutase suggests that this energy is involved in the killing of ingested bacteria. Exactly *how* this energy is translated into microbial death remains to be clearly defined.

ACKNOWLEDGMENTS

The work reported in this chapter is supported by U.S. Public Health Service research grants AI 10286 from the National Institute of Allergy and Infectious Diseases, CA 13148 from the National Cancer Institute, DE 02670 from the National Institute of Dental Research, and GM 00091 from the National Institute of General Medical Sciences.

REFERENCES

1. Fridovich, I.: Superoxide radical and superoxide dismutase. *Accounts Chem. Res.* 5:321–326, 1972.
2. McCord, J. M., and Fridovich, I.: The reduction of cytochrome *c* by milk xanthine oxidase. *J. Biol. Chem.* 243:5753–5760, 1968.
3. Rajagopalan, K. V., and Handler, P.: Hepatic aldehyde oxidase. II. Differential inhibition of electron transfer to various electron acceptors. *J. Biol. Chem.* 239:2022–2026, 1964.
4. Beauchamp, C., and Fridovich, I.: Superoxide dismutase: Improved assays and an assay applicable to acrylamide gels. *Anal. Biochem.* 44:276–287, 1971.
5. Misra, H. P., and Fridovich, I.: The role of superoxide anion in the autoxidation of epinephrine and a simple assay for superoxide dismutase. *J. Biol. Chem.* 247:3170–3175, 1972.
6. McCord, J. M., and Fridovich, I.: Superoxide dismutase: An enzymic function for erythrocuprein (hemocuprein). *J. Biol. Chem.* 244:6049–6055, 1969.
7. McCord, J. M., Keele, B. B., Jr., and Fridovich, I.: An enzyme-based theory of obligate anaerobiosis: The physiological function of superoxide dismutase. *Proc. Natl. Acad. Sci.* 68:1024–1027, 1971.
8. Baehner, R. L., and Nathan, D. G.: Quantitative nitroblue tetrazolium test in chronic granulomatous disease. *N. Engl. J. Med.* 278:971–976, 1968.
9. Babior, B. M., Kipnes, R. S., and Curnutte, J. T.: Biological defense mechanisms: The production by leukocytes of superoxide, a potential bactericidal agent. *J. Clin. Invest.* 52:741–744, 1973.
10. Johnston, R. B., Jr., Klemperer, M. R., Alper, C. A., and Rosen, F. S.: The enhancement of bacterial phagocytosis by serum: The role of complement components and two cofactors. *J. Exp. Med.* 129:1275–1290, 1969.
11. Baehner, R. L., and Karnovsky, M. L.: Deficiency of reduced nicotinamideadenine dinucleotide oxidase in chronic granulomatous disease. *Science* 162:1277–1279, 1968.
12. Babior, B. M., Curnutte, J. T., Hull, W. E., and Kipnes, R. S.: Production by granulocytes of superoxide, a possible bactericidal agent. *J. Clin. Invest.* 52:5a, 1973.
13. Johnston, R. B., Jr., Keele, B., Webb, L., Kessler, D., and Rajagopalan, K. V.: Inhibition of phagocytic bactericidal activity by superoxide dismutase: A possible role for superoxide anion in the killing of phagocytized bacteria. *J. Clin. Invest.* 52:44a, 1973.
14. Baehner, R. L., and Johnston, R. B., Jr.: Metabolic and bactericidal activities of human eosinophils. *Br. J. Haematol.* 20:277–285, 1971.
15. Johnston, R. B., Jr., and Baehner, R. L.: Improvement of leukocyte bactericidal activity in chronic granulomatous disease. *Blood* 35:350–355, 1970.
16. Johnston, R. B., Jr., Anderson, P., and Newman, S. L.: Opsonization and phagocytosis of *Hemophilus influenzae,* type b. In Sell, S. H. W., and Karzon, D. T. (eds): *Hemophilus Influenzae.* Vanderbilt University Press, Nashville, Tenn., pp. 99–112. 1973.
17. Webb, L. S., Keele, B. B., Jr., and Johnston, R. B., Jr.: Inhibition of phagocytosis-associated chemiluminescence by superoxide dismutase. *Infect. Immun.* 9:1051–1056, 1974.
18. Haber, F., and Weiss, J.: The catalytic decomposition of hydrogen peroxide by iron salts. *Proc. Roy. Soc. London, Ser. A* 147:332–351, 1934.
19. Beauchamp, C., and Fridovich, I.: A mechanism for the production of ethylene from methional: The generation of the hydroxyl radical by xanthine oxidase. *J. Biol. Chem.* 245:4641–4646, 1970.
20. Allen, R. C., Stjernholm, R. L., and Steele, R. H.: Evidence for the generation of an electronic excitation state(s) in human polymorphonuclear leukocytes and its participation in bactericidal activity. *Biochem. Biophys. Res. Commun.* 47:679–684, 1972.
21. Stjernholm, R. L., Allen, R. C., Steele, R. H., Waring, W. W., and Harris, J. A.: Impaired chemiluminescence during phagocytosis of opsonized bacteria. *Infect. Immun.* 7:313–314, 1973.
22. Khan, A. U., and Kasha, M.: Chemiluminescence arising from simultaneous transitions in pairs of singlet oxygen molecules. *J. Am. Chem. Soc.* 92:3293–3300, 1970.
23. Arneson, R. M.: Substrate-induced chemiluminescence of xanthine oxidase and aldehyde oxidase. *Arch. Biochem. Biophys.* 136:352–360, 1970.
24. Finazzi Agró, A., Giovagnoli, C., DeSole, P., Calabrese, L., Rotilio, G., and Mondoví, B.: Erythrocuprein and singlet oxygen. *FEBS Lett.* 21:183–185, 1972.
25. Goda, K., Chu, J., Kimura, T., and Schaap, A. P.: Cytochrome c enchancement of singlet

molecular oxygen production by the NADPH-dependent adrenoxin reductase-adrenoxin system: The role of singlet oxygen in damaging adrenal mitochondrial membranes. *Biochem. Biophys. Res. Commun.* 52:1300–1306, 1973.
26. Stauff, J., Schmidkunz, H., and Hartmann, G.: Weak chemiluminescence of oxidation reactions. *Nature* 198:281–282, 1963.
27. Weisiger, R. A., and Fridovich, I.: Superoxide dismutase: Organelle specificity. *J. Biol. Chem.* 248:3582–3592, 1973.
28. Keele, B. B., Jr., McCord, J. M., and Fridovich, I.: Superoxide dismutase from *Escherichia coli* B: A new manganese-containing enzyme. *J. Biol. Chem.* 245:6176–6181, 1970.
29. Yost, F. J., and Fridovich, I.: An iron-containing superoxide dismutase from *Escherichia coli*. *J. Biol. Chem.* 248:4905–4908, 1973.
30. Beckman, G., Lundgren, E., and Tarnvik, A.: Superoxide dismutase isoenzymes in different human tissues: Their genetic control and intracellular localization. *Hum. Hered.* 23:338–345, 1973.
31. DeChatelet, L. R., McCall, C. E., McPhail, L. C., and Johnston, R. B., Jr.: Superoxide dismutase activity in leukocytes. *J. Clin. Invest.* 53:1197–1201, 1974.
32. Stossel, T. P., Pollard, T. D., Mason, R. J., and Vaughn, M.: Isolation and properties of phagocytic vesicles from polymorphonuclear leukocytes. *J. Clin. Invest.* 50:1745–1757, 1971.

DISCUSSION

Mandell: How do you explain the nearly complete inhibition of killing with both catalase and dismutase? You had nearly 100 percent with either one tied onto latex.

Johnston: I guess there are at least two possibilities. One is that what appears to be complete inhibition is really not. This is a dynamic system; at what point you interfere with it is going to make a difference—the bacteria outside are replicating, etc. I would really hesitate to say that we inhibited all killing; the net result was a standstill in terms of number of bacteria. A second possibility is that these two agents must interact or act together, for example, to generate hydroxyl radical.

Mandell: Does dismutase have any effect on peroxide at all?

Johnston: I think it may have some. The dogma at the moment, as I understand it, is that it has no appreciable effect under physiologic conditions. Certainly superoxide becomes peroxide very rapidly when peroxide doesn't accumulate.

Baehner: I assume these are peripheral blood polys?

Johnston: Yes.

Baehner: As you are well aware, one problem involved in working with peripheral blood is isolating pure polys because of the contamination by lymphocytes, platelets, and red cells. As you know, the red cell was the first cell used to purify superoxide dismutase. I therefore wonder about the purity of the preparations you are showing us here.

Johnston: The preparations used to determine dismutase location were about 97 percent polys. The rest were monos or lymphs. We could not find platelets in these preparations. (We started with defibrinated blood.) We separate lymphocytes reasonably well, and then lyse the erythrocytes, so that none are detectable in the preparation.

Karnovsky: I was concerned about the fact that although I think you tried hard to demonstrate that your effects were not due to defective phagocytosis *per se,* nevertheless, the question isn't quite solved. The killing data are all on a good kinetic curve, but the uptake data are really done under different conditions and we have only a single time point. We don't know whether you are at some final concentration in the cells. I really would wonder if it is not possible to obtain uptake and killing data in the same experiment so that the two curves can be rigorously compared. And this leads me to ask if you are satisfied that the benzoate effect was sufficient to let you really believe that the benzoate was acting in the way that you had hoped it might act.

Johnston: To get at the last point first—I really don't feel very confident about what benzoate is doing. The extent of inhibition that we showed there is very reproducible and it does not vary much whether you use latex in the system or not. How it works and whether it's scavenging something other than the hydroxyl radical, I don't know. Your point about kinetics is certainly a good one, and we will do that. All of our experiments have been done with a fluid, tumbling system, and we would prefer to retain that system at this point.

Klebanoff: Did you try other hydroxyl radical scavengers such as mannitol?

Johnston: We haven't tried mannitol. We looked at ethyl alcohol; it inhibits killings but there is no telling what else it does besides scavenging hydroxyl radical.

Cohn: This is a question for either Dr. Klebanoff or Dr. Johnston. If we consider cytotoxic mechanisms, I wonder if we can also bring in some of the cytotoxic systems in which mammalian cells are killed by other cells in the immune response. I wonder how these cytotoxic systems might operate free in the extracellular environment or with perhaps intimate contact between an affector and target cell.

Johnston: That is a very interesting question, especially in regard to antibody-dependent cytotoxicity, in which there is said to be direct contact between the mononuclear effector cell and the target cell, usually an erythrocyte coated with antibody. The cytolysis might be the result of oxidative metabolism, but I know of no data in this regard.

Cohn: Dr. Kelbanoff, do you think it might be responsible in the environment?

Klebanoff: I can't answer that. We have looked at the cytotoxic effect of the peroxidase system on tumor cells using xanthine and xanthine oxidase as the hydrogen peroxide-generating system, attempting to compare the cytotoxicity of the complete peroxidase system to that of the oxygen radicals formed by the xanthine oxidase system. Our results are very preliminary, but they suggest that xanthine and xanthine oxidase alone, under the conditions employed, have little or no cytotoxicity as measured by chromium release, but, that when combined with the other components of the peroxidase system, they are strongly cytotoxic. This suggests that the products of the xanthine oxidase system, which include the oxygen radicals, are only weakly cytotoxic when compared to the complete peroxidase system.

Holmes-Gray: In your last figure what is the staining reagent?

Johnston: NBT is reduced by superoxide from a photoreduction system except in areas to which superoxide dismutase has moved in the electrophoretic field.

Ward: I have a question for Drs. Cohn or Klebanoff. In the lymphocyte-target cell killing, has anyone demonstrated the halogenation of the target cell?

Klebanoff: You can iodinate the surface of the cell by the cell-free peroxidase system.

Ward: But under the conditions of lymphocyte target-cell killing.

Cohn: It would be an easy thing to do but I don't think anybody has done it with intact cells.

The Phagocytic Cell in Host Resistance, edited
by Joseph A. Bellanti and Delbert H. Dayton.
Raven Press, New York © 1975.

Advances in the Study of Cytoplasmic Granules of Human Neutrophilic Polymorphonuclear Leukocytes

John K. Spitznagel

Department of Bacteriology, University of North Carolina School of Medicine, Chapel Hill, North Carolina 27514

In order to evaluate fully the latent functional capacities of polymorphonuclear leukocytes (PMN), it is essential to have information concerning their cytoplasmic granules. PMN's from humans have at least two classes of granules, the azurophil or primary granules and the specific or secondary granules which have been described morphologically (1), and biochemically (2). Until very recently the composition of the granules of human cells was only partially understood, available information being limited to and largely derived from studies on their azurophil granules, which are readily identified histochemically (1) and biochemically (3). Since the granules of rabbit PMN were more completely understood (summarized in ref. 2), the tendency of those writing on the subject was to extrapolate from rabbit to human PMN. That this extrapolation is unsound was first suggested by the results of Richard Welsh working in my laboratory (4) and of Burton West (5) working at the National Institutes of Health. Both workers found the alkaline phosphatase of human PMN associated with the cell membranes. This was surprising because in rabbit PMN 90% of the alkaline phosphatase sedimented with the specific granules (6, 7). Leffell (8) subsequently showed that the specific granules of human PMN contain most of the lactoferrin of these cells as well as one-half of their lysozyme and confirmed that those granules had no alkaline phosphatase.

In this chapter I will summarize studies on cytoplasmic granules of human PMN (2) that set forth in one place for the first time quantitative immunochemical studies on the distribution of myeloperoxidase and lactoferrin in the cytoplasmic granules of human PMN along with observations on the distribution of catalytically measured lysozyme, peroxidase, neutral protease, lysozyme, acid β-glycerolphosphatase, β-glucuronidase, and alkaline phosphatase.

The important point that emerges from this work is that all of the myeloperoxidase of the human PMN is in the azurophil granules whereas the lactoferrin is in the specific granules. These two substances can be measured immunochemically and quantitatively with material from 4×10^7 PMN from 10 ml of venous blood. Hence these measurements are potentially useful for screening the integrity of azurophil and specific granules of PMN from small children as well as from adults. In order to establish this, we had to use methods that yield more information and are more exacting but are also more cumbersome.

The velocity sedimentation studies described here, for example, were done with suspensions of 1×10^9 cells (90 to 99% PMN) isolated from samples of 400 ml of peripheral blood. These PMN's, homogenized in 0.34 M sucrose until 60 to 70% of them appeared broken when viewed with phase microscopy, provided cell homogenates from which nuclei and unbroken cells were removed in a centrifuge at $400 \times g$ min. The supernatant cytoplasmic fraction with its granules was layered onto density gradients, linear from 56 to 30% sucrose in 60-ml tubes, and then centrifuged in the S27.2 rotor of a Beckman L2–65B centrifuge until the time-velocity integral, ${}_0\int^t \omega^2\, dt$, was 1.2×10^{10}, 2.3×10^{10}, or 4.6×10^{10} sec^{-1} (see Fig. 1). With great regularity three turbid bands separated from the material layered on the gradient and sedimented through the medium. The most rapidly sedimenting band was termed III, the next most rapid II, and the slowest, I. As the velocity-time integral increased, all bands sedimented further into the gradients. It was found that ${}_0\int^t \omega^2\, dt = 2.3 \times 10^{10}$ gave the widest separation between the bands and so that condition was used for most of the studies. With this condition, band III was in 44 to 46.4% sucrose, band II in 38.4% sucrose, and band I in 30.5 sucrose (Figs. 1 and 2). Two important findings were observed when the cell cytoplasm was brought to 25% sucrose before being layered on the gradients rather than being layered on, as is usually done, in 0.34 M (11%) sucrose (see Fig. 3). First, aggregation of particles was greatly reduced; and second, band III was resolved into two bands that sedimented within 5 ml (11% of the gradient) of each other. We have designated these bands IIIs (III slower) and IIIf (III faster). Band IIIs was in 44% sucrose and band IIIf in 46.4% sucrose.

Immunochemical and biochemical analyses were done by methods described in Spitznagel (2). Table 1 shows the values obtained for whole cell homogenates of normal polymorphs.

Immunochemical analysis showed that 90% of the myeloperoxidase (MPO) of the PMN is associated with III and IIIs (Figs. 2 and 4). Of the lactoferrin, 77% was associated with band II, as Leffell found earlier (8) (see Fig. 4). Biochemical analysis showed (Fig. 3) that more than 90% of the neutral protease of the PMN is precisely associated with the MPO of band IIIs and so is 65% of the β-glucuronidase. The lysozyme of the cell is equally distributed between

→

FIG. 1. Post-nuclear cytoplasm from three donors, A, B, and C, was resolved by centrifuge into three bands labeled I, II, and III in order of increasing sedimentation. Band IV, detectable only as a peak of spectrophotometrically measured peroxidase, was obtained in gradients contaminated with specific granules from eosinophils. The centrifuge treatments were: A = ${}_0\int^t \omega^2\, dt = 1.2 \times 10^{10}$, B = ${}_0\int^t \omega^2\, dt = 2.3 \times 10^{10}$, and C = ${}_0\int^t \omega^2\, dt = 4.6 \times 10^{10}$ sec^{-1}. Total recoveries for each constituent respectively were: alkaline phosphatase 96, 71, and 74%; peroxidase 95, 75, and 86%; neutral protease 98, 95, and 84%; lysozyme 86, 75, and 72%; βGU 70, 74, and 74%; βGP 103, 94, and 91%; protein 110, 109, and 93%. The PMN were dextran purified and the contents of each subject's cell suspension were: A—PMN 90%, lymphs 7%, monocytes 1%, and eosinophils 2%; B—PMN 74%, lymphs 18%, monocytes 0.2%, and eosinophils 7.8%;

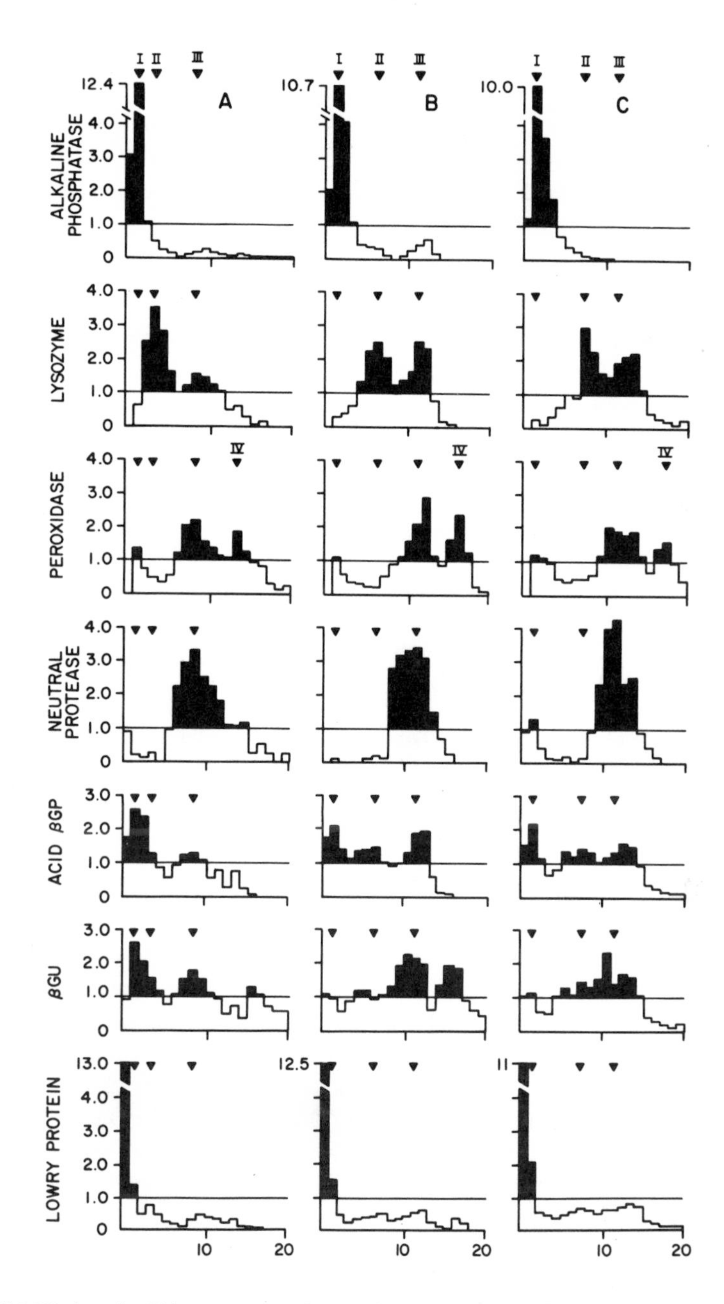

C—PMN 90%, lymphs 7%, monocytes 3%, and eosinophils 1%. Platelets were one per PMN or less in all preparations. Scale on ordinate calculated by methods of Beaufay et al. (16). A line is drawn across each histogram and corresponds to 1 on the ordinate. The bars are blackened where they extend above the line to indicate that the constituent has been concentrated in that fraction. Numbers on abscissa indicate the number of fractions collected from the gradients. The granules sedimented from left to right.

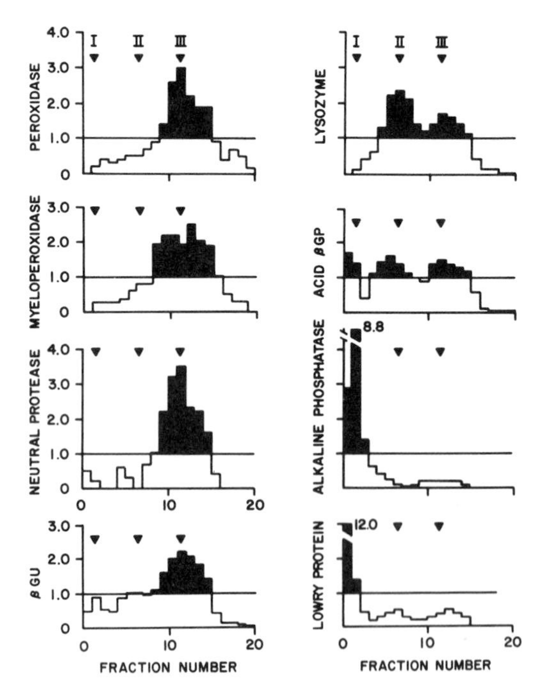

FIG. 2. Resolution of granules from 99% pure PMN and immunological detection of MPO. Recoveries were: peroxidase 74%, MPO 70%, neutral protease 110%, βGU 75%, βGP 77%, lysozyme 74%, alkaline phosphatase 85%, and protein 100%. Note that most constituents were undetectable or in relatively low concentration in the loading zone (fraction 1). Post-nuclear cytoplasm was applied and centrifuged at 2.3×10^{10} sec^{-1} through a gradient. PMN were purified with dextran and then with Ficoll-Hypaque producing a suspension with PMN 99%, lymphocytes 0%, monocytes 0.4%, and eosinophils 0.6%. No platelets were found. Results presented as in Fig. 1.

bands III and II (Fig. 2). But the lysozyme of band III is mostly in IIIf rather than IIIs (Fig. 3). There is a skewness of the MPO, neutral protease, and β-glucuronidase of band IIIs which provides a shoulder extending across IIIf. Likewise an opposite skewness of IIIs leaves a shoulder across IIIs. Thus it appears that band III has two components. One, IIIs, is richer in MPO, neutral protease, and β-glucuronidase while the other IIIf has relatively more lysozyme.

Ultrastructural histochemistry, which will be described below, confirmed the interpretation of the peroxidase distribution.

The distribution of acid β-glycerolphosphatase is of interest because this enzyme is characteristically found in lysosomal granules. About 20% of this enzyme appears to be associated with each of bands IIIs and IIIf (Fig. 3). Another 35% of this enzyme is distributed in a well-defined peak (see above) with 35% of β-glucuronidase. This peak sediments a little less rapidly than band II and well ahead of band I. It may contain granules similar to the acid-phosphatase positive tertiary granules described in ultrastructural studies on rabbit PMN (9). For the

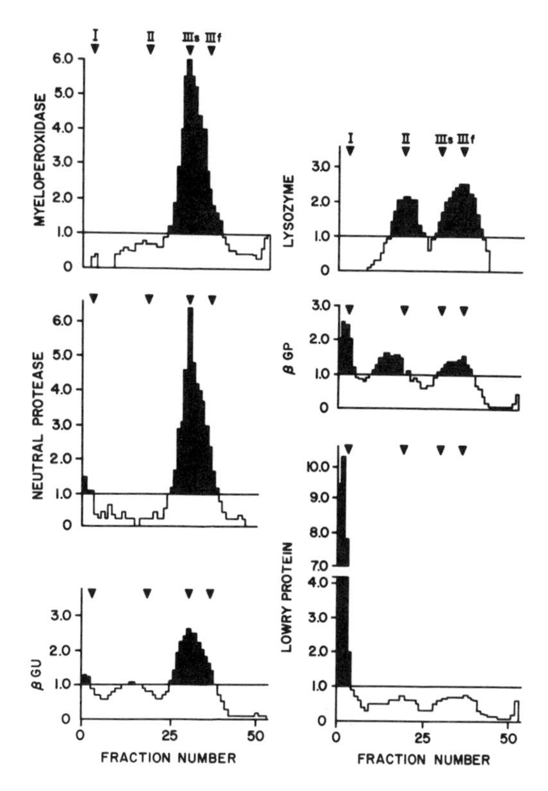

FIG. 3. Band III resolved into IIIs and IIIf. Total recoveries were: MPO 90%, neutral protease 90%, βGU 82%, lysozyme 117%, βGP 93%, and protein 106%. PMN were purified as for Fig. 2. PMN 96%, lymphocytes 0.5%, monocytes 0%, and eosinophils 3.5%. Granules applied in 25% sucrose. Other conditions were as described for Fig. 2. The gradient was collected in 54 1-ml fractions.

time being both this fraction of human PMN and the tertiary granules of rabbit PMN await further elucidation.

The alkaline phosphatase, which is plentiful in human PMN, was also accounted for. We found all of it in band I, which comprises empty membranous vesicles or microsomes and is devoid of granules.

The ultrastructure of material in bands III and II was of special interest (see ref. 2). Bands IIIs and IIIf were morphologically similar in several respects and comprised membrane-bounded granules 0.3 μ broad with profiles roughly round or oval. These granules were peroxidase positive when stained with the procedure of Graham and Karnovsky (see ref. 2) and viewed by electron microscopy.

Band II also comprised granules. These were membrane-bounded, 0.13 μ broad and round or elongated. Some were dumbbell shaped. Their matrices were densely stained by uranyl and lead and they were peroxidase negative according to the Graham-Karnovsky stain. Thus the granules of bands IIIs and IIIf resembled the azurophil granules of intact PMN and the granules of band II resembled

TABLE 1. *Peroxidase, myeloperoxidase, hydrolase and lactoferrin content of PMN*

Substance [a]	Specific activity [b]	SD	n [c]
1. MPO	75.0	19.0	11
2. PO, pH 7	1,095.0	397.0	20
3. Protease, pH 7	1.4	0.3	12
4. βGU, pH 4.5	4.5	1.0	16
5. Lysozyme, pH 6.2	114.0	31.0	21
6. Lactoferrin	112.0	21.0	11
7. βGP, pH 4.8	12.0	2.6	17
8. Phosphatase, pH 10.2	21.1	8.1	16

[a] (1) Myeloperoxidase measured by single radial immunodiffusion, (2) peroxidase measured spectrophotometrically, (3) enzyme hydrolyzing denatured hemoglobin, (4) enzyme hydrolyzing phenolphthalein glucuronide, (5) lysozyme activity measured spectrophotometrically, (6) lactoferrin measured by single radial immunodiffusion, (7) enzyme hydrolyzing βGP; (8) enzyme hydrolyzing *p*-nitrophenylphosphate.
[b] Values show the mean specific activity in milliunits per milligram cell protein. For 4, 7, and 8: 1 unit is the amount of enzyme needed to split 1 micromole of substrate/min at 37°C; for 1 and 6: 1 unit = 1 mg of protein; for 5: 1 unit of lysozyme is the amount causing a 10.0 OD units/min reduction in the suspended substrate at 25°C; for 2: 1 unit of peroxidase is the amount causing a 10.0 OD units/min increase at 25°C; for 3: 1 unit of protease is the amount causing a 1.0 OD units/min increase in TCA soluble fragments (at 280 nm); all other conditions specified in the methods section.
[c] Number of subjects.

specific granules. These morphological findings correlated exactly with the biochemical results that the azurophil granules contained all of the MPO and the specific granules were devoid of MPO.

In other studies Folds et al. (10) have found that the neutral protease of human PMN is distributed in the azurophil granules of band IIIs along with myeloperoxidase and neutral protease. In more detailed studies Ohlsson and Olsson have prepared antibodies in rabbits against collagenase (11) and elastase (12) isolated from a mixed granule fraction of PMN from patients with chronic granulocytic leukemia (CGL). Collaborative studies now in progress between our laboratories show that these antibodies detect antigens in the IIIs azurophil granules of normal human PMN.

Another antigen has turned out to be distributed in the azurophil granules of normal PMN. This antigen is detected by antibody prepared by Olsson and Venge (13) against cationic protein they isolated from the granules of PMN from patients with CGL. They found that this cationic protein has primary antimicrobial capacity (Ohlsson and Venge, *in press*) against both *Staphylococcus aureus* and *Eschericia coli.*

Finally, Leffell (14) has used the lactoferrin and MPO markers to study the potency of various stimuli in inducing degranulation. She has also been able to study independently and to compare with each other the translocation of specific granule contents (lactoferrin) and the translocation of azurophil granule contents. She has found that antigen and antibody complexes more effectively stimulate degranulation of both kinds of granules than do antigen or antibody alone. Surprisingly, specific granule contents (lactoferrin) are primarily translocated

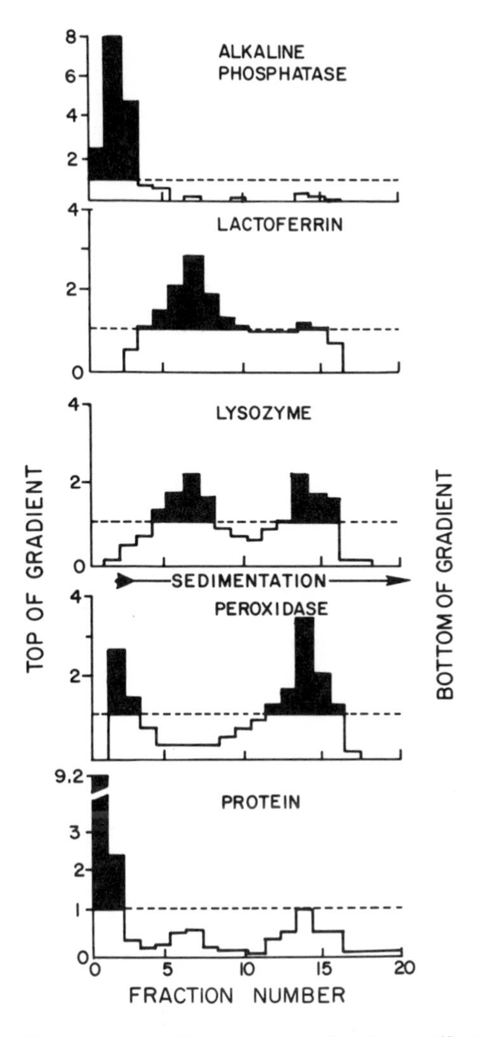

FIG. 4. Fractionation of leukocyte granules by sucrose density centrifugation. Graphs are normalized distribution histograms as a function of the total protein or total enzymatic activity recovered. Ordinate is concentration in fraction relative to concentration corresponding to uniform distribution throughout the gradient. Recoveries were 92% for alkaline phosphatase, 69% for lactoferrin, 74% for lysozyme, 83% for peroxidase, and 87% for protein.

into the extracellular fluid. Only 8% of the lactoferrin degranulated remained in the phagolysosome. Conversely, 50% or more of the MPO and more than 50% of the neutral protease translocated from the azurophil granules remained in the phagolysosome. Presumably specific and azurophil granule constituents that reached the extracellular fluid left the cells through clefts that connected nascent phagocytic vesicles to the extracellular space while degranulation had already begun. Possibly larger amounts of lactoferrin and lesser amounts of MPO left the cells because the specific granules degranulate earlier (as suggested by Bainton's work with rabbit PMN, 15). Alternatively, the lactoferrin may be less fixed to the cell membrane than may be the case with MPO.

Most important to the present discussion, Leffell's studies (14) showed the advantage of lactoferrin and MPO, immunochemically measured, as markers for specific and azurophil granules in studies of the mechanisms of degranulation.

In the course of our studies on granules of PMN from peripheral blood of humans we found several precautions were essential. The PMN suspensions had to be as free from other formed elements as possible, and clearcut distributions of enzymes were only achieved with 95% or more PMN free of platelets, monocytes, lymphocytes, and eosinophils. Eosinophils were especially troublesome contaminants because they possess peroxidase which turned out to be catalytically eight times more active than the MPO with PMN (2). Contaminant eosinophil granule peroxidase produces a misleading distribution of catalytically active peroxidase when PMN granules are separated by velocity or by isopynic centrifugation. Since 2 to 6% eosinophil contamination is difficult to avoid, we used rabbit antibody against MPO and measured MPO with single radial immunodiffusion. MPO and eosinophil peroxidase are immunologically distinct. Therefore it was possible through this device to measure the MPO of PMN independently of eosinophil peroxidase. It cannot be overemphasized that, in order for a substance to serve as an unambiguous marker for an organelle or its contents, it must be measurable by a method capable of distinguishing it from similar substances from other organelles from the same cell type as well as from similar substances from other cells. MPO measured immunochemically and lactoferrin measured in like manner appear well suited for this.

The advantage of applying to gradients post-nuclear supernatants suspended in 25% sucrose rather than 11% (0.34 M) has also been mentioned. This maneuver greatly reduced aggregation and made possible the resolution of the azurophil granules into what we have tentatively identified as two substances: one richer in MPO, neutral protease, and β-glucuronidase, the other in lysozyme.

A surprising discovery has been the complete absence of alkaline phosphatase from the granules of human PMN (2, 4, 5, 8) and the recognition that it is confined to cell membranes. The practical significance is that alkaline phosphatase cannot be used as a marker for specific granules of human PMN nor can the presence or absence of this enzyme in PMN be considered indicative of the integrity or sufficiency of specific granules. Moreover, there are theoretical implications, for only if the precise location of this enzyme is appreciated can its role in the metabolism of the cell be understood.

SUMMARY

In order to assess the integrity of PMN granules, it is helpful to be able to measure a substance that unambiguously reflects the components of a particular granule class and can be detected with specificity and sensitivity. MPO is a suitable substance of assessment of azurophil granules. In like manner lactoferrin appears suitable for assessment of specific granules. Similar methods are being developed to facilitate the localization and quantitation of important PMN granule constituents such as the proteases and cationic proteins of human PMN. In addition, these methods and markers should help to analyze the translocation of granule constituents in response to physiological stimuli imposed during phagocytosis.

REFERENCES

1. Bainton, D. F., Ullyot, J. L., and Farquhar, M. G.: The development of neutrophilic polymorphonuclear leukocytes in human bone marrow. Origin and content of azurophil and specific granules. *J. Exp. Med.* 134:907–934, 1971.
2. Spitznagel, J. K., Dalldorf, F. G., Leffell, M. S., Folds, J. D., Welsh, I. R. H., Cooney, M. H., and Martin, L. E.: Character of azurophil and specific granules purified from human polymorphonuclear leukocytes. *Lab. Invest.* 30:774–785, 1974.
3. Schultz, J., Corlin, R., Oddi, F., Kaminker, K., and Jones, W.: Myeloperoxidase of the leukocyte of normal human blood. III. Isolation of the peroxidase granule. *Arch. Biochem. Biophys.* 111:73–79, 1965.
4. Welsh, I. R. H., Zeya, H. I., and Spitznagel, J. K.: Heterogeneity of lysosomes from human peripheral blood polymorphonuclear leukocytes. *Fed. Proc.* 30:599 abs., 1971.
5. West, B. C., Gelb, N. A., and Kimball, H. R.: Human blood granulocyte granules. *Fed. Proc.* 31:253 abs., 1972.
6. Baggiolini, M., Hirsch, J. G., and De Duve, C.: Resolution of granules from rabbit heterophil leukocytes into distinct populations by zonal sedimentation. *J. Cell Biol.* 40:529–541, 1969.
7. Zeya, H. I., and Spitznagel, J. K.: Characterization of cationic protein-bearing granules of polymorphonuclear leukocytes. *Lab. Invest.* 24:229–236, 1971.
8. Leffell, M. S., and Spitznagel, J. K.: Association of lactoferrin with lysozyme in granules of human polymorphonuclear leukocytes. *Infect. Immun.* 6:761–765, 1972.
9. Murata, F., and Spicer, S. S.: Morphologic and cytochemical studies of rabbit heterophilic leukocytes. *Lab. Invest.* 29:65–72, 1973.
10. Folds, J. D., Welsh, I. R. H., and Spitznagel, J. K.: Neutral proteases confined to one class of lysosomes of human polymorphonuclear leukocytes. *Proc. Soc. Exp. Biol. Med.* 139:461–463, 1972.
11. Ohlsson, K., and Olsson, I.: The neutral proteases of human granulocytes: Isolation and partial characterization of two granulocyte collagenases. *Eur. J. Biochem.* 36:473–481, 1973.
12. Ohlsson, K., and Olsson, I.: The neutral proteases of human granulocytes: Isolation and partial characterization of granulocyte elastase. *Eur. J. Biochem.* 42:519–527, 1974.
13. Olsson, I., and Venge, P.: Cationic proteins of human granulocytes: Isolation of the cationic proteins from the granules of leukemic myeloid cells. *Scand. J. Haematol.* 9:204–214, 1972.
14. Leffell, M. S., and Spitznagel, J. K.: Intracellular and extracellular degranulation of human polymorphonuclear azurophil and specific granules induced by immune complexes. Submitted for publication, 1974.
15. Bainton, D. F.: Sequential degranulation of the two types of polymorphonuclear leukocyte granules during phagocytosis of microorganisms. *J. Cell Biol.* 58:249–264, 1973.
16. Beaufay, H., Jacques P., Baudhuin, P., Sellinger, O. Z., Berthet, J., and de Duve, C.: Resolution of mitochondrial fractions from rat liver into three distinct populations of cytoplasmic particles by means of density equilibration in various gradients. *Biochem. J.* 92:184, 1964.

The Phagocytic Cell in Host Resistance, edited
by Joseph A. Bellanti and Delbert H. Dayton.
Raven Press, New York © 1975.

Complement and Phagocytosis

Hans J. Müller-Eberhard

Department of Molecular Immunology, Scripps Clinic and Research Foundation, La Jolla, California 92037

THE DUAL ROLE OF COMPLEMENT IN PHAGOCYTOSIS

Complement appears to play a dual role in facilitating the phagocytic reaction. It gives rise to leukotactic factors and to opsonization of particles. The chemotactic factors are generated through fission (C3a and C5a) or through fusion (C5b, 6, 7) of complement proteins. Opsonization is primarily a function of bound C3b and, to a lesser extent, of C4b. The opsonic function is based on the ability of these fragments to bind to immune complexes, bacteria, and other cells and to display, in their bound form, sites that can specifically interact with receptors on the surface of phagocytic cells. Complement-dependent opsonization of infectious agents may be particularly important in the early phase of host invasion when effective amounts of specific antibody may not be available. But even in the presence of adequate antibody, complement appears to exert a cooperative effect in the induction of immune phagocytosis.

In the following I will briefly summarize the molecular dynamics of the complement reaction, discuss the structure-function relationship of C3a, C5a, and C3b, and present a tentative model of the C3 molecule because this protein occupies a key position in complement-dependent host resistance to infections.

MOLECULAR DYNAMICS

The Classic Pathway

Two pathways of complement function have been distinguished: the first, or classic, and the second, or alternate, pathway. The latter is intimately related to the properdin system of Pillemer.

The first pathway consists of three operationally defined functional units: the recognition unit (C1), the activation unit (C2, C3, C4), and the membrane attack mechanism (C5, C6, C7, C8, C9) (for detailed references see 1–6).

C1 constitutes a complex of three kinds of proteins: C1q is a collagen-like protein with binding sites for IgG and IgM; C1r is the activating enzyme of the critical catalytic site of the C1 complex; and C1s is a proenzyme which is activated by C1r. When C1 collides with antigen-antibody complexes located, for instance, on the surface of a cell, C1 is bound to the antibody molecules through its C1q subunit. Presumably through a change in conformation of C1q, a conformational change of C1r is effected which renders the C1r molecule enzymatically active ($C1\bar{r}$). Subsequently, C1s is activated to $C1\bar{s}$ by cleavage of its single polypeptide chain. The two resulting fragments are held together by a disulfide bond and the active site is resident in the smaller fragment having a molecular weight of 33,000 dalton (7, 8).

The activation unit is assembled in two steps. C3 convertase ($C\overline{4b,2a}$) is formed by $C\bar{1}$ (active site located in $C1\bar{s}$) through consecutive cleavage of C4 and C2. The major C4 fragment, C4b, in its nascent state, can attach to membrane surface receptors and thus may become firmly bound to the target cell. The major C2 fragment, C2a, in its nascent state, can bind to C4b. Upon fusion of these two fragments into a bimolecular complex, enzymatic activity appears that is directed against C3. C3 convertase cleaves this molecule into a small fragment, C3a (anaphylatoxin I), and a large fragment, C3b, which can attach to membrane receptors and to its own activation enzyme, thereby evoking immune adherence reactivity and causing conversion of C3 convertase to C5 convertase. The latter enzyme consists of three fragments ($C4\overline{b,2a,3b}$) and has substrate specificity for C5.

Assembly of the membrane attack mechanism is initiated by cleavage of C5 into C5a (anaphylatoxin II) and C5b. This hydrolytic step is accomplished by the C5 convertase of the classic or the alternate pathways (see below) and represents the last enzymatic event in the entire complement reaction. Nascent C5b binds C6 and C7 by adsorption and the resulting trimolecular complex, which can attach to membrane receptors, binds C8 and C9. Fully assembled, the membrane attack complex consists of one molecule of C5b, C6, C7, and C8 and up to six molecules of C9. Its cumulative molecular weight is one million (9). In its cell-bound form it injures the outer cell membrane and causes cell death.

The Alternate Mechanism of Complement Activation

The alternate mechanism of complement activation is set in motion by naturally occurring polysaccharides and lipopolysaccharides (10) and by aggregates of IgA (11). This mechanism bypasses C1, C2, and C4 and enters the classic pathway at the C3 reaction step (12). Operationally, we distinguish a segment of the reaction which is distal to C3 and which involves properdin from one that is proximal to C3 and requires the C3 proactivator.[1]

The proximal segment is most readily understood; it constitutes a C3b-dependent positive feedback reaction (13). C3 proactivator (C3PA) (11) is a proenzyme with a molecular weight of 80,000 dalton. Enzymatic activation generates a 60,000 dalton fragment which is endowed with enzyme activity having specificity for C3. We call the enzyme C3 activator since it cleaves C3 into its physiological

[1] Abbreviations used in this chapter with synonyms used by others: C3PA, C3 proactivator (GBG, Factor B); C3A, C3 activator (GGG, β_2-glycoprotein II); C3PAse, C3PA convertase (GBGase, Factor D); HSF or C3, hydrazine sensitive factor or the third component of complement (Factor A); HSFa or C3b, activated HSF or the b-fragment of C3; P, properdin; $\overline{P}$, activated properdin; C3b INA, C3b inactivator (KAF).

products C3a and C3b much like the $\overline{C4b,2a}$ complex. C3b then enables the enzyme C3PA convertase (C3PAse) to activate C3PA. Thus a product of C3 leads to modulation of the enzyme system which activates C3. It should be emphasized here that cleavage of C3PA is not an essential prerequisite for expression of its enzymatic activity. We have found that the enzyme can be reversibly switched on in the cold in serum of a patient with focal glomerulonephritis. In normal serum, cobra factor has a similar effect on C3PA, if the reaction is carried out at 0°C (14).

The initiation of the C3b-dependent feedback requires properdin (P) (15, 16), C3PAse, native C3, and probably two additional serum factors. The latter two factors appear to be involved in the activation of P. One of these factors has been tentatively identified as the normal analogue of the so-called nephritic factor (C3NeF) and we call the normal equivalent the initiating factor or IF (17). The other factor appears to act subsequent to IF and prior to P, because serum depleted of this factor (we call it factor X) cannot be activated by C3NeF, inulin, or other activators of the alternate pathway, although such serum contains P, C3, C3PAse, and C3PA.

Conversion of C3 by $\bar{P}$ requires C3PA and C3PAse and conversion of C3PA by $\bar{P}$ requires C3 and C3PAse (15). We have therefore proposed that in the early steps of the alternate pathway $\bar{P}$ cooperates with native C3 in the activation of C3PAse. Following this event, the C3b-dependent positive feedback mechanism is initiated.

For formation of C5 convertase of the alternate pathway, additional require-

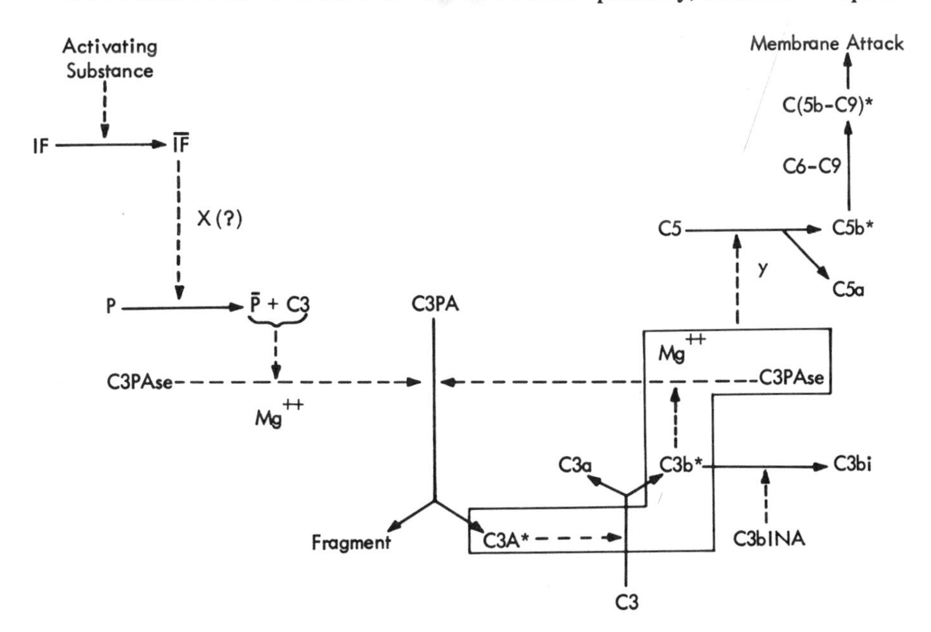

FIG. 1. The current concept of the second complement pathway. The asterisks denote enzymatically activated, labile-binding sites. The components enclosed by the solid line together with an additional factor (Y) constitute the ingredients for generation of C5 convertase activity.

ments have been recognized. In whole serum a surface may be required, such as that provided by yeast cell walls or endotoxin particles, allowing assembly of the enzyme from its various subunits (15). These may include C3 activator, C3PAse, C3b, and possibly an additional factor, called factor Y, or factor E (18). The present concept of the action of the components of the alternate pathway is summarized schematically in Fig. 1.

Regardless of which pathway is set in motion, the molecular consequences are nearly identical: (1) the two anaphylatoxins C3a and C5a are liberated, (2) C3b is formed, and (3) the C5b-9 complex is assembled. With generation of the anaphylatoxins, histamine-releasing, smooth muscle-contracting, and chemotactic activity appear; bound C3b exhibits immune adherence reactivity and free C3b modulates C3PAse and C3 convertase; nascent C5b-9 kills cells. One biologically active fragment is produced only in the classic reaction sequence: C4b, which in its bound form also exhibits immune adherence reactivity like C3b (19).

THE C3b-FRAGMENT

The Labile, Enzymatically Activated Binding Site

Nascent C3b is endowed with a labile binding site (Sbl) which is activated through cleavage of native C3 by C3 convertase of the classic pathway or the C3 activator of the alternate pathway (20). By virtue of the Sbl site, C3b can bind to a wide variety of particulate or colloidal substances: immune aggregates, particulate polysaccharides and lipopolysaccharides, bacterial cell walls, animal cell membranes, and basement membranes. Apparently the receptor for the Sbl site of C3b is either ubiquitous or different chemical groups can fulfill this function. Due to the inherent lability of the activated site, binding to potential receptors must occur shortly after activation; failing this, C3b remains permanently unbound in the fluid phase.

The Stable, Immune Adherence Site

C3b bound by the above mechanism to antigen-antibody complexes, cells, or other particles exhibits the ability to react with the C3b receptor of cell membranes. This ability resides in a stable site (Sbs) and depends on the structural integrity of the bound C3b fragment. Unlike the Sbl-receptor, the Sbs receptor is restricted to a limited species of cells and exhibits a high degree of specificity for C3b. It is usually called the C3b- or immune adherence (IA) receptor. Its chemical identity is unknown. It is readily removed from the surface of cells by trypsin. The reaction allows close physical contact between the C3b-coated particle and cells such as polymorphs, monocytes, erythrocytes, a subspecies of B-lymphocytes, and platelets. In the case of polymorphs and monocytes the C3b-mediated adherence induces phagocytosis of the adhering particles.

The experimental model of IA consists of sheep erythrocytes (E) coated with antibody (A), having reacted with C1, C2, C3, C4 (EAC1,4,2,3), and of human blood group O erythrocytes that bear the C3b receptor and serve as indicator cells. Approximately 100 bound C3b molecules per sheep E are required to give a marginal IA reaction (19). A strongly positive IA phenomenon necessitates several thousand bound C3b molecules per cell (20). Since only 10 to 20% of the C3 offered is attached to the cells upon activation, an input of 1,000 to 10,000 C3 molecules per cell is required for efficient IA. Although this may seem a large number of molecules, it is relatively small in terms of the supply available in a milliliter of serum (1,500 μg).

Comparison with C4-Dependent Immune Adherence

Cooper (19) showed that EAC1,4 also produced the IA phenomenon. The minimal number of C4b molecules per cell required for a positive reaction was approximately 3,000. A strong reaction was caused by 9,000 to 10,000 bound C4b molecules per cell. Recently, Sobel and Bokisch (21) found that EAC1,4 also react with human peripheral lymphocytes. The observed rosette formation was inhibitable with soluble C3b, indicating that bound C4b probably reacts with the C3b receptor of lymphocytes and perhaps other cells.

The demonstrated IA activity of C4b has raised the question as to a possible cooperative effect of C3b and C4b in IA. It is conceivable that the number of C3b molecules required for IA is inversely proportional to the number of C4b molecules present. This hypothesis is presently under investigation. If C4b reacts with the C3b receptor, as has been suggested, the specificity of this receptor would be less restricted than previously assumed. On the other hand, recent comparative analyses of the chain structure of C3 and C4 have revealed certain striking similarities.

Cooperativity of C3b and IgG in the Induction of Phagocytosis

The interplay between C3b and its cellular receptor represents an essential process in immune phagocytosis. That erythrophagocytosis *in vitro* requires C3b was first shown by Gigli and Nelson (22). A more intricate function of C3b, described in our laboratory, pertains to the ingestion of antibody-covered erythrocytes by human monocytes (23). In this system IgM-type antibody was ineffective as opsonin and ingestion of the erythrocytes required approximately 1,000 bound C3b molecules per cell. In contrast, ingestion of erythrocytes sensitized with IgG antibody was independent of complement due to the presence of IgG receptors on the phagocytic cell. However, the reaction was inhibited by a concentration of free IgG far below that in normal serum. Inhibition by free IgG was overcome by approximately 100 bound C3b molecules per cell. Apparently, contact established between the erythrocytes and monocytes by C3b enables IgG antibody to come into play. The following conclusions were drawn: the IgG and C3b receptors of monocytes may function independently in the induction of phagocytosis. Or, more importantly, the two receptors may exert a cooperative effect on ingestion by monocytes or erythrocytes coated with IgG antibody in the presence of inhibitory amounts of free IgG. The latter situation clearly pertains to *in vivo* conditions and stresses the importance of the role of C3 as an inducer of phagocytosis.

Other Functions of C3b

Nascent C3b can attach to the $C\overline{4b,2a}$ complex, thus forming the trimolecular C5 convertase ($C\overline{4b,2a,3b}$). C3b also appears to be a subunit of the complex C5 convertase of the alternate pathway of complement activation. Free C3b, which has lost its Sbl site, retains the ability to mediate the interaction between C3PAse and C3PA and thus functions as an apparent activator of the C3PAse enzyme (13). Free C3b retains also some IA reactivity, that is, the Sbs site remains functional to a certain degree. Residual IA reactivity in free C3b was first demonstrated with human Burkitt lymphoma cells of the Raji line (24). These cells possess the C3b receptor and bind free C3b through its Sbs site. Since this site is engaged in the binding process, C3b coated Raji cells do not display IA reactivity. However, in the presence of fresh serum, the C3b on the cell surface activates C3PAse, which ultimately results in formation of C5b-9 and killing of the cells.

EFFECT OF C3b-INACTIVATOR ON C3b STRUCTURE AND FUNCTION

C3b INA (25), also called KAF (26), is a heat-stable serum enzyme with the mobility of a β-globulin and a molecular weight of 100,000 dalton. The enzyme cleaves C3 into the antigenically distinct C3c and C3d fragments (27). With fission of C3b, all of its known functions are abrogated. Specifically, KAF destroys the IA activity or the Sbs site, the modulator function in C5 convertase or the SM-1 site, and the activator function of C3PAse or the Sm-2 site.

Action of KAF on cell-bound C3b results in release of C3c but leaves C3d firmly attached to the cell, indicating that the binding site of C3b (Sbl) is resident in the C3d portion. Bound C3d displays a new reactivity of the C3 molecule, namely the ability to react with the C3d receptor on certain lymphocytes (28). As far as I know, phagocytic cells such as polymorphs and monocytes are not endowed with the C3d receptor. The biological relevance of C3d and its receptor on lymphocytes is unknown.

THE RELATIONSHIP BETWEEN STRUCTURE AND FUNCTION OF C3a AND C5a

According to Ward (29), both C3a and C5a of human origin are chemotactic for polymorphs and monocytes, the C5a fragment being the more active one. Their activity is under the control of the serum chemotactic factor inactivator that appears to be distinct from the anaphylatoxin inactivator. According to

Becker (30), both peptides effect activation of a serine esterase in leukocytes as an essential part of their chemotactic action.

In guinea pig serum only C5a is said to be leukotactic, whereas C3a does not have this activity (31). Further, according to Wissler (32), who worked with rat and porcine serum, chemotactic activity is a function of two interacting peptides, one being anaphylatoxin (probably C5a) and the other an as yet unidentified entity, which he calls cocytotaxin.

We have limited our studies to the analysis of the physical and chemical properties of the two peptides and the relationship of their structure to anaphylatoxin activity. This activity expresses itself by causing smooth muscle contraction, release of histamine from mast cells, and, *in vivo,* formation of edema and erythema in the skin. It is probable that certain of the structural requirements for these activities are also requirements for the leukotactic function.

The molecular weight of C3a is 8,900, that of C5a 15,000 dalton. The electrophoretic mobility at pH 8.6 of C3a and C5a is respectively +2.1 and −1.7 × 10^{-5} cm^2 V^{-1} $sec.^{-1}$. Both peptides contain arginine in COOH-terminal position.

The circular dichroism (CD) spectra of C3a (33) and C5a (34) show a considerable magnitude of mean residue ellipticity at 208 and 222 nm. Calculations indicate that both molecules contain approximately 40 to 45% α-helical structure. Treatment of human C3a with either mercaptoethanol or 6 M guanidinium chloride produced a marked decrease in ellipticity at 222 nm without significantly affecting biological activity. Simultaneous treatment with mercaptoethanol and guanidinium chloride eliminated the ellipticity at 222 nm and abolished biological activity. Removal of the denaturant and reducing agent restored both the characteristic CD spectrum and anaphylatoxin activity.

In the case of C5a, mercaptoethanol treatment resulted in progressive decline in the magnitude of ellipticity at 222 nm and a parallel decline in biologic activity. Upon removal of the reducing agent by dialysis, the original CD spectrum was restored and so was C5a activity.

In vitro, C3a is active at a minimal concentration of 1.3×10^{-8} M and C5a at 7.5×10^{-10} M. The activity of both peptides is totally abolished by removal of the COOH-terminal basic amino acid residue. Cleavage of this residue is efficiently accomplished by the serum anaphylatoxin inactivator, which is a 300,000 dalton α-globulin with carboxypeptidase B-like activity (35). CD examination showed that removal of the COOH-terminal arginine from C3a had no effect on the peptide's secondary structure (33).

In conclusion, the biologic activity of both anaphylatoxins depends on at least two independent structural requirements: the COOH-terminal arginine residue and a high degree of ordered secondary structure maintained by disulfide bonds and noncovalent forces.

A MODEL OF THE C3 MOLECULE

To facilitate an understanding of the multiple, distinct functions of C3, it appears appropriate to propose a tentative model of the C3 molecule. A schematic

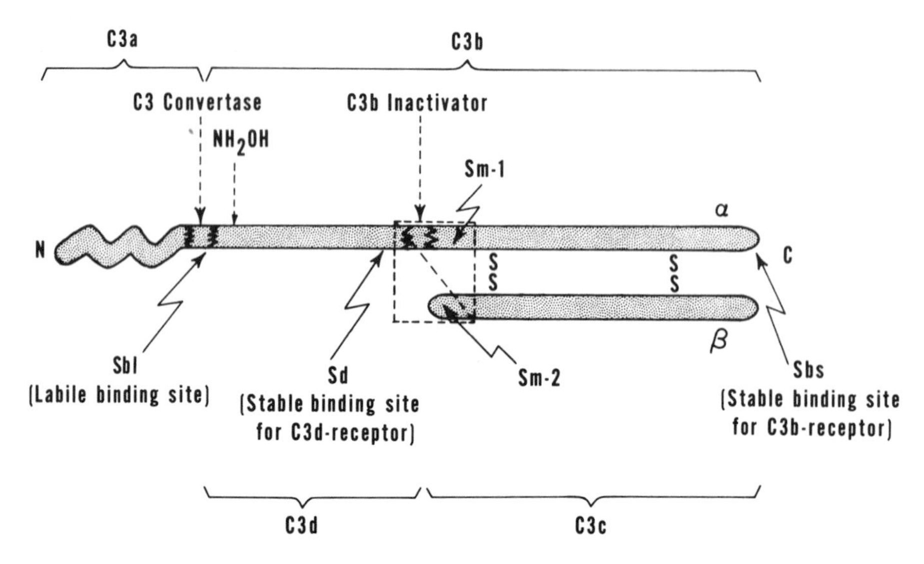

FIG. 2. A tentative model of the C3 molecule proposing topological relationships between chains (α, β) fragments (a–d), functional sites (Sbl, Sbs, Sd, Sm-1, Sm-2), hydroxylamine and enzymatic attack regions (C3 convertase, C3b inactivator).

summary of our knowledge of the topology of the various functional sites, chains, enzymatic attack regions, and fragments of the C3 molecule is depicted in Fig. 2.

C3, having a molecular weight of 180,000 dalton, consists of two polypeptide chains, α and β, the molecular weights of which are respectively 110,000 and 70,000 dalton (36). The chains are linked by disulfide bonds and noncovalent forces. Whereas most of the molecule has random coil structure, the small C3a-portion, accounting for 4.9% of its mass, has a high degree of secondary structure. It represents the amino-terminal segment of the α-chain which comprises 77 amino acid residues, contains three intrachain disulfide bonds, and possesses 45% α-helical configuration as revealed by its CD spectrum (37).

C3a, having a molecular weight of 8,900 dalton and being endowed with leukotactic and anaphylatoxin activity, is split from the C3 molecule by the action of C3 convertase of either the classic or the alternate pathway of complement activation. A peptide bond of the α-chain is cleaved, which involves the carboxyl group of an arginyl residue and which is highly susceptible to enzymatic attack (38). As a result, a binding site (Sbl) is generated through which C3b can attach to the surface of cell membranes, immune complexes, particulate polysaccharides, etc. This binding site, which is capable of reacting with seemingly ubiquitous receptors, is located in the d-portion of C3b. The site is very labile and is rapidly and irreversibly lost unless collision with a suitable receptor occurs within a fraction of a second after its activation. Bound C3b and, to some extent, free C3b exhibit the ability to react with the specific C3b or immune adherence receptor of a variety of cellular elements including polymorphs and monocytes. This function (Sbs) is probably located in the c-portion of C3b, and, unlike Sbl, Sbs is a stable site.

At least two additional functional sites must be postulated for C3b: the region by means of which it modulates the function of the $C\overline{4,2}$ enzyme (Sm-1) and the site responsible for activation of C3PAse (Sm-2). Their topology is unknown; however, since their function depends on the structural integrity of C3b, both the c- and the d-portion may contribute to their structure.

The C3b-fragment can be cleaved by the C3b-inactivator or KAF into C3c (140,000 dalton) and C3d (31,000 dalton). By reduction with dithiothreitol in sodium dodecyl sulfate, the molecular weight of C3c is reduced to 70,000 dalton (39). This observation indicates that C3c consists of the β-chain (70,000 dalton) and a COOH-terminal fragment of the α-chain of similar size. An identical treatment of C3d does not result in a molecular weight change, indicating that C3d represents a fragment of the α-chain only (39). By implication, the C3b-inactivator is envisaged to act on the α-chain portion of the C3b-fragment. With cleavage of C3b, all three functions, namely those resident in Sbs, Sm-1, and Sm-2, are lost. C3d, however, remains bound through Sbl and, after removal of C3c, exhibits a new, previously concealed site (Sd) which has specificity for the C3d-receptor of certain lymphocytes and lymphoblastoid cells (24, 28).

ACKNOWLEDGMENTS

This is publication number 819 from the Department of Molecular Immunology, Scripps Clinic and Research Foundation, La Jolla, California 92037. This work was supported by U.S. Public Health Service grant AI-07007.

REFERENCES

1. Müller-Eberhard, H. J.: Complement. In: Snell, E. E. (ed.): *Annual Review of Biochemistry,* Annual Reviews, Inc., Palo Alto, Calif., Vol. 38, p. 389, 1969.
2. Müller-Eberhard, H. J.: The molecular basis of the biological activities of complement. In: *The Harvey Lectures,* Series 66, Academic Press, New York, p. 75. 1972.
3. Rapp, H. J., and Borsos, T.: *Molecular Basis of Complement Action.* Appleton-Century-Crofts, New York, 1970.
4. Ruddy, S., Gigli, I., and Austen, K. F.: The complement system of man. *N. Engl. J. Med.* 287:489, 545, 592, 642, 1972.
5. Schultz, D. R.: The complement system. In: *Monographs in Allergy,* S. Karger, Basel, Vol. 6, 1971.
6. Complement Workshop: Abstracts of the Fifth International Complement Workshop, Hotel Del Coronado, Coronado, Calif., February 23–25, 1973. *J. Immunol.* 111:286, 1973.
7. Sakai, K., and Stroud, R. M.: Purification, molecular properties and activation of C1 proesterase, C1s. *J. Immunol.* 110:1010, 1973.
8. Valet, G., and Cooper, N. R.: Isolation and characterization of the proenzyme form of the C1s subunit of the first complement component. *J. Immunol.* 112:339, 1974.
9. Kolb, W. P., and Müller-Eberhard, H. J.: The membrane attack mechanism of complement. Verification of a stable C5–9 complex in free solution. *J. Exp. Med.* 138:438, 1973.
10. Gewurz, H., Shin, H. S., and Mergenhagen, S. E.: Interactions of the complement system with endotoxin lipopolysaccharides: Consumption of each of the six terminal complement components. *J. Exp. Med.* 128:1049, 1968.

11. Götze, O., and Müller-Eberhard, H. J.: The C3-activator system: An alternate pathway of complement activation. *J. Exp. Med.* 134:90s, 1971.
12. Sandberg, A. L., Osler, A. G., Shin, H. S., and Oliveira, B.: The biologic activities of guinea pig antibodies. II. Modes of complement interaction with $\gamma 1$ and $\gamma 2$ immunoglobulins. *J. Immunol.* 104:329, 1970.
13. Müller-Eberhard, H. J., and Götze, O.: C3 proactivator convertase and its mode of action. *J. Exp. Med.* 135:1003, 1972.
14. Day, N. K., and Müller-Eberhard, H. J.: Cold-dependent activation of the alternate complement pathway. *Fed. Proc.* 33:775, 1974.
15. Götze, O., and Müller-Eberhard, H. J.: The role of properdin in the alternate pathway of complement activation. *J. Exp. Med.* 139:44, 1974.
16. Pensky, J., Hinz, C. F., Jr., Todd, E. W., Wedgwood, R. J., Boyer, J. T., and Lepow, I. H.: Properties of highly purified human properdin. *J. Immunol.* 100:142, 1968.
17. Vallota, E. H., Spiegelberg, H. L., Götze, O., Forristal, J., West, C. D., and Müller-Eberhard, H. J.: A serum factor in chronic hypocomplementemic nephritis distinct from immunoglobulins and activating the alternate pathway of complement. *J. Exp. Med.* 139:1249, 1974.
18. Ruddy, S., Fearon, D. T., and Austen, K. F.: Participation of factors B, D, E and C3b inactivator in cobra venom (CoVF)-induced activation of the alternate complement pathway. *J. Immunol.* 111:289, 1973.
19. Cooper, N. R.: Immune adherence by the fourth component of complement. *Science* 165:396, 1969.
20. Müller-Eberhard, H. J., Dalmasso, A. P., and Calcott, M. A.: The reaction mechanism of β_{1C}-globulin (C'3) in immune hemolysis. *J. Exp. Med.* 123:33, 1966.
21. Sobel, A. T., and Bokisch, V. A.: Receptor for the fourth component of complement on human B-lymphocytes. *Fed. Proc.* 33:759, 1974.
22. Gigli, I., and Nelson, R. A., Jr.: Complement dependent immune phagocytosis. I. Requirements for C'1, C'4, C'2, C'3. *Exp. Cell Res.* 51:45, 1968.
23. Huber, H., Polley, M. J., Linscott, W. D., Fudenberg, H. H., and Müller-Eberhard, H. J.: Human monocytes: Distinct receptor sites for the third component of complement and for immunoglobulin G. *Science* 162:1281, 1968.
24. Theofilopoulos, A. N., Bokisch, V. A., and Dixon, F. J.: Receptor for soluble C3 and C3b on human lymphoblastoid (Raji) cells: Properties and biological significance. *J. Exp. Med.* 139: 696–711, 1974.
25. Tamura, N., and Nelson, R. A., Jr., Three naturally-occurring inhibitors of components of complement in guinea pig and rabbit serum. *J. Immunol.* 99:582, 1967.
26. Lachmann, P. J., and Müller-Eberhard, H. J.: The demonstration in human serum of "conglutinogen-activating-factor" and its effect on the third component of complement. *J. Immunol.* 100:691, 1968.
27. Müller-Eberhard, H. J., and Bayne, A.: C5 convertase of human complement. *J. Exp. Med.* (in press).
28. Ross, G. D., Polley, M. J., Rabellino, E. M., and Grey, H. M., Two different complement receptors on human lymphocytes. One specific for C3b and one specific for C3b inactivator-cleaved C3b. *J. Exp. Med.* 138:798, 1973.
29. Ward, P. A.: Complement-derived leukotactic factors in pathological fluids. *J. Exp. Med.* 134:-109s, 1971.
30. Becker, E. L.: The relationship of the chemotactic behavior of the complement-derived factors, C3a, C5a, and C567, and a bacterial chemotactic factor to their ability to activate the proesterase 1 of rabbit polymorphonuclear leukocytes. *J. Exp. Med.* 135:376, 1972.
31. Snyderman, R., Phillips, J. K., and Mergenhagen, S. E.: Biological activity of complement *in vivo.* Role of C5 in the accumulation of polymorphonuclear leukocytes in inflammatory exudates. *J. Exp. Med.* 134:1131, 1971.
32. Wissler, J. H., Stecher, V. J., and Sorkin, E.: Chemistry and biology of the anaphylatoxin related serum peptide system. III. Evaluation of leucotactic activity as a property of a new peptide system with classical anaphylatoxin and cocytotaxin as components. *Eur. J. Immunol.* 2:90, 1972.
33. Hugli, T. E., Morgan, W. T., and Müller-Eberhard, H. J.: Circular dichroism of C3a anaphylatoxin: Effects of pH, guanidinium chloride and mercaptoethanol on conformation and function. *J. Biol. Chem.* (in press).

34. Morgan, W. T., Vallota, E. H., and Müller-Eberhard, H. J.: Structure-function relationship of porcine C5a anaphylatoxin. *Biochem. Biophys. Res. Commun.* 57:572, 1974.
35. Bokisch, V. A., and Müller-Eberhard, H. J.: Anaphylatoxin inactivator of human plasma: Its isolation and characterization as a carboxypeptidase. *J. Clin. Invest.* 49:2427, 1970.
36. Nilsson, U. R., and Mapes, J.: Polyacrylamide gel electrophoresis (PAGE) of reduced and dissociated C3 and C5: Studies of the polypeptide chain (PPC) subunits and their modifications by trypsin (TRY) and $C\overline{4,2}$–$C\overline{4,2,3}$. *J. Immunol.* 111:293, 1973.
37. Hugli, T. E., Vallota, E. H., and Müller-Eberhard, H. J.: Purification and partial characterization of human and procine C3a anaphylatoxin. *J. Biol. Chem.* (in press).
38. Budzko, D. B., Bokisch, V. A., and Müller-Eberhard, H. J.: A fragment of the third component of human complement with anaphylatoxin activity. *Biochemistry* 10:1166, 1971.
39. Bokisch, V. A., and Müller-Eberhard, H. J.: *To be published.*

DISCUSSION

Gallin: I would like to ask a question about the C3a fragment. How does this compare with the C3 fragment resulting from brief trypsinization of C3, which contains both chemotactic and anaphylatoxic activity, and the C3 fragment resulting from prolonged trypsinization, which loses the anaphylatoxic but retains the chemotactic activity? Would you also comment on the heat lability of the C3a fragment?

Müller-Eberhard: The C3a fragment is quite heat stable. I think its secondary structure is responsible for it. You cannot denature it by just heating it to 56 degrees. The trypsin-generated fragment, of course, does not compare with the C3 convertase-generated fragment functionally or structurally. Because there are additional cleavages in C3a occurring with trypsin but not with C3 convertase. The latter is strictly limited to the cleavage of one bond. Therefore, if you wish to have a highly active and structurally intact C3a, you have to produce it by the physiological complement enzymes.

Quie: In one of your figures it appeared that C2-deficient serum did not function as opsonin for either *S. aureus* or *E. coli* but did have opsonic activity for other bacterial species.

Müller-Eberhard: Yes, these are randomly selected bacterial products, not even well defined in some cases. Out of 32 products that we had been able to collect 50 percent activated C3 in C2-deficient serum and 50 percent did not.

Quie: It may have been because we used different strains of bacteria, but we found different opsonic requirements for *E. coli* and *S. aureus.* When calcium was chelated with EGTA, there was sufficient Mg in serum so that there was activity of the alternate pathway of complement activation. When EGTA was added to serum, we found opsonization of *E. coli* but not *S. aureus,* suggesting that *E. coli* can activate the alternate pathway but *S. aureus* cannot. From your data it seems that neither *E. coli* nor *S. aureus* effectively activate the alternate pathway.

Müller-Eberhard: I think that is quite comparable. The EGTA must be handled just right. It doesn't work very well in everyone's hands. And it is a little safer to be dealing with a serum that is clearly deficient in one of the early classical components.

Frank: Does bacterial lipopolysaccharide activate the alternate pathway?

Müller-Eberhard: Yes. What microorganism did you use, Dr. Hirsch?

Hirsch: Staphylococcus.

Müller-Eberhard: It was staphylococcus and utilizing the alternate pathway. I don't think this table was very representative. It just showed that some bacterial products are very efficient in activating the alternate pathway.

Snyderman: What is your feeling about C5a in and of itself being chemotactic?

Müller-Eberhard: This work has really been done together with Dr. Ward and he should comment on it. As far as we can tell, there is no clear-cut evidence for the requirement of an additional peptide. Although I must say that it is very difficult to obtain highly purified C5a from either human or porcine serum. There are little peptides that do tend to contaminate it and you have to have very stringent chemical composition data in order to be sure that a given preparation is not contaminated. I would not want to over emphasize this point, whether there is a secondary peptide required as suggested by Wissler or not.

Alper: Do you consider that hydrazine and ammonia attack the same bond as does hydroxylamine?

Müller-Eberhard: No, different ones.

Alper: Where are the points of attack on the C3 molecule?

Müller-Eberhard: I don't know. A C3a-like fragment is not liberated from C3 on ammonia or hydrazine treatment. That is all I can say.

Alper: Yet there is conversion?

Müller-Eberhard: Yes.

Alper: As far as hydroxylamine is concerned, what kind of bond do you think is involved? And what is the reaction?

Müller-Eberhard: In collagen it has been demonstrated. It is a bond between an asparinyl and a glycyl residue which is particularly susceptible to hydroxylamine treatment.

Cohn: Would you comment on the substrate specificity of the enzymatic steps and sequence? Is it possible there are substrates on cell surfaces which are modified by various portions of the reaction?

Müller-Eberhard: We have no evidence that cell—let's say cell surface constituents, peripheral or integral subunits of membranes—are directly attacked by enzymes of either pathway.

Bellanti: In one of the references in an unpublished article that you referred to, I noticed the attachment of C3b to human Burkitt lymphoma cells of the Raji line. I wonder if you could comment on whether this is a virally-induced change.

Müller-Eberhard: That is interesting. Dr. Bokisch in our lab has seen that free C3b as well as native C3 can react with the C3b receptors of Raji cells. In the case of C3, nothing happens. In the case of C3b, the Raji cell is killed due to the activation of the alternate pathway and the formation of the C5b to 9 complex in the immediate vicinity of the cell surface.

Bellanti: This may be a virally-induced change on the membranes.

Müller-Eberhard: They are virus-infected, yes, but it doesn't seem to be the virus acting on it from the outside. For instance, after one of the cell lines loses this receptor, then you have to start out with an original batch of cells.

Stossel: What is the evidence that C3b is the opsonically active fragment of C3?

Müller-Eberhard: This is not just our work. This has been shown by Gigli and Nelson originally, I think.

Stossel: They showed that C3 in some form is fixed, but they didn't analyze it.

Müller-Eberhard: Yes, but there is no other way. There is no way of getting C3 bound to a particle other than Raji cells, to my knowledge, than after activation by an enzyme. And then what you find on the cell surface is C3b. There is always a little bit of C3a adhering, too, which hasn't yet diffused off or dissociated itself from the b fragment. But this should not matter.

Stossel: But what is the evidence that C3b is the opsonically active fragment?

Müller-Eberhard: C3c is coming off and d is staying behind and the opsonic activity has been lost.

Becker: In that regard, does anti-C3b inhibit opsonization? Would that answer your question?

Stossel: No, that wouldn't be critical because C3b contains most of the C3 molecule. We have looked at particles which are opsonized and which when vigorously treated appear to have no complement protein on them other than something relating to C3. When the protein eluted, the loss of ingestiblity correlates with the loss of C3 from the surface, and the protein has a subunit molecular weight of 70,000 (see Alper, Stossel, and Rosen, *this volume*). I think there is no hard evidence that C3b as defined by C3 from which C3a is removed is the opsonically active piece.

Müller-Eberhard: Certainly it is the one that allows contact between particles coated with C3b (if you don't mind) and cells that have the C3b receptor on their surface. And if you, either by trypsin or by the C3b inactivator enzyme, impair C3b, it loses its activity and what is coming off is C3c.

Stossel: It is questionable whether the monocyte system described, which looks at phagocytosis morphologically or immune adherence, is the same as evaluating opsonically active C3 in a rigorous way.

The Phagocytic Cell in Host Resistance, edited
by Joseph A. Bellanti and Delbert H. Dayton.
Raven Press, New York © 1975.

Studies of the Interaction of Antibody, Complement, and Macrophages in the Immune Clearance of Erythrocytes

Michael M. Frank, Alan D. Schreiber, and John P. Atkinson

Clincial Immunology Section, Laboratory of Clinical Investigation, National Institute of Allergy and Infectious Diseases, National Institutes of Health, Bethesda, Maryland 20014

For the past 3 years our laboratory has been engaged in the systematic evaluation of the *in vivo* function of antibody and complement in the interaction of particles with fixed macrophages of the reticuloendothelial system (RES). These studies were begun in an animal model and more recently have included a series of observations in human beings.

The studies have emphasized the fact that the fate of a particle circulating in the blood stream is dependent upon a number of factors. These include (a) the nature of the particle, (b) whether specific antibody coats the particle and, in turn, the class of antibody, (c) whether complement is activated and bound to the particle surface, (d) the state of activation of the fixed macrophages of the RES, (e) the distribution within various organs of the fixed phagocytic cells and the cellular architecture of the RES.

Some particles are more easily phagocytosed than others. For example, rough pneumococci may be phagocytosed easily whereas heavily encapsulated organisms are phagocytosed with difficulty (1). For the purpose of these studies we wished to examine the clearance and phagocytosis of a particle which was completely dependent upon antibody and complement for its removal from the circulation. We, therefore, chose to study the clearance of isologous erythrocytes.

The format of these experiments was straightforward. Erythrocytes were removed from the study subject in the case of humans or from guinea pigs of the study strain in the guinea pig experiments. They were radiolabeled with ^{51}Cr and reinfused into the donor in the human studies, or other animals of the same strain in the animal studies. If the red cells were unsensitized, they survived normally and had a typical half-life of about 7.5 days in the case of guinea pigs or 55 days in the case of humans. If the cells were sensitized with specific antibody, their pattern of survival was altered and this could be quantitated in terms of amount of cell-bound antibody and degree of erythrocyte clearance. Because we were interested in the interaction of antibody and complement, we quantitated the cell-bound antibody in terms of complement (C1) fixing sites generated by use of the C1a fixation and transfer test (2). This test allows one to measure the average number of complement-fixing sites per erythrocyte in absolute molecular terms, thereby circumventing the problems raised in trying to compare antibody classes which differ widely in molecular weight and in their efficiency in mediating various antibody-dependent biological functions.

In the guinea pig experiments, small aliquots of erythrocytes were sensitized with highly purified high-avidity rabbit anti-guinea pig erythrocyte antibody and then reinfused into recipient animals. Multiple samples of blood were obtained from the retro-orbital plexus with a calibrated bleeding pipette and the clearance of the cells was followed. At selected time intervals animals were killed and the organ localization of the cells removed from the circulation was determined. Cells were sensitized with either IgM or IgG antibody fractions. In the case of IgM antibody every antibody molecule was capable of fixing C1; therefore, the number of C1-fixing sites was a direct measure of the number of antibody molecules per cell (2, 3). A doublet of IgG antibody, two molecules side by side, is reported to be necessary for C1 fixation (4), and in fact several thousand IgG molecules were required to form one C1-fixing site on the erythrocyte membrane (3).

When erythrocytes were coated with IgM antibody and infused into guinea pigs, at least 60 molecules of IgM (60 complement-fixing sites) were required to initiate clearance (5). The results obtained with 117 sites per cell are shown in Fig. 1. The cells were removed from the circulation within 10 min after injection

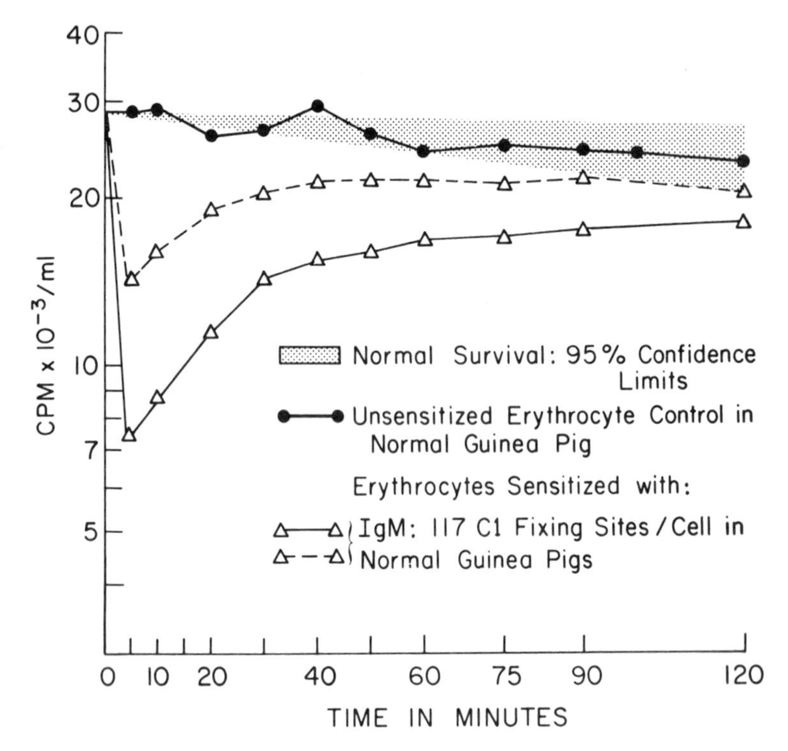

FIG. 1. Survival of ^{51}Cr-labeled guinea pig erythrocytes: 117 IgM C1-fixing sites/erythrocyte in two normal guinea pigs. (Reprinted from *J. Clin. Invest.*)

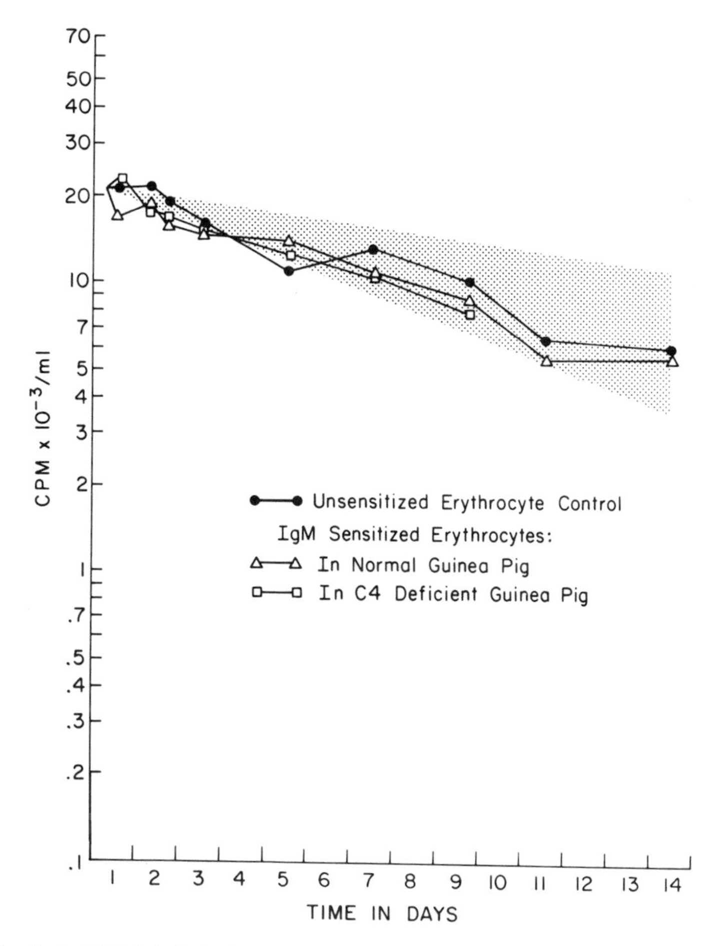

FIG. 2. Survival of ^{51}Cr-labeled guinea pig erythrocytes with 117 IgM C1-fixing sites/erythrocyte from 2 hr to 14 days after injection. (Reprinted from *J. Clin. Invest.*)

and then slowly reappeared in the circulation over the course of the next several hours. Thereafter, the sensitized cells survived normally (Fig. 2), even though coated with antibody and complement. Organ localization studies demonstrated that the liver was responsible for the sequestration of IgM-sensitized erythrocytes (5). In fact, the cells appeared to be removed from the circulation in one passage through the liver and the rate of clearance appeared to be determined by liver blood flow. Complement activation was required for clearance, and no clearance was observed in the C4-deficient strain of guinea pigs (Fig. 3) (5). C4-deficient animals have a complete block in the classical complement pathway but an intact alternative pathway (6, 7). The fact that no clearance of IgM-coated particles was obtained in C4-deficient animals was related to an inability of the IgM-coated erythrocytes to effectively activate the alternate complement pathway. In this

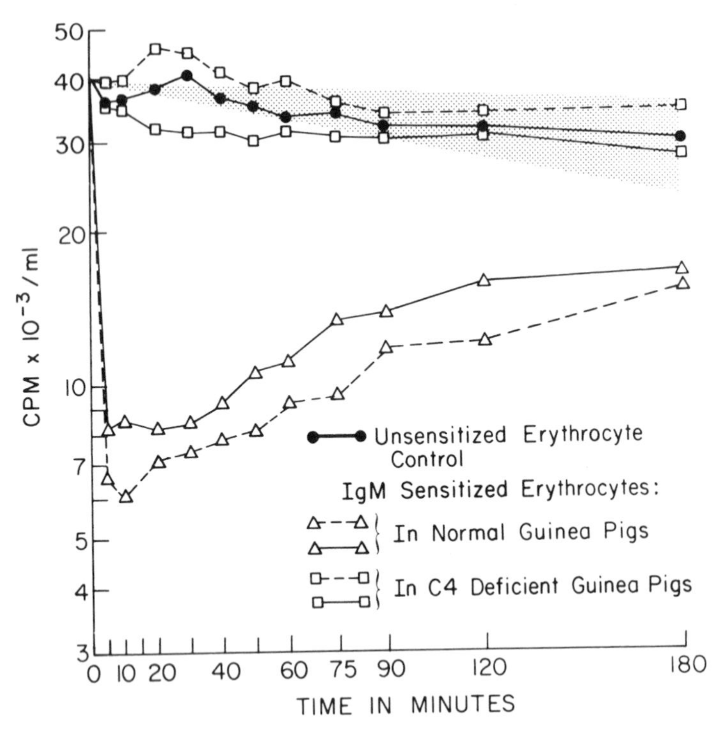

FIG. 3. Survival of ^{51}Cr-labeled erythrocytes with 234 IgM C1-fixing sites/erythrocyte in two normal and two C4-deficient guinea pigs. (Reprinted from *J. Clin. Invest.*)

regard, IgM-coated erythrocytes resembled several other types of nucleated and non-nucleated cells in that antibody directed at the normal cell membrane activated the alternate pathway in guinea pig serum poorly (8, 9). There is no receptor on phagocytic cells for heterologous IgM (10, 11), and in the absence of effective complement activation, the IgM-sensitized erythrocytes when injected into the C4-deficient animals were not adequately opsonized.

In the case of IgG the situation was very different (5). Although several thousand IgG molecules were required to form a C1-fixing site, there was virtually no clearance unless one C1-fixing site was generated by the antibody. However, in contrast to IgM, as few as one complement fixing site per cell could effectively mediate clearance. IgG clearance curves resembled the more usually published clearance patterns; clearance was progressive and the cleared cells were never returned to the circulation (Fig. 4). In the absence of complement activation clearance was inefficient, but large numbers of IgG molecules could effect clearance. Macrophages have been shown to possess a membrane IgG receptor (12, 13) and presumably were thereby able to mediate clearance in the absence of complement activation. It is of interest that the macrophage IgG receptor can be blocked by normal serum IgG *in vitro* and this may account for the inefficiency

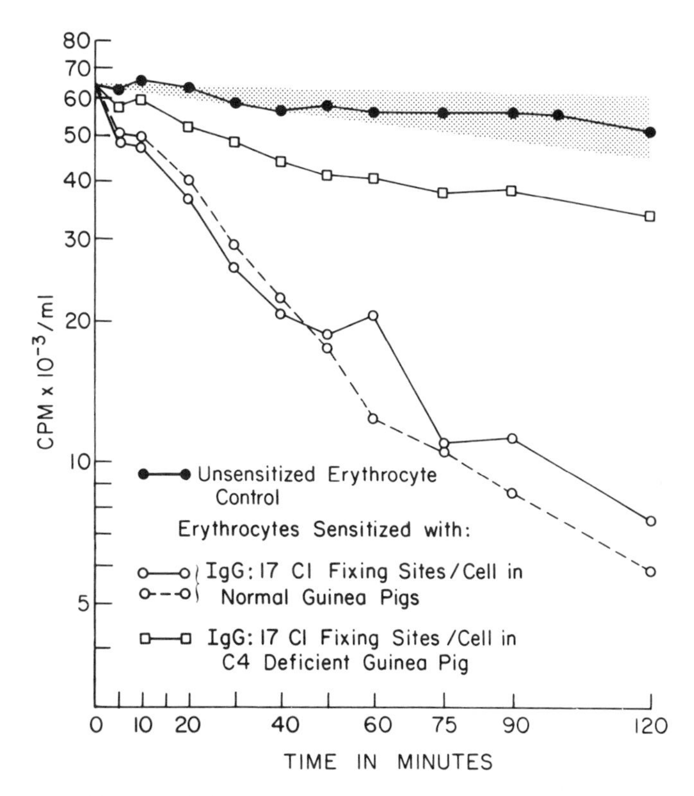

FIG. 4. Survival of ^{51}Cr-labeled erythrocytes with 17 IgG C1-fixing sites/erythrocyte in two normal and one C4-deficient guinea pig. (Reprinted from *J. Clin. Invest.*)

of this receptor *in vivo.* Thus, complement markedly augmented the clearance of IgG-coated erythrocytes *in vivo.* The organ primarily responsible for the clearing of IgG-coated cells, both in the presence and absence of complement activation, was the spleen unless erythrocytes were coated with larger quantities of antibody (5). With the larger amounts of antibody, the liver sequestered a large percentage of the cells. In no case was the IgM pattern of sequestration and subsequent release obtained. The IgM-sensitized erythrocytes were therefore cleared by complement-dependent adherence to fixed phagocytes within the liver and IgG-sensitized erythrocytes were cleared by the spleen by a mechanism which was largely complement dependent.

In this series of experiments we examined the effect of a number of factors which may influence the state of macrophage activation on the clearance of cells that had reacted with antibody and complement. First, we examined the effect of corticosteroid therapy (14, 15). Corticosteroids are known to decrease the metabolic activity of macrophages. They are often used in treatment of patients with the clinical counterpart of our experimental model, autoimmune hemolytic anemia. We found that corticosteroid therapy decreased the clearance of cells

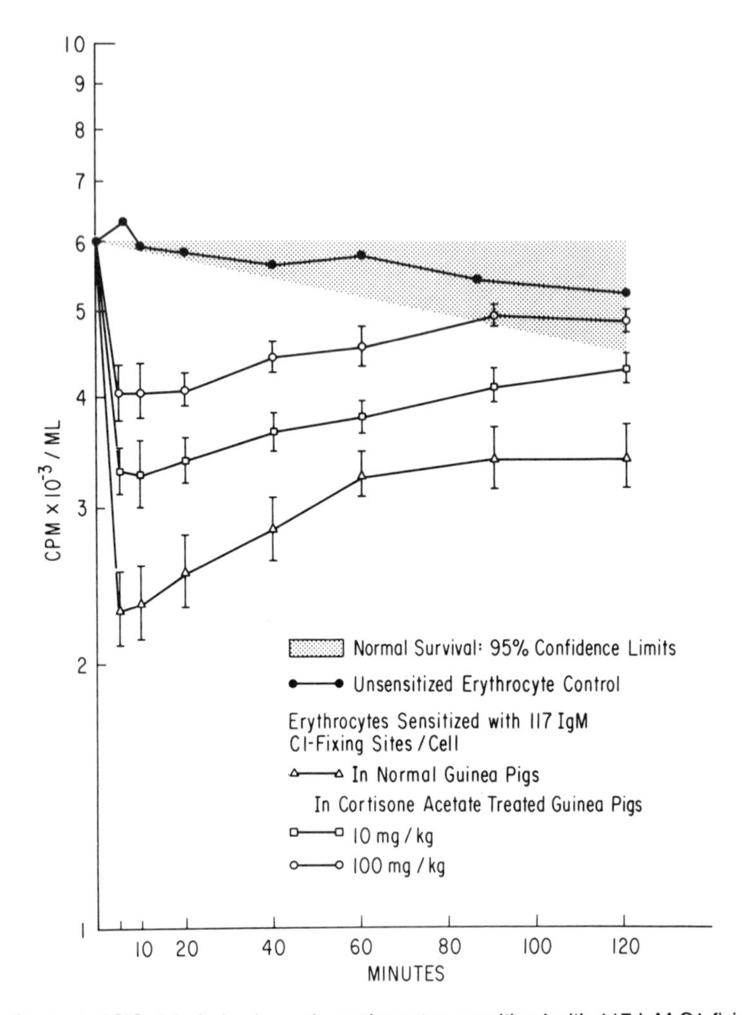

FIG. 5. Survival of ^{51}Cr-labeled guinea pig erythrocytes sensitized with 117 IgM C1-fixing sites per cell: comparison between normal and corticosteroid-treated guinea pigs. These data represent the ± SEM of 12, eight, and six animals in the control, 10 mg, and 100 mg groups, respectively. The clearance curve in guinea pigs treated with 20 mg/kg per day of cortisone acetate fell approximately halfway between those for 10 and 100 mg. The shaded area in this and subsequent figures represents the 95% confidence limits for decay curve slopes of 20 normal animals. (Reprinted from *J. Clin. Invest.*)

sensitized with both IgM and IgG antibody (Figs. 5 and 6) (14, 15). This decrease in clearance was more marked in the case of IgG-coated cells and was dose dependent. Moreover, the cortisone effect was greatly dependent on the amount of antibody used to sensitize the cells. With large numbers of complement-fixing sites, cortisone had little effect. As the number of complement-fixing sites on the erythrocyte membrane was decreased, the cortisone effect became more pronounced. The activity of the corticosteroids was first manifest after 4 to 5 days

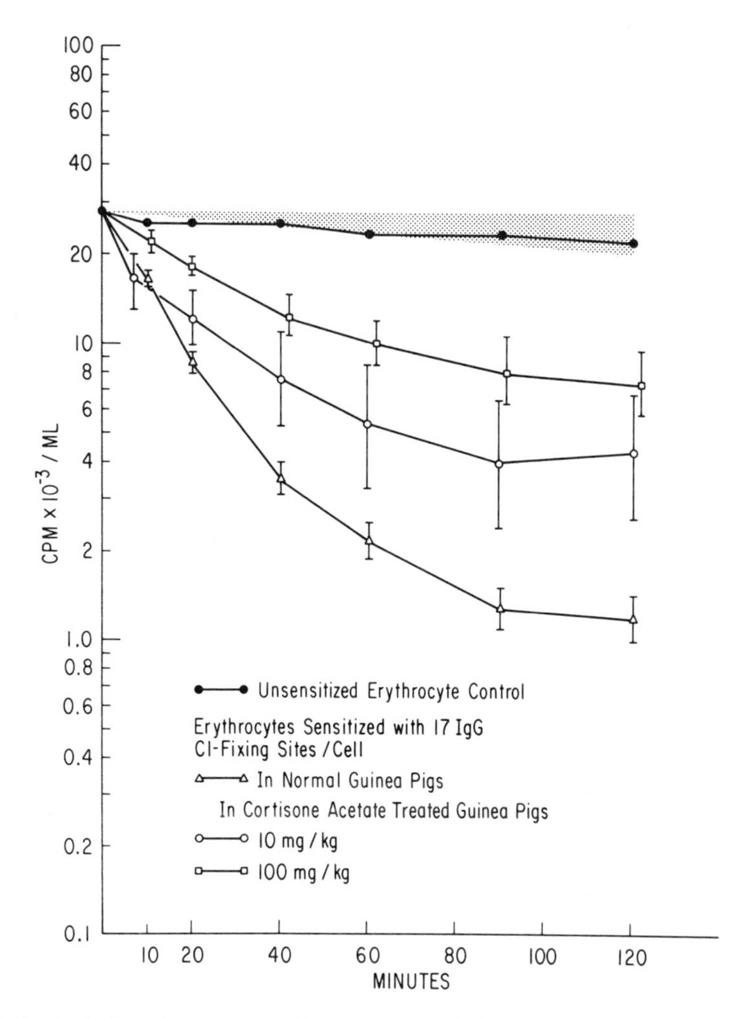

FIG. 6. Survival of erythrocytes sensitized with 17 IgG C1-fixing sites per cell: comparison between normal and corticosteroid-treated guinea pigs. Each point in these clearance slopes represents the ± SEM of 12, 10, and four animals in the untreated control, 10 mg, and 100 mg groups, respectively. The clearance slope for the 20 mg group was not significantly different from the 100 mg group. (Reprinted from *J. Clin. Invest.*)

of treatment and became maximal after 8 days. In corticosteroid-treated animals, erythrocytes were cleared as if they had fewer complement-fixing sites; the pattern of clearance typical for each immunoglobulin class was unchanged. Complement-independent clearance was also examined in the C4-deficient strain of guinea pigs. Here corticosteroids were very effective at lowering clearance rates, even at high antibody site density (Fig. 7). We advanced the hypothesis that one of the *in vivo* effects of corticosteroids was to decrease the number and/or avidity of macrophage receptors for IgG and C3.

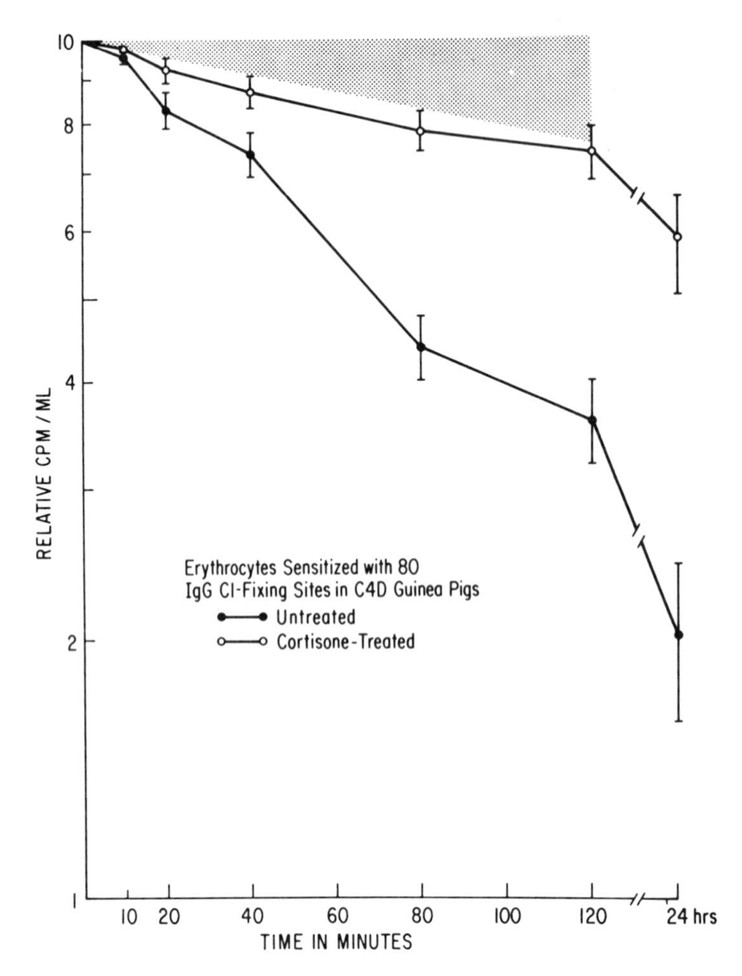

FIG. 7. Survival of ^{51}Cr-labeled erythrocytes sensitized with 80 IgG C1-fixing sites in untreated and cortisone treated C4-deficient guinea pigs. These data represent the ± 1 SEM for six animals in each group. The cortisone group represents a composite mean for animals treated with 10, 20, or 100 mg of cortisone acetate. (Reprinted from *Blood*.)

We next attempted to increase the state of macrophage activation by infecting the animals with BCG (Phipps strain) (16). Within 4 days after BCG infection, the animals showed an increased rate of clearance of IgG-sensitized cells (Fig. 8). In the case of IgM the increase in the extent of clearance was not marked. However, the cleared cells were not returned to the circulation but were phagocytosed by hepatic macrophages (Fig. 9). The adherence of C3-coated erythrocytes to the surface of mouse macrophages is a poor stimulus for ingestion (17). The presence of IgG as well as C3, however, markedly stimulates phagocytosis. In the normal animal the C3-coated erythrocytes adhered to the membrane of phagocytic cells presumably via the C3 receptor. The cells were not rapidly

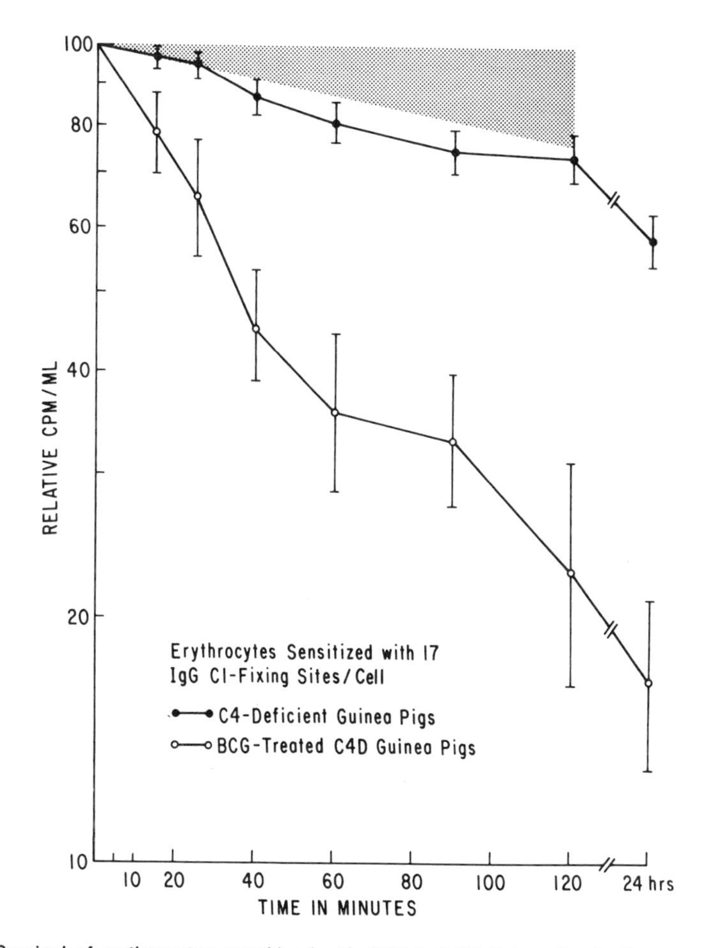

FIG. 8. Survival of erythrocytes sensitized with 17.0 IgG C1-fixing sites/cell: comparison between the ± SEM of six C4D and six BCG-infected guinea pigs. (Reprinted from *J. Clin. Invest.*)

ingested and it was possible for a C3-cleaving protein in serum, the C3 inactivator, to cleave the erythrocyte-bound C3, thereby freeing the cells to circulate normally. In the BCG-treated animals the adherent cells appeared to be phagocytosed before the C3 inactivator could cleave C3 and release the cells. This also was seen in normal animals but only when cells were injected that contained very large numbers of complement-fixing sites. Therefore in BCG-treated animals, sensitized erythrocytes behaved as if they were coated with many more molecules of antibody per cell. In both the case of IgM-sensitized erythrocytes and IgG-sensitized erythrocytes, the sensitized cells localized to the usual organs—IgM to the liver and IgG to the spleen via a complement-dependent mechanism. The data are compatible with the concept that activated macrophages have an increased number and/or avidity of receptors.

Our most recent studies have attempted to relate these findings in an animal

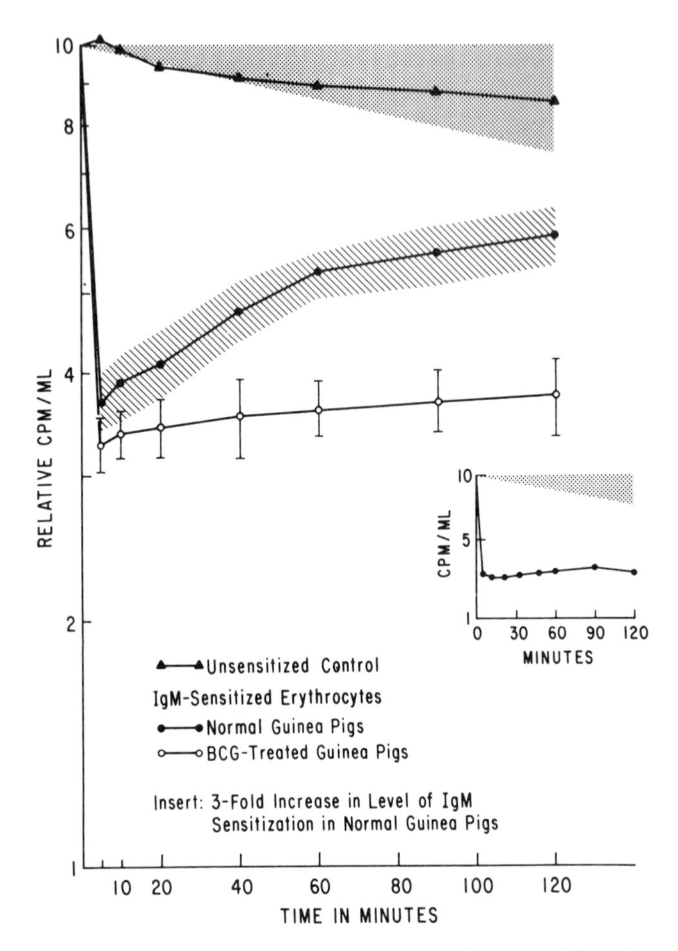

FIG. 9. Survival of ^{51}Cr-labeled guinea pig erythrocytes sensitized with 117 IgM C1-fixing sites/cell: comparison between the ± SEM of four normal and four BCG-infected animals. The inset is the mean clearance curve of four normal animals at 351 IgM C1-fixing sites/cell. The hatched area represents the clearance (± 1 SEM) of IgM-sensitized cells in normal animals. (Reprinted from *J. Clin. Invest.*)

model to the situation noted in humans (18). Thus far we have completed that segment of the work which relates to the function of IgM antibody. Highly purified human IgM anti-A blood group substance was utilized to sensitize cells from type A individuals and the sensitized cells were reinjected into the donors. As noted in Fig. 10 the cells were rapidly cleared from the circulation and a portion of the cleared cells were released at a later time back into the circulation where they survived normally. Release was not as extensive as that noted in the guinea pig model. In the human as few as 20 IgM sites per cell, an amount that could not be detected by conventional antiglobulin tests, led to clearance. In general the data were strikingly similar to those obtained in the guinea pig model.

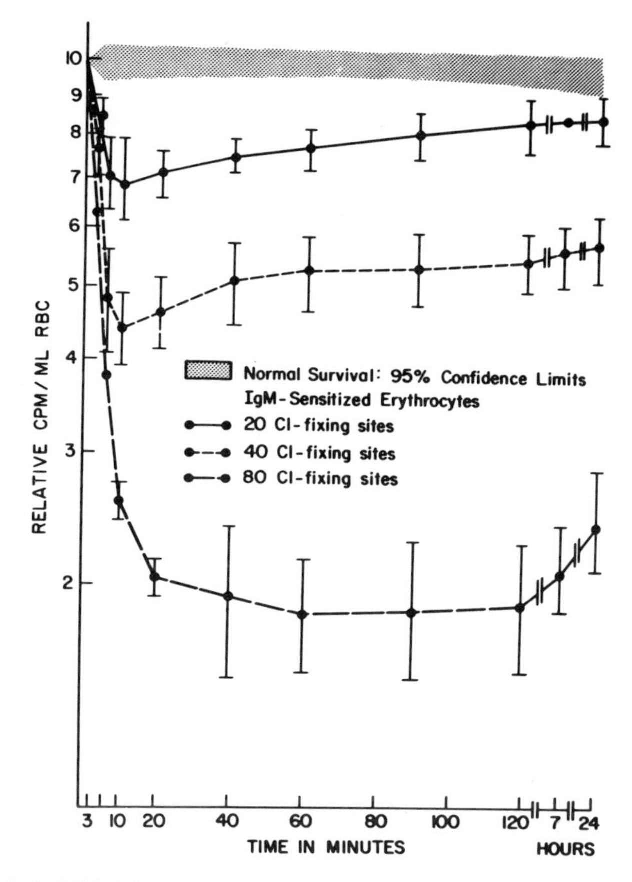

FIG. 10. Survival of ^{51}Cr-labeled human erythrocytes: shown are clearance patterns at three levels of sensitization with anti-A IgM isoagglutinin. These data represent the ± 1.0 SEM for three, five, and three normal subjects, respectively, at 20, 40, and 80 IgM C1-fixing sites/erythrocyte. The shaded area in this figure represents the 95% confidence limits for survival of radiolabeled unsensitized cells in five normal individuals. Subjects received a total dose of about 5 μC ^{51}Cr and counts were corrected to a 0 time figure of 1,000 cpm. (Reprinted from *J. Clin. Invest.*)

The cleared cells could be localized to the liver as shown by studies performed in the whole body counter utilizing separate scintillators over liver and spleen (Fig. 11). Clearance was dependent upon the classical complement pathway (Fig. 12) and sensitized erythocytes were not cleared in two individuals with the disease hereditary angioedema who had nondetectable C4 and C2. These patients had a normally functioning alternate complement pathway reemphasizing in man the importance of the classical pathway in the clearance of IgM-sensitized erythrocytes.

It was possible to correlate clearance with the number of C3 molecules on the cell surface and nature of the C3 fragment. Exposure of IgM-sensitized ery-

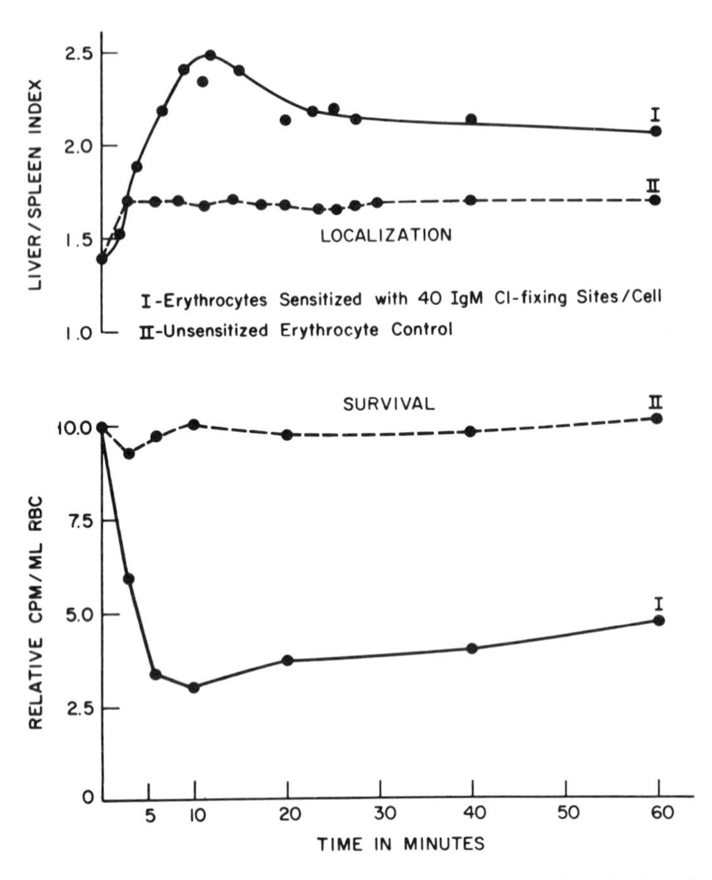

FIG. 11. Localization and survival of sensitized and unsensitized chromated erythrocytes in normal subjects. Chromated cells were injected at 0 time and localization of the injected erythrocytes was determined in the whole body counter. Simultaneous samples were obtained for determination of cell clearance. Individual I, who received sensitized cells, showed the typical clearance pattern and an associated increase in the liver/spleen index. Liver/Spleen = net counts collected by liver detector/net counts collected by spleen detector. This was not seen in individual II, who received unsensitized erythrocytes. (Reprinted from *J. Clin. Invest.*)

throcytes to fresh serum led to the deposition of C3 (500 to 800 molecules/IgM site) on the erythrocyte membrane in the form of the fragment C3b. These cells were positive in tests of immune adherence (19) and were rapidly cleared from the circulation by trapping within the liver. It was possible to expose these cells with surface-bound antibody and C3b to heated serum which could serve as a source of the C3b inactivator but would not mediate further C3 deposition. After exposure to heated serum, the cells could be shown to be negative in immune adherence. They no longer had C3b on their surface but did have the cleavage fragment C3d. Such cells were no longer cleared by fixed phagocytes and survived

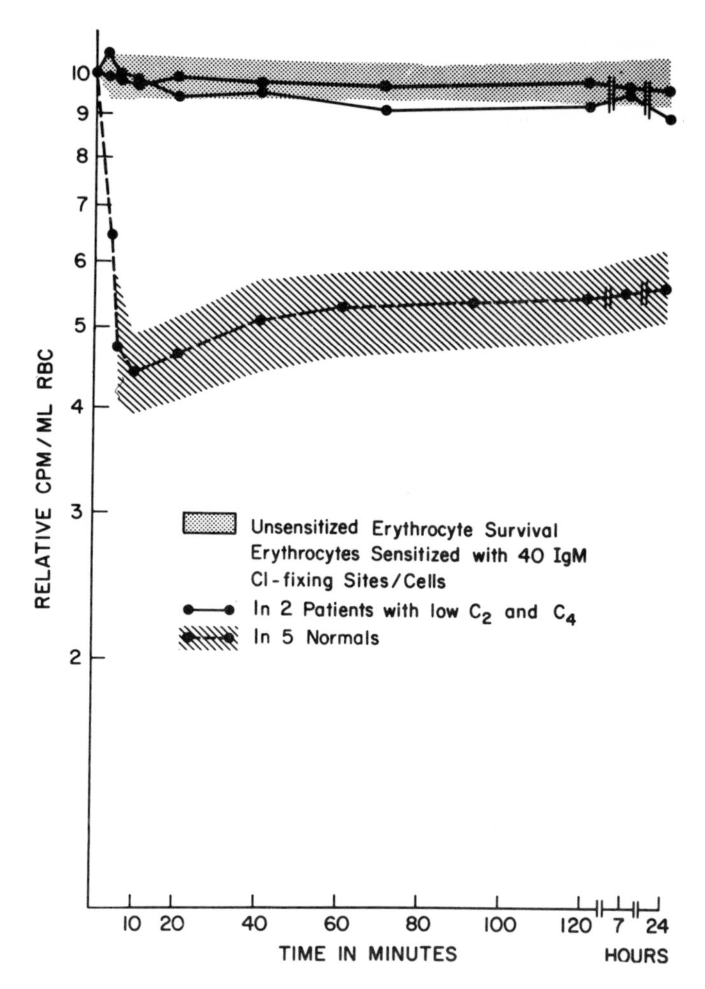

FIG. 12. A comparison of survival of IgM-sensitized erythrocytes in normals and patients with no detectable C2 and low C4 levels. The area enclosed by the hatching represents the ±SEM for five normals at 40 IgM C1-fixing sites/erythrocyte. (Reprinted from *J. Clin. Invest.*)

normally in the circulation although they remained sensitized with antibody and complement fragments (Table 1).

In summary, in both an animal model and in man the clearance of isologous erythrocytes depends upon the nature of the immunoglobulin sensitizing the cells, the ability of the immunoglobulin to activate complement, and the state of activation of cells of the fixed phagocytic system. In these models clearance is not the result of nonspecific membrane damage but depends upon the deposition of opsonic proteins (Ig or complement) which can interact with specific membrane receptors on the phagocytic cell.

TABLE 1. *Correlation of Cell-bound C3 fragments with clearance and immune adherence reactivity*

Experimental groups	Serum incubation (min)		Agglutination anti-C3 fragments		Immune adherence	% Clearance at 10 min (± 1 SEM)
	Fresh	Heated[a]	C3b	C3d		
1	0	0	—	—	—	45–62[b]
2	15	0	++++	++++	++++	45–62
3	60 or 120	0	+++	++++	+++	30–40
4	15	60	±	++++	—	0–10

Red cells sensitized with 40 IgM C1-fixing sites/cell.
[a] Serum was heated at 56°C for 30 min to destroy complement but leave the C3 inactivator activity intact.
[b] Complement components are bound upon injection into normal subjects and then their reactivity would be identical to that of group 2.

REFERENCES

1. Austen, K. F., and Cohn, Z. A.: Contribution of serum and cellular factors in host defense. I. Serum factors in host defense. *N. Engl. J. Med.* 268:933, 1963.
2. Borsos, T., Colten, H. R., Spalter, J. S., Rogentine, N., and Rapp, H. J.: the Cla fixation and transfer test: Examples of its applicability to the detection and enumeration of antigens and antibodies at cell surfaces. *J. Immunol.* 101:392, 1968.
3. Schreiber, A. D., and Frank, M. M.: Role of antibody and complement in the immune clearance and destruction of erythrocytes. II. Molecular nature of IgG and IgM complement-fixing sites and effects of their interaction with serum. *J. Clin. Invest.* 51:583, 1972.
4. Boros. T., and Rapp, H. J.: Complement fixation on cell surfaces by 19s and 7s antibodies. *Science* 150:505, 1965.
5. Schreiber, A. D., and Frank, M. M.: The role of antibody and complement in the immune clearance and destruction of erythrocytes. I. *In vivo* effects of IgG and IgM complement-fixing sites. *J. Clin. Invest.* 51:575, 1972.
6. Ellman, L., Green, I., and Frank, M.: Genetically controlled total deficiency of the fourth component of complement in the guinea pig. *Science* 170:74, 1970.
7. Ellman, L., Green, J., Judge, F., and Frank, M: *In vivo* studies in C4-deficient guinea pigs. *J. Exp. Med.* 134:162, 1971.
8. May, J. E., and Frank, M. M.: Complement-mediated tissue damage: Contributions of the classical and alternate complement pathways in the Forssman reaction. *J. Immunol.* 108:1517, 1972.
9. May, J. E., Green, I., and Frank, M. M.: The alternate complement pathway in cell damage: Antibody-mediated cytolysis of erythrocytes and nucleated cells. *J. Immunol.* 109:595, 1972.
10. Huber, H., and Douglas, S. D.: Receptor sites on human monocytes for complement: Binding of red cells sensitized with cold autoantibodies. *Br. J. Haematol.* 219:19, 1970.
11. Lay, W. H., and Nussenzweig, V.: Ca^{++} dependent binding of antigen-19S antibody complexes to macrophages. *J. Immunol.* 102:1172, 1969.
12. Lo Buglio, A. F., Cotran, R. S., and Jandl, J. H.: Red cells coated with immunoglobulin G: Binding and sphering by mononuclear cells in man. *Science* 158:1582, 1967.
13. Huber, H., Polley, M. J., Linscott, W. D., Fudenberg, H. H., and Müller-Eberhard, H. J.: Human monocytes: Distinct receptor sites for the third component of complement and for immunoglobulin G. *Science* 162:1281, 1968.
14. Atkinson, J. P., Schreiber, A. D., and Frank, M. M.: Effect of corticosteroids and splenectomy on the immune clearance and destruction of erythrocytes. *J. Clin. Invest.* 52:1509, 1973.
15. Atkinson, J. P., and Frank, M. M.: Cortisone inhibition of complement independent erythrocyte clearance. *Blood (in press).*

16. Atkinson, J. P., and Frank, M. M.: The effect of Bacillus Calmette-Guerin induced macrophage activation on the *in vivo* clearance of sensitized erythrocytes. *J. Clin. Invest.* 53:1742–1749, 1974.
17. Mantovani, B., Rabinovitch, M., and Nussenzweig, V.: Phagocytoses of immune complexes by macrophages: Different roles of the macrophage receptor sites for complement (C3) and for immunoglobulin (IgG). *J. Exp. Med.* 135:780, 1972.
18. Atkinson, J. P., and Frank, M. M.: Studies on the *in vivo* effects of antibody: Interaction of IgM antibody and complement in the imune clearance and destruction of erythrocytes in man. *J. Clin. Invest.* 54:339–348, 1974.
19. Nelson, D. S.: Immune adherence. In Wolstenholme, G. E. W., and Knight, J. (eds): *Ciba Foundation Symposium on Complement.* J. S. A. Churchill, Ltd., London, p. 222, 1965.

DISCUSSION

Bellanti: I think these findings have profound biological implications in terms of subsequent processing events and specific immunologic events. Have you had an opportunity to employ nonautologous cells in studies of antibody production?

Frank: Nonautologous cells are cleared from the circulation fairly rapidly in most cases. We have done a few experiments in the guinea pig model but obviously not with humans and these have not been performed in a systematic way. But if you examine the clearance of a bacterium such as *E. coli* you find rapid clearance in C4-deficient animals suggesting activation of the alternate pathway. Isologous red cells coated with antibody are unsuccessful in activating the alternate pathway and therefore are not cleared in C4-deficient animals. This is also true in humans as shown in the experiments with patients with hereditary angioedema who have an intact alternate pathway but cannot clear IgM-sensitized erythrocytes. We have not yet looked into the effect of IgG in humans or into the effects on sensitization.

Bellanti: The obvious example is in the case of Rhogam.

Frank: We are studying Rhogam at the present time. Perhaps I should make a few comments on the nature of the Fe and C3 receptors, although this work has not been done by us. The Fc receptor resists trypsin treatment of cells and appears to persist in long term *in vitro* culture of macrophages. The C receptor is sensitive to trypsin treatment and appears to be lost on long term *in vitro* culture of macrophages in serum-free medium.

We have performed studies *in vivo* where we have attempted to activate macrophages or suppress their activity. Four days after animals were injected with BCG there was a marked augmentation in clearance. This would persist for a very long period of time *in vitro,* in fact for many weeks. Obviously BCG does many things in addition to activating macrophages. We have specifically looked to see if the BCG effect was mediated by a serum factor and found that it is not.

Cohn: I am told that the complement receptor of lymphocytes is sensitive to proteolytic cleavage.

Frank: That may be.

Snyderman: When you inject the cells and they are picked up by the liver, do they still contain the IgM on them?

Frank: They do contain the IgM. In our experiments we have shown that the antibody has high avidity for the cells. We have even been able to demonstrate the antibody on the few percent of circulating radiolabeled cells. We suspect that the reason that we note less release in the case of human cells is that the human IgM continues to activate C3 and deposit it on the cell surface whereas this is not true to the same extent in the guinea pig system.

The Phagocytic Cell in Host Resistance, edited
by Joseph A. Bellanti and Delbert H. Dayton.
Raven Press, New York © 1975.

Complement-Derived Inflammatory Mediators. The C5-Cleaving Enzyme in Biological Reactions

Peter A. Ward

Department of Pathology, University of Connecticut Health Center, Farmington, Connecticut 06032

Inflammatory mediators derived from the complement system are now well known to consist of those factors capable of increasing vascular permeability (1, 2) and those factors that attract neutrophils and monocytes (3, 4). The former group of mediators, termed the anaphylatoxins, have been reviewed by Müller-Eberhard *(this volume)* and will not be discussed in detail here. In general, the anaphylatoxins appear not to be direct effectors of permeability but, rather, the effectors of vasoactive amine release from mast cells and basophils. Consequently, most of the permeability changes induced by the anaphylatoxins can be blocked by the antagonists to histamine. As can be presumed on the basis of the work of Bokisch, the role of anaphylatoxins in inflammatory reactions is difficult to discern because, like the kinins, rapid inactivation of the anaphylatoxins takes place in human serum, thus preventing direct demonstration of their generation in whole serum (5). However, the enormous biological activity of these peptides in human skin suggests that the anaphylatoxins constitute some of the most biologically active peptides known to man (6, 7).

The leukotactic factors are less well defined as far as their structures are concerned, in contrast to the emerging knowledge about the amino acid composition and amino acid sequence for C3 anaphylatoxin. On the other hand, considerably more information is available regarding the presence of C3- and C5-derived leukotactic factors in biological reactions. For instance, C3-related leukotactic fragments have been found in extracts of the rat heart during the first few hours following infarction, and the critical role of C3 fragments in mediating the acute cellular inflammatory reaction to this form of tissue injury has been documented (8). In inflammatory nonrheumatoid arthritis of humans, C3 leukotactic fragments have been found in the synovial fluids. Simultaneously, a significant number of these same synovial fluids have been found to possess a C3-cleaving enzyme, which is capable of producing more chemotactic activity upon the addition of C3, but not C5 (9). Situations in which C5-related leukotactic factors have been found in biological fluids include rheumatoid arthritis (9) and immunologic vasculitis in the rat (10). In humans, both the C5 leukotactic fragment and the activated C567 complex ($\overline{C567}$) have been demonstrated in nearly two-thirds of all rheumatoid synovial fluids tested. In addition, a C5-cleaving enzyme is present in at least one-half of the synovial fluids from the same patients (9).

The origin of this enzyme appears to be lysosomal granules of the neutrophil (9, 11).

In reactions of experimental immunologic vasculitis, using the reversed passive Arthus reaction as the model, it has been demonstrated that developing Arthus reactions contain leukotactic factors that consist of C5 fragments and $C\overline{567}$. It was earlier shown that complement depletion prevented development of the acute vasculitis in the Arthus reaction (12). Recently it has been shown that, under the same conditions, leukotactic factors fail to appear in dermal skin sites of complement-depleted animals, whereas in complement-intact animals extracts of the skin sites are rich in C5-related leukotactic factors. These mediators are found at a time when the acute cellular inflammatory infiltrate first appears (10). This has provided strong support for the role of C5 leukotactic factors in the mediation of the acute inflammatory reaction triggered by presence of immune complexes in walls of dermal vessels.

Recently Ward and Zvaifler (13) have demonstrated that, like other lysosomal enzymes, the C5-cleaving enzyme of the neutrophil is released during the process of phagocytosis. The following studies were designed to determine some of the circumstances in which the C5-cleaving enzyme is present in tissue fluids or developing inflammatory reactions. The data in Table 1 indicate several types of particulate matter that will cause rabbit neutrophils to release the C5-cleaving enzyme. Various substances were incubated with 2×10^7 rabbit neutrophils isolated from glycogen-induced peritoneal exudates. Details of the procedures are listed elsewhere (13). Briefly, neutrophils are incubated with the phagocytic substances for 30 min at 37°C. The cells and particles are then removed by centrifugation and the culture medium assayed for the presence of enzyme activity by measuring the amount of chemotactic activity generated following incubation with C5. Bentonite and latex particles coated with factors present in Cohn Fraction II of human serum as well as immune complexes containing rabbit antibody to bovine serum albumin (with antigen added at equivalence) induced

TABLE 1. *Release of C5-cleaving enzyme from rabbit neutrophils*

Material inactivated with 2×10^7 neutrophils [a]	Chemotactic activity generated by cell culture fluid added to C5 [a] (chemotactic counts)
Bentonite particles, 1.5 mg, uncoated	5
Bentonite particles, 1.5 mg, coated with fraction II[b]	95
BSA-anti BSA precipitate (20 μg antibody N)	245
5-mg latex particles coated with fraction II	50
None	0

[a] See reference 13 for details of methodology.

[b] Particles incubated ½ hr at room temperature in a solution of Cohn Fraction II containing 10 μg protein/ml.

TABLE 2. *Fractional release of rabbit neutrophil enzymes during phagocytosis*

Cell treatment [a]	Total intracellular enzyme release (%) into culture fluid [b]				
	β-glucuronidase	Acid phosphatase	Alkaline phosphatase	β-galactosidase	C5-cleaving enzyme
Incubated in culture medium	5.7	6.1	14.3	17.9	6.9
Incubated in presence of immune complexes	33.4	10.9	35.7	37.3	52.0

[a] 2×10^7 neutrophils incubated in a volume of 0.3 ml at 37°C for 30 min. Where present, immune complexes were used in the same amounts described in Table 1.
[b] Assayed according to details in ref. 13. All enzyme assays were spectrophotometric except in the case of the C5-cleaving enzyme.

significant enzyme release. These data confirm and extend those in the preceding study where only immune precipitates were used (13). It seems likely that any phagocytic event will lead to similar enzyme release.

The fractional release of various lysosomal enzymes from rabbit neutrophils is shown in Table 2. Although the amount of enzyme released from "resting cells" varies according to the enzyme being measured, from 5.7 to 17.9% of the total amount of intracellular enzyme, incubation of neutrophils with immune complexes led to considerable enhancement in the release of lysosomal enzymes. Assays for three of the four hydrolases demonstrated that one-third of the entire measurable cell content of enzyme had been released. In the case of the C5-cleaving enzyme, one-half of the entire cell content of enzyme was discharged during phagocytosis, confirming an earlier study (13). In all cases, release of a cytoplasmic enzyme, lactic dehydrogenase, failed to exceed 8% of total cellular enzyme content.

Attention was then turned to an inflammatory reaction in the rabbit, the glycogen-induced peritoneal exudate. Samples from one rabbit were obtained 4 and 8 hr after intraperitoneal injection of a 0.1% glycogen (in saline) solution. At both intervals the lysed (freeze thawed) cell pellets as well as the supernatant fluids from the exudate were examined for the presence of C5-cleaving activity. The cell pellets obtained at both intervals of time had the expected C5-cleaving enzyme demonstrable in the supernates of freeze-thawed cells. Why the activity obtained in cell lysates at the 8-hr interval was only one-half the activity found in cells from the 4-hr exudate is not presently known. Of interest was the finding of C5-cleaving activity of the exudate at 4, but not at 8, hr (Table 3). An explanation for the presence of the limited amount of C5-cleaving activity is that the enzyme activity in the 4-hr exudate fluid could be a consequence of the internalization of glycogen particles by neutrophils with concomitant discharge of enzyme, or it could be due to breakdown of neutrophils in the peritoneal cavity. To what extent the C5-cleaving enzyme might play a role in the developing peritoneal inflammatory reaction following instillation of glycogen is unclear. The

TABLE 3. *Presence of C5-cleaving enzyme in peritoneal exudates of a rabbit*

Material tested	Chemotactic activity	
	observed	corrected [a]
4-hr exudate		
supernate, 50 μl	5	
supernate, 50 μl + C5 (25 μg)	70	65
cell lysate, 50 μl [b]	20	
cell lysate, 50 μl +C5 (25 μg)	190	170
8-hr exudate		
supernate, 50 μl	20	
supernate, 50 μl + C5 (25 μg)	30	10
cell lysate, 50 μl [b]	5	
cell lysate, 50 μl + C5 (25 μg)	95	90

[a] Counts in lysate or supernate subtracted from those in mixture also containing C5.
[b] Cell lysates from freeze-thawed neutrophils (2×10^7/ml) obtained from peritoneal exudates, washed and resuspended in buffered saline.

fact that little, if any, leukotactic activity was present in the supernates as they were harvested from the animal (Table 3) suggests either the lack of availability of the C5 substrate or disappearance of any C5-generated leukotactic activity by the 4- and 8-hr intervals.

The next approach involved a study of the possible role of the C5-cleaving enzyme in developing Arthus reactions. It has been shown previously that damage to blood vessels in this reaction depends upon the influx of neutrophils into perivascular deposits of immune complexes contained within walls of vessels (12). There is abundant evidence that the direct cause of tissue injury is due to the battery of enzymes (including hydrolases for basement membrane, collagen, and elastin) delivered by the neutrophil. The recognition of the C5-cleaving enzyme in the neutrophil suggests the possibility that this enzyme may accentuate the inflammatory reaction and thus be indirectly involved in the amplification of tissue damage. A potential problem in studies of the C5-cleaving enzyme, using tissue extracts of Arthus reactions, is related to the fact that the C5-cleaving enzyme derived from lysosomal granules of neutrophils in only one of at least three enzymes with the same substrate specificity. Trypsin and the enzyme $C\overline{423}$ generated from activation of the classical complement pathway (and also perhaps an enzyme generated from activation of the properdin pathway) are examples of other enzymes that will also cleave C5. The experiments described in Tables 4 and 5 were designed to resolve this question. In Table 4 extracts were obtained from reversed passive Arthus reaction sites in rats 3 hr after the intradermal injection of antibody and the intravenous injection of antigen. The tissues were homogenized and then subjected to centrifugation (see ref. 10). Sediments as well as the supernates were tested for C5-cleaving activity, as measured by chemotactic activity generated in the incubated mixture. In order to avoid the problem of preformed chemotactic activity in the tissue extracts (11), relatively small

TABLE 4. *The presence of a C5-cleaving enzyme in extracts of Arthus reactions*

Material tested [a]	Chemotactic activity		
Animal	1	2	3
Supernatant of Arthus reactions			
20 μl	15	10	20
20 μl + C5 (20 μg)	110	135	125
20 μl + C3 (20 μg)	5	10	0
Sediment of Arthus reactions			
20 μl	5	5	20
20 μl + C5 (20 μg)	0	75	40
20 μl + C3 (20 μg)	10	35	20
Saline site (supernate)			
20 μl	5	5	15
20 μl + C5 (20 μg)	20	30	25
20 μl + C3 (20 μg)	15	5	35

[a] Details of methodology are the same as those described in refs. 10 and 13. Purified human C3 and C5 were used in these experiments.

samples (20 μl) were used (Table 4). Little preformed chemotactic activity was found in either the sediments or the supernates under these conditions. However, when C5 was added to the samples, the supernate fluids of the tissue extracts showed substantial ability to generate leukotactic activity whereas very limited activity was generated when the sediment of the tissue extract was used. Neither the supernate nor the sediment generated significant leukotactic activity from C3 (Table 4). In the case of the saline-injected (control) sites, no significant chemotactic activity could be generated when supernates or sediments of tissue sites were incubated with either C3 or C5. These data indicate the supernates of extracts of developing Arthus reactions are rich in a C5-, but not a C3-, cleaving enzyme which specifies the production of leukotactic fragments. Because the C5-cleaving enzyme was present in the supernates rather than the sediments of tissue extracts, this would favor a C5-cleaving enzyme derived from the neutrophil rather than the complement system. In the latter case the enzyme $C\overline{423}$, capable of cleaving C5, would be expected to be bound to the immune precipitate in the sediment.

In order to determine features of the C5-cleaving enzyme in soluble extracts of Arthus reactions, the experiment listed in Table 5 was devised. Three extracts of developing Arthus reactions were obtained (similar to those in Table 4) and supernates of these extracts isolated. As the data in Table 5 show, relatively little leukotactic activity was present in 20 μl samples of the supernates of each of three tissue extracts. The addition of C5 (20 μg) led to generation of large amounts of leukotactic activity in the extracts. The prior addition to the supernate of 20 μl rabbit antibody to rat C3, before incubation of the supernate with C5, failed to suppress more than 25% of the leukotactic activity generated from C5. On the other hand, prior addition of soybean trypsin inhibitor (known to block the

TABLE 5. *Features of the C5-cleaving enzyme in extracts of developing Arthus reactions*

	Chemotactic activity		
Material tested [a]	Animal 1	2	3
20 μl supernate from tissue extract	30	0	30
20 μl supernate from tissue extract + C5 (20 μg)	105	200	195
20 μl supernate from tissue extract + anti C3 (20 μl) then C5 (20 μl)	190	150	180
20 μl supernate + 100 μg soybean trypsin inhibitor, then C5 (20 μg)	45	20	70
20 μl supernate + C5 (20 μg), then 100 μg soybean trypsin inhibitor	135	120	80

[a] Supernates are obtained from extracts of 3 hr Arthus reactions, as in previous tables. Supernates were either incubated alone or with C5 or trypsin inhibitor for ½ hr at 37°C, followed by incubation with buffered saline, or C5, or trypsin inhibitor for another 30 min at 37°C. After this, leukotactic assays were performed.

C5-cleaving enzyme of the neutrophil lysosome, ref. 11), before addition of C5, markedly suppressed the ability of the supernate to generate leukotactic activity. The late addition of the trypsin inhibitor, that is, following incubation of the supernate with C5, had a much diminished effect in two of the three extracts (Table 5). These results are compatible with the hypothesis that the C5-cleaving enzyme found in extracts of developing Arthus reactions is lysosomal in nature, rather than a complement associated enzyme, such as $\overline{C423}$ from the classical complement pathway.

In Table 6 the characteristics of the three known C5-cleaving enzymes are listed. The data are derived from recent studies (11). Except for molecular weight determinations and the site and storage form of the enzymes, the C5-cleaving enzyme from the human, rabbit, and rat neutrophils is very similar to trypsin. The susceptibilities of these two enzymes to competitive and noncompetitive inhibitors are strikingly similar. A comparison of the C5-cleaving enzymes is given in Table 6. The origin as well as the susceptibility of the complement-derived $\overline{C423}$ enzyme to various inhibitors is, as far as can be determined, quite different from patterns obtained with trypsin and the lysosomal-derived C5-cleaving enzyme. As mentioned above, activation of the complement system with immune complexes in either serum or tissues would be expected to result in a complement-derived enzyme physically bound to the immune precipitate in the sediment. For several reasons, it seems likely that the C5-cleaving enzyme found in the Arthus extracts is either trypsin in nature or lysosomal in origin (neutrophils), rather than complement derived. This does not detract from the presumed critical role of the $\overline{C423}$ enzyme in initiating the early generation of C5 leukotactic factors, which are necessary for the initial accumulation of neutrophils in tissues (11, 12). On the other hand, the delivery of the C5-cleaving enzyme from neutrophils would greatly amplify the inflammatory response.

An enzyme released from herpes simplex virus-infected cells has been described

TABLE 6. *Comparisons of C5-cleaving activators*

Characteristic	Enzyme		
	trypsin	lysosomal enzyme	$\overline{C423}$
Estimated molecular weight	20,000	65,000	unknown
Natural form	precursor	active	precursor
Source	pancreas	neutrophil lysosomal granules	plasma and extracellular fluid
Method of entry into body fluid	secretion	phagocytic release	activation of complement system
Susceptibility to inhibition by:			
DFP	+	+	—
trypsin inhibitor	+	+	—
TAMe, BAMe	+	+	—
ε-aminocaproic acid	+	+	—
EDTA	—	—	—

by Brier et al. (14). This enzyme has the ability to generate leukotactic activity by inducing cleavage of C5; it may well represent a similar, if not identical, lysosomal enzyme to the one described in neutrophils (11). If so, two very different and independent mechanisms leading to release of lysosomal-bound C5-cleaving enzymes would have to be kept in mind whenever such enzymes are found in tissue fluids.

On the basis of the data presented in this chapter, there is good evidence that the C5-cleaving enzyme derived from lysosomal granules of neutrophils is present in certain inflammatory reactions. It seems likely this enzyme plays an important role in the generation of leukotactic mediators and the subsequent inflammatory cellular infiltrate. How and under what conditions, in addition to phagocytosis, discharge of the lysosomal-associated C5-cleaving enzyme is effected will be important to determine if a detailed understanding of inflammatory responses is to be obtained.

ACKNOWLEDGMENT

The work reported in this chapter is supported in part by National Institutes of Health grant AI 09651.

REFERENCES

1. Dias da Silva, W., Eisele, J. W., and Lepow, I. H.: Complement as a mediator of inflammation. III. Purification of the activity with anaphylatoxin properties generated by interaction of the first four components of complement and its identification as a cleavage product of C3. *J. Exp. Med.* 126:1027, 1967.
2. Bokisch, V. A., Müller-Eberhard, H. J., and Cochrane, C. G.: Isolation of a fragment (C3a) of the third component of human complement containing anaphylatoxin and chemotactic activity

and description of an anaphylatoxin inactivator of human serum. *J. Exp. Med.* 129:1109–1130, 1969.
3. Ward, P. A.: Neutrophil chemotactic factors and related clinical disorders. *Arthritis Rheum.* 13:181–186, 1970.
4. Shin, H. S., Snyderman, R., Friedman, E., Mellors, A., and Mayer, M. M.: Chemotactic and anaphylatoxic fragment cleaved from the fifth component of guinea pig complement. *Science* 162:361–363, 1968.
5. Bokisch, V. A., and Müller-Eberhard, H. G.: Anaphylatoxin inactivator of human plasma: Its isolation and characterization as a carboxypeptidase. *J. Clin. Invest.* 49:2427–2436, 1970.
6. Wuepper, K. D., Bokisch, V. A., Müller-Eberhard, H. J., and Stoughton, R. B.: Cutaneous responses to human C3 anaphylatoxin in man. *Clin Exp. Immunol.* 11:13–20, 1972.
7. Lepow, I. H., Willms-Kretschmar, K., Patrick, R. A., and Rosen, F. S.: Gross and ultrastructural observations on lesions produced by intradermal injection of human C3a in man. *Am. J. Pathol.* 61:13–23, 1970.
8. Hill, J. H., and Ward, P. A.: The phlogistic role of C3 leukotactic fragments in myocardial infarcts of rats. *J. Exp. Med.* 133:885, 1971.
9. Ward, P. A., and Zvaifler, N. J.: Complement derived leukotactic factors in inflammatory synovial fluids of humans. *J. Clin. Invest.* 50:606, 1971.
10. Ward, P. A., and Hill, J. H.: Biological role of complement products. Complement-derived leukotactic activity extractable from lesions of immunologic vasculitis. *J. Immunol.* 108:1137, 1972.
11. Ward, P. A., and Hill, J. H.: C5 chemotactic fragments produced by an enzyme in lysosomal granules of neutrophils. *J. Immunol.* 104:535, 1970.
12. Ward, P. A., and Cochrane, C. G.: Bound complement and immunologic vasculitis. *J. Exp. Med.* 121:215, 1965.
13. Ward, P. A., and Zvaifler, N. J.: Quantitative phagocytosis by neutrophils. II. Release of the C5-cleaving enzyme and inhibition of phagocytosis by rheumatoid factor. *J. Immunol.* 111:-1777–1782, 1973.
14. Brier, A. M., Snyderman, R., Mergenhagen, S.E., and Notkins, A. L.: Inflammation and herpes simplex virus: Release of a chemotaxis-generating factor from infected cells. *Science* 170:-1104–1106, 1970.

DISCUSSION

Bellanti: Is the failure to generate chemotactic activity from the supernatants at 8 versus 4 hours reflective of any differences in the cell composition of these preparations? Are these standardized for similar cell types, numbers, and so on?

Ward: At 8 hours nearly all cells are neutrophils. Obviously a lot of things are going on. As the exudate progresses, the neutrophils begin to aggultinate and presumably a fair amount of breakdown of these cells commences. By 12 hours cell degeneration becomes very evident.

Bellanti: Could these differences be explained by differences of this type?

Ward: I think they might be. We have not done parallel studies with some of the other lysosomal enzymes to see if their levels correlate with the C5 cleaving activity. This is obviously something that would be useful in deciding whether the presence of the C5 cleaving enzyme is due to actual cell breakdown or the result of an active secretory process.

Hill: Is there any evidence that the enzyme could be taken up by the neutrophil?

Ward: There is no evidence the enzyme can be taken up. On the other hand, there might be other proteases in the neutrophil that would lead to destruction of this enzyme. But we have no evidence for this.

Miller: You indicated there were no detectable biological or physicochemical differences in the C5 cleavage products produced by the various enzymes. Could you tell us what were the functions, if this was a clinical test?

Ward: My statement was made to reflect the fact that, if one tests biological activity of the fragments produced by trypsin versus the neutral protease versus the C1423 system of the complement pathway, from a biological point of view the products are indistinguishable. There may very well be quantitative differences and there are surely structural differences between the various fragments, because, if the trypsin treatment of C5 is prolonged, anaphylatoxin is destroyed whereas the chemotactic activity is retained.

Spitznagel: Do any of the serum inhibitors inhibit this activity from your polymorph?

Ward: The antitrypsin inhibitors, etc.? Is that what you're referring to?

Spitznagel: Yes, or just whole serum.

Ward: I don't know.

Spitznagel: But certainly the whole serum does, for example, inhibit neutral proteases of the neutrophil.

Ward: I would expect serum trypsin inhibitors will block the C5 cleaving enzymes.

Gallin: I would like to report that Dr. Daniel Wright, working with me, has confirmed your observations using human cells (Wright, D. G., and Gallin, J. I.: Generation of chemotactic activity from serum by a product released from human polymorphonuclear leukocytes during phagocytosis. *Fed. Proc.* 33:631 abs., 1974). In addition, we found that the material released by phagocytizing human PMN's will generate chemotactic activity from normal human serum. This reaction is inhibited by EDTA, but not EGTA, and did not occur in serum deficient in C3 unless C3 was added back to the serum suggesting this product of phagocytosis may also directly activate the complement system. Have you studied the ability of your C5 cleaving enzyme to work in whole serum?

Ward: I can't remember any experiments where we have looked at the ability of the C5 cleaving enzyme to generate activity in whole serum.

Snyderman: I think Dr. Spitznagel's point is a good one in terms of serum factors blocking the protease activity. Because if you look at an *in vivo* situation and inject endotoxin or immune complexes into the peritoneal cavities of guinea pigs or mice, you see the early appearance of a chemotactic activity and a large number of neutrophils come in, but shortly thereafter the chemotactic activity falls off markedly. I think it would be important to look at what factors in serum might shut off the production of additional chemotactic activity and it might be well to go back and look for blocking factors of this activity kinetically in terms of the inflammatory cycle.

Ward: I would agree with you. I would be extremely surprised if the antitrypsin did not block the C5 cleaving enzyme. And, like all inflammatory actions, there is dual control, control of the actions that generate the mediator and inactivation of the mediators so generated.

Baum: Would you speculate a bit on the nonrheumatoids that have a persistent inflammation which is probably due to activation of C3. What would be the source of the activation of the C3? Do you think it might be from local inflammatory tissue?

Ward: My guess has been for a long time that in these inflammatory non-rheumatoid arthritis states the origin of this enzyme is probably a local one or regional one derived from synovial-lining cells or tissues. As far as we can tell, the C3 cleaving enzyme found in some of the synovial fluid is the same enzyme that can be extracted from a variety of normal tissues, including heart. The enzyme is released in the case of a myocardial infarct. We have only done a few experiments examining extracts of homogenized synovial tissues and the results so far have been rather equivocal.

Baum: It is an attractive theory because in the person with classic rheumatoid arthritis, many of the cells that are found in the synovial tissue have an abundance of lysosomal enzymes. However, in many of these other inflammatory states, you don't have the remarkable reduplication of these cells in the synovial tissue. So it could be due to cells deeper in the inflammatory tissue.

Ward: I think it is necessary to make one important distinction also. When I have used the terms C3 and C5 cleaving enzyme, this is with the bias with which I look at C3 and C5 cleavage. There must be production of a chemotactic activity. There are many proteases that will cleave these components without producing a chemotactic substance. Therefore, the words I have used should be considered only in that context, and I am sure if one looks at these various fluids one finds many enzymes that cleave, C3 or C5, but just in a manner productive of a biological factor.

Park: Do you find these enzymes in the activated lymphocytes? For example, the activation by a specific antigen or nonspecific activation?

Ward: I can't recall that we have really looked in activated lymphocytes to see if these enzymes are released.

Park: Would you like to elaborate your myocardial infarction model? How did you make it?

Ward: I can refer you to a paper which will give the details (Hill, J. H., and Ward, P. A.: The phlogistic role of C3 leukotactic fragments in myocardial infarcts in rats. *J. Exp. Med.* 133:885–900, 1971).

The Phagocytic Cell in Host Resistance, edited
by Joseph A. Bellanti and Delbert H. Dayton.
Raven Press, New York © 1975.

Genetic Defects Affecting Complement and Host Resistance to Infection

Chester A. Alper, Thomas P. Stossel, and Fred S. Rosen

Center for Blood Research, Divisions of Hematology and Immunology, Children's Hospital Medical Center, and Department of Pediatrics, Harvard Medical School, Boston, Massachusetts 02115

There are many biological activities generated during activation of the complement and properdin systems that have important roles in the inflammatory response and in host resistance to infection. The bulk of the important activities, such as, the enhancement of phagocytosis of red cells (1) and certain bacteria (2), immune adherence (3), chemotaxis for polymorphonuclear leukocytes (4), and anaphylatoxin generation (5), are elaborated with the activation and cleavage of C3. Further anaphylatoxin and chemotactic activity is generated with the participation of C5 and C5–7 but optimal lysis of antibody-sensitized cells requires the full classical sequence through C9. The requirements for the capacity of serum to kill certain smooth strains of Gram-negative bacteria are not entirely clear, but it seems probable that the properdin system, the classical sequence, and C3–C9 are necessary. Both the properdin system and the classical sequence through at least C4 are necessary for virus neutralization.

The relative importance *in vivo* of these complement-mediated functions is probably best ascertained from study of persons and animals with inherited deficiency states of single proteins in the system. A growing number of such deficiency states have been uncovered, particularly over the past few years. A strain of guinea pigs, unfortunately now lost, genetically deficient in an undefined later-acting component (6), or in C4 (7), rabbits (8) or humans (9) deficient in C6, mice (10,11) and humans (12) deficient in C5, and humans deficient in C2 (13) or C7 (14) do not appear to be more susceptible to infections than their counterparts who have normal concentrations of these proteins. One explanation for the lack of such increased susceptibility in C4 and C2 deficiency is the presence of the properdin system (15), which represents a pathway alternative to the classical C1, 4, 2 route to C3 activation. This pathway, if activated by the appropriate pathogen, through its action on C3 and later-acting components, could mediate virtually all the complement-mediated functions. The normal health of the C5-deficient mice, C6-deficient rabbits, and humans and C7-deficient humans may be explained by the duplication at the C3 step of the functions (anaphylatoxin generation and chemotaxis) derived from C5 and C6.

Families have been reported (16, 17) in which there is eczema and infection with Gram-negative bacteria and with *Staphylococcus aureus* during the first year of life (Leiner's syndrome). Serum from affected individuals is defective in the enhancement of the phagocytosis of yeast and this defect is reportedly corrected by the addition to the patient's serum of purified human C5 or normal mouse serum but not C5-deficient mouse serum. C5 is present in normal concentrations in these sera and C5 isolated from such serum has normal hemolytic function. Nevertheless, because of the restoration experiments, the defect is thought to represent C5 dysfunction. Several other observations contradict this interpretation. First of all, mouse serum congenitally devoid of any detectable C5 shows only slight reduction in enhancement of pneumococcal phagocytosis when compared with normal mouse (2, 18). Secondly, and even more importantly, humans with genetic deficiency of C5 have been found very recently (12) and their serum exhibits normal enhancement of phagocytosis of yeast.

C3, by virtue both of its crucial position in the complement cascade at the junction of the classical and properdin pathways and of the many important functions associated with its activation, is the most critical of the complement proteins. One would expect that defects affecting this protein would result in immunological impairment and increased susceptibility to infection. Nevertheless, patients with prolonged acquired depression of C3 concentration, as, for example, in membranoproliferative glomerulonephritis, do not seem to be infection-prone. Similarly, patients with half-normal C3 levels as the result of inheritance of a single "nonexpressed" C3 gene (19) are asymptomatic. On the other hand, some patients with systemic lupus erythematosus may be more than normally susceptible to infection.

We have studied several patients with disorders affecting C3 who have markedly increased susceptibility to infection with pyogenic organisms. In three of these patients the hereditary bases of their defects have been clearly established, whereas in the fourth such a basis is suspected but not yet proved. The specific abnormalities in these patients are different.

HOMOZYGOUS C3 DEFICIENCY

One patient homozygous for C3 deficiency (20) is a 15-year-old girl who has had more than 20 hospital admissions for recurrent infections since infancy. Of these, 14 were for bacterial pneumonia, two were for meningococcal meningitis, and the remainder were for recurrent otitis media, impetigo, and paronychia. Pathogenic bacteria were isolated from her sputum on only a few occasions during her episodes of pheumonia and included *Diplococcus pneumoniae, Streptococcus pyogenes,* and *Klebsiella aerogenes.* All of these infections responded to antibiotic therapy. At no time was there peripheral blood neutrophilia despite her severe bacterial infections. No other member of her family had a history of undue susceptibility to infection.

Humoral antibody levels (including to a thymus-independent antigen), delayed hypersensitivity, and polymorphonuclear number and function revealed no abnormality. In contrast, her total serum complement was less than 1 CH_{50} U/ml (normal: 32 to 45 U/ml). The concentration of C3 in the patient's serum was less than 2.5 μg/ml (normal: 1,000 to 2,000 μg/ml) as determined immunochemically and 13 U/ml by a functional assay (normal: 15,000 to 30,000 U/ml). The serum concentrations of C1, C2, C4, C5, C6, C7, C8, C9, C$\bar{1}$ inhibitor, C3 inactivator, and properdin factor B were normal. Family studies revealed that serum C3 concentrations in the patient's mother, father, and five of her six siblings were approximately half-normal and in one sibling was normal. Hemolytic complement was slightly reduced in those family members with half-normal concentrations of C3. Results of C3 typing in this family were consistent with the presence of nonexpressed C3 genes in both the maternal and paternal relatives. The patient's parents were first cousins, as were her paternal grandparents.

Incubation of the patient's serum with zymosan failed to result in activation of the properdin system, confirming the observation of Müller-Eberhard and Götze (21) that C3 or one of its fragments is necessary for the activation of the enzyme that cleaves properdin factor B.

The patient's serum was deficient in such complement-mediated functions as the enhancement of phagocytosis of type II pneumococci (2) or of endotoxin-paraffin oil emulsion (22) and chemotaxis for peripheral blood polymorphonuclear leukocytes. Addition of C3 to normal concentration to her serum corrected these deficiencies.

A second patient with a closely related, if not identical, form of inherited C3 deficiency was uncovered by Dr. John S. Davis, IV. This patient is 3 years old and has had pneumonia, otitis media, and an episode of acute arthritis, probably septic in origin. The father of this patient was not available for typing but the patient's mother, grandfather, and several other family members had half-normal C3 concentrations. The patient's serum contained about 2% of the normal level of C3 but other complement components were in normal concentration. As in the case of the other homozygous C3-deficient patient, complement-mediated functions were abnormal in the patient's serum but could be corrected by the addition of purified C3. In contrast to the first patient, a leukocytosis with a "shift to the left" was observed during at least two episodes of bacterial infection, although this response was blunted in relation to the severity of infection.

TYPE I ESSENTIAL HYPERCATABOLISM OF C3 (KAF DEFICIENCY)

The patient with this disorder (23) is a 28-year-old man with a lifelong history of increased susceptibility to infection with pyogenic organisms such as β-hemolytic *Streptococci, Neisseria meningitidis,* and *Hemophilus influenzae.* All aspects of the immune response were intact when tested in his serum save for complement-mediated functions. Bactericidal activity for smooth Gram-negative bacteria, chemotaxis, and the enhancement of phagocytosis of Type II pneumococci or endotoxin-paraffin oil emulsions were grossly deficient. Of the classical complement proteins all were in normal concentration except for C3. Total C3 measured immunochemically was 300 μg/ml (normal range: 1,000–2,000 μg/ml) but of this about three-fourths was in the form of the inactive conversion product,

C3b, so that only about 70 μg/ml was native, functional C3. These findings suggested that C3 inactivation and cleavage was occuring in the patient *in vivo.* Metabolic studies with purified ^{125}I-labeled C3 confirmed that this was, indeed, the case. By 2 hr after administration, some 40% of the ^{125}I-C3 was converted to ^{125}I-C3b and the fractional catabolic rate for C3 was about five times the rate in normal subjects.

Complement-mediated functions could not be restored to his serum simply by adding purified C3 *in vitro,* as could be done in the case of serum from the C3-deficient patients. Chemotaxis, bactericidal activity, and hemolytic activity were restored by whole normal serum or by a 5–6S β-pseudoglobulin fraction of normal serum. For the restoration of opsonization, both this fraction and purified C3 were required. It is clear that a group of proteins are deficient in the patient's serum and that these are found in the 5–6S β-pseudoglobulin fraction of normal serum which even contains low concentrations of C3.

The patient's primary genetic deficiency (24, 25) is in the C3 inactivator (26), an enzyme which destroys the immune adherence and hemolytic activities of cell-bound $C\bar{3}$ or C3b (27), cleaves fluid phase C3b (24), and renders EAC $\overline{(1)4(2)3}$ conglutinable (agglutinable by the bovine serum protein conglutinin) (28). In this latter capacity, the C3 inactivator has been designated conglutinogen-activating factor (KAF). KAF is also and probably most importantly an inhibitor of the properdin or alternate complement pathway (25) via both its attack on C3b and its inhibition of GBGase (29), an enzyme which cleaves glycine-rich β-glycoprotein (GBG) (30) or properdin factor B (31, 32) (Fig. 1). C3b has been

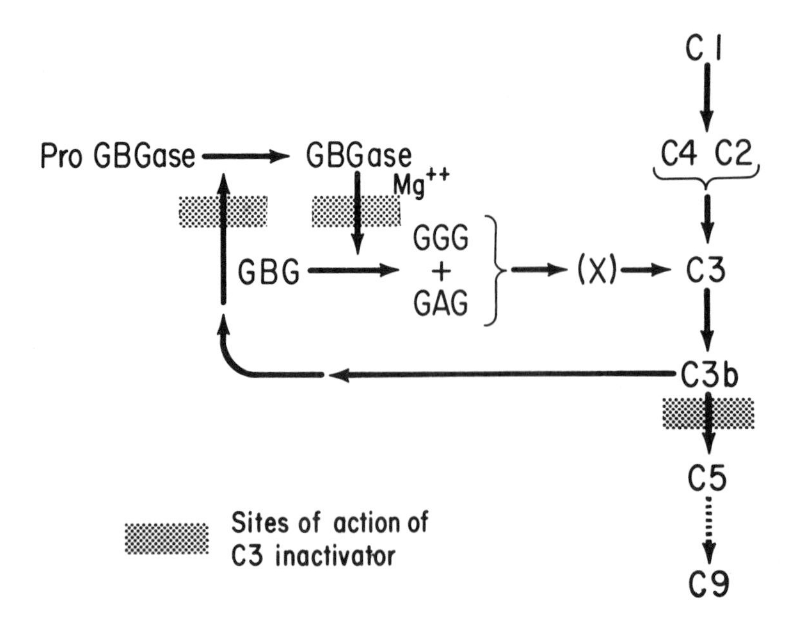

FIG. 1. Scheme of the alternate complement pathway.

shown (33) to be capable of activating GBGase. GBG is undetectable in the patient's serum, although fragments of this molecule are found in low concentration in fresh plasma drawn into EDTA. Active GBGase is present in his serum (34), and added GBG is rapidly cleaved on incubation with his serum and its factor B activity is destroyed (32). Since neither purified C3 alone nor C3 with added GBG is cleaved on addition to the patient's serum, it seems likely that an additional protein (or proteins) (X) is also deficient in his serum. Further evidence for this additional protein is the inability of a mixture of the patient's serum, KAF, GBG, and C3 to enhance the phagocytosis of endotoxin-paraffin oil emulsions.

It is thus clear that, owing to the genetic absence of KAF in this patient, there is spontaneous activation and consumption of the proteins of the alternate or properdin pathway in his circulating plasma, including C3. His defects have been mimicked *in vitro* by the depletion of KAF from normal serum and subsequent incubation (33). Normal plasma produces a remarkable normalization of this patient's abnormalities lasting for over 2 weeks when administered *in vivo* (35). These effects could also be produced by the intravenous infusion of purified KAF (36).

In addition to the postulated "X," a protein in normal serum, which forms a complex with a protein in the venom of *Naja naja* (called cobra factor or CoF) (37) and mediates the attack on C3, is also missing from the patient's serum. The addition of this protein to the mixture of KAF, GBG, C3, and the patient's serum fails to restore opsonization for endotoxin-paraffin oil emulsions. The exact role of the CoF-binding protein in the alternate pathway and the question of its requirement for opsonization is thus unclear. Its deficiency in this patient, however, bespeaks its place somewhere in the alternate or properdin pathway. Even more puzzling is the fact that properdin itself is present in the patient's serum in normal or near-normal concentration.

TYPE II ESSENTIAL HYPERCATABOLISM OF C3

The fourth patient (38) is a 34-year-old woman with partial lipodystrophy and a history of meningococcal meningitis and meningococcemia, β-hemolytic streptococcal tonsillitis on two occasions, and two episodes of pneumonia, one of them pneumococcal. Immunoglobulins were in normal concentration in her serum and her humoral antibody response was adequate. There were no abnormalities in cell-mediated immunity, nor in peripheral blood leukocyte function. Complement-mediated functions in her serum were absent or markedly diminished. These could be normalized or considerably improved by the addition of purified C3 alone to her serum. All the proteins missing from the serum of the Type I patient with KAF deficiency, including GBG, KAF, and CoF-binding protein were present in normal concentrations in the serum of the Type II patient. The properdin concentration was slightly increased.

The CH_{50} was 8 U/ml compared with the normal range of 32 to 45 U/ml.

Immunochemical and functional measurements of C1, C4, C2, C5, and C6 revealed no abnormality. Her total serum C3 concentration, in contrast, was 70 μg/ml or approximately 5% of the normal mean value. Of this immunochemically determined C3, about 50% in fresh-drawn plasma was in the form of inactive conversion products C3c and C3d.

Isotopically labeled purified C3 administered intravenously was more rapidly catabolized than normal, but it was also shown that C3 synthesis was reduced. In contrast to the patient with Type I disease, an enzymic activity was directly demonstrable in this patient's serum *in vitro* in that added labeled C3 converted to C3c and C3d on incubation at 37°C. Far from being inhibited by normal serum, this activity was enhanced when the patient's serum and normal serum were mixed. Both the activity in the patient's serum and the protein in normal serum responsible for enhancement were heat-labile 6S β-pseudoglobulins. The enzymic activity for C3 required Mg^{2+} but not Ca^{2+} and the attack on C3 was temperature-dependent. The enhancing protein was present in normal concentration in the sera of patients with hereditary angioneurotic edema and of the patient with Type I essential hypercatabolism of C3. The enhancing protein in normal serum may be an inactive precursor of the enzyme in the serum of the patient with Type II, and there may be autoactivation of the zymogen by the active enzyme.

Several patients with partial lipodystrophy and similar complement abnormalities have been reported (39, 40) although none has had the increased susceptibility to infection exhibited by the first patient. Some of the patients have membranoproliferative glomerulonephritis whereas others, as our patient, had no evidence of renal disease. Therefore, the relationships between partial lipodystrophy, hypercatabolism of C3, increased susceptibility to infection, and glomerulonephritis remain tantalizingly unclear.

CONCLUSIONS FROM COMPLEMENT-DEFICIENT ANIMALS AND HUMANS

It is clear from the studies of animals and humans with deficiencies of complement proteins, including regulators, that the complement system, including the properdin or alternate pathway, does play an important part in host resistance to infection. The C3-deficient subjects have infections with organisms very similar to those of agammaglobulinemic boys. Thus, at least for certain pyogens, complement is required as an effector mechanism for antibodies in the host's defense against them. It seems probable that the most important function in this regard is the enhancement of phagocytosis. For certain organisms, such as perhaps *Staphylococcus aureus,* which have not been prominent among the organisms causing infections in persons with abnormalities affecting C3, antibody alone when present in high concentration may suffice to enhance phagocytosis, even in the absence of all detectable complement proteins (41, 42).

The fact that neither humans nor animals with deficiencies of later acting complement components (C5–7) have increased numbers or severity of bacterial infections suggests that the full system is not essential for host resistance. This indicates that neither bactericidal activity for certain smooth Gram-negative organisms nor the closely related hemolytic activity for animal cells is crucial *in vivo.* Similarly, deficiency states of C4 or C2 are associated with defects in immune adherence but not with increased susceptibility to bacterial infection. Thus, immune adherence does not appear to be a critical function *in vivo,* at least with respect to host resistance to bacterial invasion.

Chemotaxis is probably an important function *in vivo.* This function is carried at two, and possibly three, stages of complement activation. Thus, a deficiency of C3 or C5 (or C6) alone may not impair this function. Deficiency of C3 obviates generation of chemotaxis by the usual sequential complement activation by either the classical or alternate pathways, but it has been shown (43) that tissue proteases (and possibly bacterial proteases) are capable of elaborating chemotactic fragments from C3 and C5 by direct attack on these proteins. In this regard, C3-deficient patients have normal responses in the Rebuck skin window test. On the other hand, the failure of C3-deficient persons to mount a normal leukocytosis in response to bacterial infection must impair resistance to infection.

Some light is shed on the relative importance of the classical and alternate pathways of complement activation in host resistance by the deficiency states. Patients with alternate pathway defects certainly seem to be more susceptible to bacterial infection than those with deficiencies of early acting or classical pathway components. There is evidence that the alternate pathway can be activated by polysaccharides including endotoxin even in the absence of antibody. It may therefore be that nonimmune activation of the properdin system is vital to host defense.

OTHER DISORDERS OF HOST DEFENSE RELATED TO THE COMPLEMENT SYSTEM

It has long been known that some patients with sickle-cell anemia suffer from unusual and severe pyogenic infections (44). Splenic ablation (45) and the glutting of mononuclear phagocytes with damaged erythrocytes (46) might contribute to this susceptibility. Nonetheless, abnormal heat-labile opsonic activity of serum from patients with sickle-cell disease has been reported (47), and recently evidence has been presented to suggest that the defect resides somewhere in the properdin pathway (48). Neonates are susceptible to bacterial sepsis. They lack certain antibodies, and, relative to adults, have lower levels of many complement components. It has been reported that the lowest complement levels are found in premature infants, and that these babies have lower heat-labile opsonic activity than normal neonates (49, 50). We found that about 15% of a series of neonates tested were markedly deficient in GBG and that these infants had significantly lower opsonic activity than those babies with normal GBG levels (51). Whether these neonates are actually at risk for infection remains to be proved.

STUDIES ON THE MECHANISM OF OPSONIZATION BY COMPLEMENT IN VITRO

Although many techniques have been applied to the study of how serum opsonizes, only methodolgy that truly quantitates engulfment of particles by phagocytes yields interpretable information. Gigli and Nelson, measuring disappearance of erythrocyte hemoglobin spectrophotometrically from the medium surrounding neutrophils (1), and Johnston et al. (2), assaying nitroblue tetrazolium reduction as an indirect measurement of ingestion of pneumococci by neutrophils, showed that C3 fixation by the sequential action of C1, C4, and C2 opsonized antibody-coated erythrocytes or pneumococci. However, Johnston et al. observed that C2-deficient serum had opsonic activity, a finding subsequently confirmed by Johnson et al. (52). In a similar fashion, heat-labile opsonic activity was found in C4-deficient, C2 and C4-deficient, C1q-deficient, and antibody-deficient sera (53–57). All of these findings suggested indirectly that opsonic activity was being generated by the alternate pathway. We have utilized *E. coli* 026:B6 lipopolysaccharide-coated paraffin oil particles containing Oil Red O to assay spectrophotometrically the initial rate of ingestion of particles by neutrophils (58). Ingestion required pretreatment of the particles with fresh unheated serum. Normal, C4-, C2-, C4- and C2-, and C6-deficient sera had equivalent opsonic activity at all concentrations, but agammaglobulinemic sera had somewhat diminished activity. The activity of normal or C2-deficient sera was enhanced by the addition of antilipopolysaccharide antisera. C3-deficient serum had no opsonic activity and purified C3 restored it in proportion to the quantity of C3 added. Furthermore, sera from various patients had opsonic activity proportional to the C3 concentration in the range of 0 to 100 mg/100 ml. GBG-deficient neonatal serum had decreased opsonic activity which was restored by purified GBG. All of the findings indicated that the opsonic activity of the serum for the lipopolysaccharide-coated particles involved C3 fixation by the alternate complement pathway alone and that measurement of ingestion of the particles represented a quantitative assay of this system. Similar findings were obtained using albumin-coated paraffin oil particles (59), and suggested that denatured protein, as well as lipopolysaccharide, has the ability to initiate reactions of the properdin system. During opsonization of lipopolysaccharide-coated paraffin oil particles in serum, ^{125}I-C3 is fixed to the particles and the ingestibility of the particles correlates with the quantity of C3 fixed. As opsonization occurs, ^{125}I-properdin and ^{125}I-GBG also become fixed to the particles. Attachment of these reagents requires divalent cations and does not occur in C3-deficient serum. Properdin and GBG but not C3 radioactivity are removed from opsonized particles by washing them in 2 M NaCl; nevertheless, the particles remain ingestible. C3 radioactivity and ingestibility of the particles withstand remarkably rough physical and chemical manipulations including washing in 8 M urea, 6 M guanidine, extremes of pH, Triton X-100, and deoxycholate and boiling (60). Dodecyl sulfate (1%) removes ingestibility and radioactivity of the particles. SDS eluates reduced and applied to polyacrylamide gels reveal one radioactive peptide with a molecular weight of approximately 70,000. This peptide has only about one-third of the radioactive tryptic peptides found in C3 or in C3b (60). Thus, the opsonically active piece of C3 is smaller than C3b and is extraordinarily stable after fixation. Opsonically active C3, however, like its immune adherence counterpart, is removed from the particles by trypsin or by activity in serum which is, in part, accounted for by KAF. The rate of removal of opsonically active C3 in serum is much slower than the rate of fixation. Properdin, but not GBG, is removed from particles in serum as well.

ABBREVIATIONS

GBG-glycine-rich β-glycoprotein = properdin factor B = C3PA (C3 proactivator) = UF (unknown factor) = HLF (Heat-labile factor)

GBGase-glycine-rich β-glycoproteinase = C3PAse (C3 proactivator convertase) = factor D

CoF-Cobra venom factor = CVF

KAF-conglutinogen-activating factor = C3 inactivator = C3b inactivator = C3INH

C3b = activated factor A = HSFa

ACKNOWLEDGMENTS

The work reported in this chapter was supported by U.S. Public Health Service grants AM 13855, AI 08173, AI 05877, FR 128, HL-1517, and AI 00366. We thank Lillian Watson and John Hartwig for expert technical assistance in the original studies cited here and Louise Viehman for untiring secretarial help.

Thomas P. Stossel is an established investigator of the American Heart Association.

REFERENCES

1. Gigli, I., and Nelson, R. A., Jr.: Complement-dependent immune phagocytosis. I. Requirements for C'1, C'4, C'2, and C'3. *Exp. Cell Res.* 51:45, 1968.
2. Johnston, R. B., Jr., Klemperer, M. R., Alper, C. A., and Rosen, F. S.: The enhancement of bacterial phagocytosis by serum. The role of complement components and two cofactors. *J. Exp. Med.* 129:1275, 1969.
3. Nelson, R. A., Jr.: The role of complement in immune phenomena. In Zweifach, B. W., Grant, L., and McCluskey, R. T. (eds): *The Inflammatory Process,* Academic Press, New York, p. 819, 1965.
4. Bokisch, V. A., Müller-Eberhard, H. J., and Cochrane, C. G.: Isolation of a fragment (C3a) of the third component of human complement containing anaphylatoxin and chemotactic activity and description of an anaphylatoxin inactivator of human serum. *J. Exp. Med.* 129:1109, 1969.
5. Dias da Silva, W., Eisele, J. W., and Lepow, I. H.: Complement as a mediator of inflammation. III. Purification of the activity with anaphylatoxin properties generated by interaction of the first four components of complement and its identification as a cleavage product of C'3. *J. Exp. Med.* 126:1027, 1967.
6. Hyde, R. R.: Complement deficient guinea-pig serum. *J. Immunol.* 8:267, 1923.

7. Ellman, L., Green, I., and Frank, M.: Genetically controlled total deficiency of the fourth component of complement in the guinea pig. *Science* 170:74, 1970.
8. Rother, U., and Rother, K.: Über einem angeborene Komplement-Defekt bei Kaninchen. *Z. Immunitaetsforsch.* 121:224, 1961.
9. Leddy, J. P., Frank, M. M., Gaither, T., Baum, J., and Klemperer, M. R.: Hereditary deficiency of the sixth component of complement in man. I. Immunochemical, biologic and family studies. *J. Clin. Invest.* 53:544, 1974.
10. Rosenberg, L. T., and Tachibana, D. K.: Activity of mouse complement. *J. Immunol.* 89:861, 1962.
11. Cinader, B., Dubiski, S., and Wardlaw, A. C.: Distribution, inheritance and properties of an antigen, MuBl, and its relation to hemolytic complement. *J. Exp. Med.* 120:897, 1964.
12. Rosenfeld, S. I., and Leddy, J. P.: Hereditary deficiency of the fifth component of complement (C5) in man. *J. Clin. Invest.* 53:67a, 1974.
13. Klemperer, M. R., Woodworth, H. C., Rosen, F. S., and Austen, K. F.: Hereditary deficiency of the second component of complement (C'2) in man. *J. Clin. Invest.* 45:880, 1966.
14. Boyer, J.: *Personal communication.*
15. Pillemer, L., Blum, L., Lepow, I. H., Ross, O. A., Todd, E. W., and Wardlaw, A. C.: The properdin system and immunity. I. Demonstration and isolation of a new serum protein, properdin, and its role in immune phenomena. *Science* 120:279, 1954.
16. Miller, M. E., Seals, J., Kaye, R., and Levitsky, L. C.: A familial, plasma-associated defect of phagocytosis: A new cause of recurrent bacterial infections. *Lancet* ii:60, 1968.
17. Miller, M. E., and Nilsson, U. R.: A familial deficiency of the phagocytosis-enhancing activity of serum related to a dysfunction of the fifth component of complement (C5). *N. Engl. J. Med.* 282:354, 1970.
18. Shin, H. S., Smith, M. R., and Wood, W. B., Jr.: Heat-labile opsonins to pneumococcus. II. Involvement of C3 and C5. *J. Exp. Med.* 130:1229, 1969.
19. Alper, C. A., Propp, R. P., Klemperer, M. R., and Rosen, F. S.: Inherited deficiency of the third component of human complement (C'3). *J. Clin. Invest.* 48:553, 1969.
20. Alper, C. A., Colten, H. R., Rosen, F. S., Rabson, A. R., Macnab, G. M., and Gear, J. S. S.: Homozygous deficiency of C3 in a patient with repeated infections. *Lancet* ii:1179, 1972.
21. Müller-Eberhard, H. J., and Götze, O.: C3 proactivator convertase and its mode of action. *J. Exp. Med.* 135:1003, 1972.
22. Stossel, T. P., Mason, R. J., Hartwig, J., and Vaughan, M.: Quantitative studies of phagocytosis by polymorphonuclear leukocytes. Use of paraffin oil emulsions to measure the rate of phagocytosis. *J. Clin. Invest.* 51:615, 1972.
23. Alper, C. A., Abramson, N., Johnston, R. B., Jr., Jandl, J. H., and Rosen, F. S.: Increased susceptibility to infection associated with abnormalities of complement-mediated functions and of the third component of complement (C3). *N. Engl. J. Med.* 282:349, 1970.
24. Abramson, N., Alper, C. A., Lachmann, P. J., Rosen, F. S., and Jandl, J. H.: Deficiency of the C3 inactivator in man. *J. Immunol.* 107:19, 1971.
25. Alper, C. A., Rosen, F. S., and Lachmann, P. J.: Inactivator of the third component of complement as an inhibitor in the properdin pathway. *Proc. Natl. Acad. Sci.* 69:2910, 1972.
26. Tamura, N., and Nelson, R. A., Jr.: Three naturally occuring inhibitors of components of complement in guinea pig and rabbit serum. *J. Immunol.* 99:582, 1967.
27. Ruddy, S., and Austen, K. F.: C3b inactivator of man. II. Fragments produced by C3b inactivator cleavage of cell-bound or fluid phase C3b. *J. Immunol.* 107:742, 1971.
28. Lachmann, P. J., and Müller-Eberhard, H. J.: The demonstration in human serum of "conglutinogen-activating factor" and its effect on the third component of complement. *J. Immunol.* 100:691, 1968.
29. Rosen, F. S., and Alper, C. A.: An enzyme in the alternate pathway to C3 activation (the properdin system) and its inhibition by a protein in normal serum. *J. Clin. Invest.* 51:80, 1972 (Abstr.).
30. Boenisch, T., and Alper, C. A.: Isolation and properties of a glycine-rich β-glycoprotein of human serum. *Biochim. Biophys. Acta* 221:529, 1970.
31. Blum, L., Pillemer, L., and Lepow, I. H.: The properdin system and immunity. XIII. Assay and properties of a heat-labile serum factor (Factor B) in the properdin system. *Z. Immunitaetsforsch. Allerg. Klin. Immunol.* 118:349, 1959.
32. Alper, C. A., Goodkofsky, I., and Lepow, I. H.: The relationship of glycine-rich β-glycoprotein

to factor B in the properdin system and to the cobra factor-binding protein of human serum. *J. Exp. Med.* 137:424, 1973.
33. Nicol, P. A. E., and Lachmann, P. J.: The alternate pathway of complement activation. The role of C3 and its inactivator (KAF). *Immunology* 24:259, 1973.
34. Alper, C. A., and Rosen, F. S.: Genetic aspects of the complement system. In Kunkel, H. G., and Dixon, F. J. (eds): *Advances in Immunology,* New York, Academic Press, p. 251. 1971.
35. Alper, C. A., Abramson, N., Johnston, R. B., Jr., Jandl, J. H., and Rosen, F. S.: Studies *in vivo* and *in vitro* on an abnormality in the metabolism of C3 in a patient with increased susceptibility to infection. *J. Clin. Invest.* 49:1975, 1970.
36. Ziegler, J., Alper, C. A., Rosen, F. S., and Lachmann, P. J.: *Unpublished observations.*
37. Müller-Eberhard, H. J.: Mechanism of inactivation of the third component of human complement (C'3) by cobra venom. *Fed. Proc.* 26:744, 1967 (Abstr.).
38. Alper, C. A., Bloch, K. J., and Rosen, F. S.: Increased susceptibility to infection in a patient with Type II essential hypercatabolism of C3. *N. Engl. J. Med.* 288:601, 1973.
39. Peters, D. K., Williams, D. G., Charlesworth, J. A., Boulton-Jones, J. M., Sissons, J. G. P., Evans, D. J., Kourilsky, O., and Morel-Maroger, L.: Mesangiocapillary nephritis, partial lipodystrophy, and hypocomplementaemia. *Lancet* ii:535, 1973.
40. Thompson, R. A., and White, R. H. R.: Partial lipodystrophy and hypocomplementaemic nephritis. *Lancet* ii:679, 1973.
41. Ward, H. K., and Enders, J. J.: An analysis of the opsonic and tropic action of normal and immune sera based on experiments with the pneumococcus. *J. Exp. Med.* 57:527, 1933.
42. Quie, P. G., Messner, R. P., and Williams, R. C., Jr.: Phagocytosis in subacute bacterial endocarditis. Localization of the primary opsonic site to Fc fragment. *J. Exp. Med.* 128:553, 1968.
43. Ward, P. A.: Complement-derived chemotactic factors and their interactions with neutrophilic granulocytes. In Ingram, D. G. (ed.): *Biological Activities of Complement,* Basel, S. Karger, p. 108, 1972.
44. Barrett-Connor, E.: Bacterial infection and sickle cell anemia. *Medicine* 50:97, 1971.
45. Pearson, H. A., Cornelius, E. A., Schwartz, A. D., Zelson, J. H., Wolfson, S. L., and Spencer, R. P.: Transfusion-reversible functional asplenia in young children with sickle-cell anemia. *N. Engl. J. Med.* 283:334, 1970.
46. Kaye, D., and Hook, E. W.: The influence of hemolysis on susceptibility to salmonella infection: Additional observations. *J. Immunol.* 91:518, 1963.
47. Winkelstein, J. A., and Drachman, R. H.: Deficiency of pneumococcal serum opsonizing activity in sickle-cell disease. *N. Engl. J. Med.* 279:459, 1968.
48. Johnston, R. B., Jr., Newman, S. L., and Struth, A. G.: An abnormality of the alternate pathway of complement activation in sickle-cell disease. *N. Eng. J. Med.* 288:803, 1973.
49. McCracken, G. H., and Eichenwald, H. F.: Leukocyte function and the development of opsonic and complement activity in the neonate. *Am. J. Dis. Child.* 121:120, 1971.
50. Forman, M. L., and Stiehm, E. R.: Impaired opsonic activity but normal phagocytosis in low-birth-weight infants. *N. Engl. J. Med.* 281:926, 1969.
51. Stossel, T. P., Alper, C. A., and Rosen, F. S.: Opsonic activity in the newborn. Role of properdin. *Pediatrics* 52:134, 1973.
52. Johnson, F. R., Angnello, V., and Williams, R. C.: Opsonic activity in human serum deficient in C2. *J. Immunol.* 109:141, 1972.
53. Jasin, H. E.: Human heat-labile opsonins: evidence for their mediation via the alternate pathway of complement activation. *J. Immunol.* 109:26, 1972.
54. Stollerman, G. H. Alberti, H., and Plemmons, J. A.: Opsonization of group A streptococci by complement-deficient blood from a patient with hereditary angioneurotic edema. *J. Immunol.* 99:92, 1967.
55. Winkelstein, J. A., Shin, H. S., and Wood, W. B., Jr.: Heat labile opsonins to pneumococcus III. The participation of immunoglobulin and of the alternate pathway of C3 activation. *J. Immunol.* 108:1681, 1972.
56. Root, R. K., Ellman, L., and Frank, M. M.: Bactericidal and opsonic properties of C4-deficient guinea pig serum. *J. Immunol.* 109:477, 1972.
57. Williams, R. C., and Quie, P. G.: Opsonic activity of agammaglobulinemic sera. *J. Immunol.* 106:51, 1971.
58. Stossel, T. P., Alper, C. A., and Rosen, F. S.: Serum-dependent phagocytosis of paraffin oil emulsified with bacterial lipopolysaccharide. *J. Exp. Med.* 137:690, 1973.

59. Stossel, T. P.: Quantitative studies of phagocytosis. Kinetic effects of cations and heat-labile opsonin. *J. Cell Biol.* 58:346, 1973.
60. Stossel, T. P., Field, R. J., Alper, C. A., and Rosen, F. S.: The opsonically active fragment of C3. *J. Clin. Invest.* 53:78a, 1974.

DISCUSSION

Spitznagel: Have you looked at this patient with the inhibitor abnormality to see if he has developed an antibody to this protein?

Alper: Yes, and we are unable to detect such antibody despite his having received whole plasma on one occasion and purified C3 inactivator on another. Similarly, the C3-deficient patient was given plasma at one point and does not have detectable antibody to C3. She, incidentally, makes normal amounts of antibody to a variety of antigens, indicating that complement is probably not necessary for the antibody response. One wonders what the role of the C3 receptor on B lymphocytes might be.

Cohn: Would you comment on the site of synthesis of C3?

Alper: Yes, it is the liver. We first showed this using C3 allotypes in a patient whose liver was transplanted. The recipient changed his allotype to that of the donor of the liver and kept this allotype until his death 45 days after transplantation.

Cohn: By the liver you mean the hepatocyte?

Alper: In subsequent studies performed with Dr. A. Myron Johnson, C3 was seen in hepatocytes using immunofluorescence.

Ward: Do you think the liver is the exclusive site of C3 synthesis?

Alper: It's the major site. Other sites may also produce C3, for example the synovium in rheumatoid arthritis as shown by Colten and Ruddy, but in health the liver accounts for at least 90% of the C3 produced.

Miller: I really feel obligated to make some comments because I think we do have a different interpretation of the data, and I think there are significant errors in some of the data you cited from our laboratory. I will try to be brief and summarize succinctly the points I think are vital.

First of all, our own experience with this entity is one that embodies approximately 16 patients. I have personally had the opportunity to look at sera from approximately 10 patients with the disorder and am aware of at least six other cases that have been observed in other laboratories. All of these cases, it should be pointed out, have been diagnosed using the yeast assay that I will describe and most of these patients have had severe life-threatening infections. In three of these patients plasma therapy supplying back C5 has proved to be effective. The idea these patients don't have life-threatening severe infections. . . .

Alper: I didn't say that.

Miller: I merely wish to establish the point that the entity we have described is associated with recurrent severe infections. Secondly, I do not share your intepretation of the animal data on C5 deficiencies. There are three sets of data from separate laboratories. The work of Morelli and Rosenberg is particularly important in our discussion. If one injects viable monilia into these animals, they die at a faster rate than normal C5-containing animals. The idea of a subtle host defect exhibiting itself in the complement system is certainly not unique, but is, rather, seen in many of the complement deficiency states. So the fact these mice appear to be normal under most circumstances doesn't say they don't have a defect. I think the *in vitro* and *in vivo* data do not support your statement.

Whether one debates that or not I think we need to clarify the basis on why we have suggested that these patients most likely have C5 dysfunctions. The work has been presented and is in press now and there are three major points which I think need to be emphasized.

First, if one purifies C5 in patients with a deficiency and from normal individuals and compares the effects on reconstitution of a C5-deficient patient, one can show, microgram for microgram, that deficient C5 has no effect whatever. In no case can one get *in vitro* opsonic activity demonstrated with the reconstituted C5.

Secondly, the issue of hemolytic activity is one I am disturbed about because we have never stated that isolated C5. . . .

Rather than debate, let me state what the data show. In terms of total hemolytic activity, this has always been normal in C5-dysfunctional patients. This is one reason why we first thought a defect of complement was not involved in this syndrome. Subsequently, we looked specifically for C5 hemolytic activity. The initial work was presented on the basis of the original C5 purification method which Ulf Nilsson and Hans Müller-Eberhard described. When C5 was purified according to that method, the isolated deficient C5 had approximately 5 percent of the hemolytic activity of normal. Subsequently, on adaptation of the new purification method, we again repeated these studies and found that C5 from both sources was normal in terms of hemolytic activity at the time of purification, but on storage for 3 or 4 days the deficient C5 had lost approximately 95 percent of its hemolytic activity while the normal retained maximum activity.

Third, in a companion article we show that if one takes normal plasma and stores it under blood bank conditions at 4 degrees centigrade and looks carefully at activity, one can show within 48 hours normal plasma has lost almost 50% of its yeast opsonic activity, and in terms of reconstitution activities we have been able to show the loss in yeast opsonic activity is due to the loss of C5. This is done on the basis of numerous C5 preparations.

In terms of quantitative amounts, it appears as little as 1 to 1.5 micrograms of C5 per milliliter is able to give normal yeast opsonic activity. This is interesting in view of what Dr. Baum said about the normal individual who had a 10 percent level. His 10 percent of C5 would, in the assays that we did, be expected to give normal activity and probably be in a range for a patient that is not symptomatic. It appears to be a highly selected, highly concentrated effect.

Alper: He said it was normal in a patient who had none. I believe the C5-deficient propositus has no detectable C5.

Miller: I will answer that point. We are presently in collaborative studies with John Leddy to ascertain why they have not found a defect in the system. There may be significant differences in the conditions of the assay they have used. Based upon the assay as I originally described it, it would not be surprising if the conditions they are using would not pick it up. The method of preparing the yeast suspension is totally different. They are using plastic tubes instead of glass tubes, and we need to test the serum in our assay to see if that particular observation is correct. If we, indeed, find serum from their patient to be normal in our assay, then I think a new set of data need to be considered with appropriate hypotheses. In summary, most of these patients have had life-threatening infection. The preparations we have used to demonstrate the C5 abnormality have included a number of different batches of purified C5, and at least three different anti-C5 preparations. We have not demonstrated an immunochemical defect, but the absence of one certainly does not rule out our hypothesis—the data we now have.

Alper: What about the genetics?

Miller: In the first three cases the parents were first cousins or there was something like that involved. Most of the cases do have a strong family history. The first two cases, as luck would have it, appear to have two genetic patterns. But we have not had the opportunity in these studies to really clarify it.

Müller-Eberhard: I'd like to go back to the C3 deficiencies that Dr. Alper described. I think one has to bear in mind here the potential immune adherence reactivity of C4 in these patients, which was demonstrated by Neil Cooper several years ago. Having normal C4 may in fact be partially responsible for their not doing all that badly. Perhaps they would be worse off if this function of C4 were not in existence. And incidentally, C4b is capable of reacting with lymphocytes.

Sbarra: I have never been exposed to C3 deficiency until today so I hope I am permitted to ask a stupid question. Could this deficiency really be increased breakdown of C3?

Alper: We have done a metabolic study with labeled C3 in a patient who has almost total deficiency, and she has a mildly increased catabolic rate in no way sufficient to account for her extremely low C3 level.

Sbarra: Does she have a liver problem?

Alper: No.

Snyderman: For what it's worth, we came across a patient with a complete isolated deficiency of C6. We studied a number of members of her family but haven't found a C6 depression of any member of the family. The interesting association we found and don't know what do do with was that this woman had primary biliary cirrhosis and Sjogren's syndrome and recently died of massive intestinal hemorrhage although her clotting functions as far as we know had been normal. Have you seen anything similar to this?

Frank: The only patient with C6 deficiency that we have studied was the patient we reported with the Rochester group. This person did appear to have a familial deficiency.

Alper: The normal range for C6 is fairly wide so even a half-normal level may not be outside of that range.

Root: Two comments. First, to add a further note of confusion into the C5 dysfunction syndrome, I have had a chance to look at their opsonic capacity for pseudomonas and *S. aureus* using strains we have in the laboratory and a radio-tagged bacterial uptake system. Three of the four patients I have studied had normal or virtually normal opsonization when compared to normal controls. I don't know how this fits into the picture of recurrent infections but perhaps it suggests that an opsonic deficiency is not operative as far as bacteria are concerned. Secondly, I was struck by your observation that the patient with a complete lack of C3 had polys in her skin on biopsy, and I wonder what skin windows of this patient and other patients with absent C3 have shown.

Alper: It was normal. The skin window depends on abrading normal tissue, and tissue proteases may cleave C5 and generate chemotaxis, as shown by Dr. Ward and his colleagues.

Ward: I think that at this time no one really knows what the skin window is measuring.

Frank: It has been reported that the skin windows are abnormal in patients with C2 deficiency.

Holmes-Gray: Yes, in one patient with C2 deficiency.

Bellanti: Are there any immunoconglutinins found in these patients or the patients that Dr. Snyderman referred to?

Alper: Immunoconglutinins are presumably antibodies against cell-bound C3 or C4. We haven't found any in our patients.

The Phagocytic Cell in Host Resistance, edited
by Joseph A. Bellanti and Delbert H. Dayton.
Raven Press, New York © 1975.

A Brief Review of Macrophage Activation by Lymphocyte Mediators

John R. David

Departments of Medicine, Harvard Medical School and the Robert B. Brigham Hospital, Boston, Massachusetts 02120

It has been apparent for many years that macrophages play a very important part in resistance to many infections (1–4). These cells ingest and dispose of a variety of organisms; when obtained from recently immunized animals, they exhibit an enhanced ability to do this and have been termed "activated" (4). More recent studies have shown that *in vivo* activation of macrophages requires the interaction of specifically sensitized T lymphocytes with the appropriate antigenic agent (5, 6). Once activated, the macrophages may exhibit a certain degree of nonspecific antimicrobial activity.

How does the interaction of lymphocytes with antigen lead to the activation of macrophages? The events that occur *in vivo* are not known. *In vitro* studies on the mechanism of cellular hypersensitivity and immunity, however, have shown that such stimulated lymphocytes produce a number of soluble mediators several of which affect macrophages (7–12). The following will be a brief review of studies we have carried out to determine whether such lymphocyte mediators "activate" macrophages *in vitro.*

Most of these studies were carried out using guinea pig cells. Casein-induced peritoneal exudates were plated on Petri dishes, and monolayers of adherent cells, predominantly macrophages, were obtained. (An irritant is required as only a few macrophages are obtainable from the peritoneal cavity when none is used, and those survive very poorly in culture.) The macrophage monolayers were incubated for varing periods of time in tissue culture medium containing lymphocyte mediators. The mediators were produced by incubating lymph node lymphocytes from guinea pigs sensitized with o-chlorobenzoyl bovine γ-globulin (OCB–BGG) for 24 hr. Control cultures were not stimulated by antigen; after incubation, the cells were removed by centrifugation and antigen was added to the control supernatant. In some studies, lymphocytes were stimulated by the mitogen concanavalin A instead of antigen. In most experiments described, the supernatants were chromatographed on Sephadex G-100 columns and fractions rich in migration inhibitory factor (MIF) and its control counterpart were used (13, 14).

ALTERED MACROPHAGE FUNCTION

Macrophages incubated in MIF-rich Sephadex G-100 fractions were found by Nathan, Karnovsky, and David (15) to exhibit a number of morphologic, metabolic, and functional changes after 3 days of culture. These include an enhanced ability to adhere to the culture dish, increased ruffled membrane motility, and spreading and enhancement in both the rate and extent of phagocytosis of dead mycobacteria. After 3 days the macrophages incubated in MIF-rich fractions also showed a fourfold increase in glucose carbon-1 oxidation through the hexose monophosphate shunt when compared to cultures incubated with control fractions (15). Similar findings have been seen with human cells; Rocklin (16) recently demonstrated that human blood monocytes, when cultured with human MIF-rich fractions for 3 days, exhibited an increase in both adherence and glucose carbon-1 oxidation.

CHARACTERIZATION OF MACROPHAGE ACTIVATING FACTOR

The guinea pig activating factor was eluted from Sephadex G-100 with molecules between 68,000 and 35,000 daltons with peak activity between 55,000 and 35,000 (17). This is the same fraction containing peak activity of guinea pig MIF, chemotactic factor for macrophages, and lymphotoxin (13, 10, 18). Further studies showed that the active fractions' ability to enhance both cell adherence and glucose oxidation was destroyed by incubation with neuraminidase, a procedure which also destroys guinea pig MIF but does not affect chemotactic factor or lymphotoxin (18–20). This finding, along with the observation that the macrophage activating factor after isopycnic centrifugation in CsCl is recovered in a band with a buoyant density slightly greater than albumin, as is MIF but not the other two mediators, indicates that with the present techniques it is indistinguishable from MIF and in all probability the same material (19).

KINETICS OF ACTIVATION

It is not clear why it takes several days for the changes in the macrophages to become manifest. If the MIF-rich fractions are removed in the last 24 hr, no change is seen. On the other hand, MIF-rich fractions need only be present the last 24 hr for increased cell adherence to occur, and only the last 48 hr for the enhancement of glucose oxidation. The data suggest that the 3-day period required by macrophages to manifest a response to the activating factor consists of two stages. In the first, requiring 1 to 2 days, the macrophages are refractory to the influence of the activating factor but undergo changes that render them receptive. In the second, they respond to activating factor with increased adherence and glucose oxidation (17). More about this latent period is discussed below.

MACROPHAGE LYSOSOMAL ENZYMES

In addition to the changes described above, macrophages incubated in MIF-rich fractions also show changes in lysosomal enzyme content and in activity of certain plasma membrane enzymes.

Remold and Mednis (21) measured the activity of acid phosphatase, cathepsin D, and β-glucuronidase in macrophage monolayers after 0, 24, 48, and 72 hr of incubation in MIF-rich and control fractions. Although no differences were observed during the first 2 days, there was a consistent decrease in the specific activity of these three enzymes (measured as activity/cell DNA) in the MIF-treated cultures compared to control was found on the third day (21). Further, the loss of enzyme activity could not be readily explained. No corresponding increase in enzyme activity was found in the supernatant fluid. The serum used did not inhibit enzyme activity. Testing of macrophage homogenates kept at 37°C for 3 days showed that the enzymes were stable under these conditions.

The loss of these three lysosomal enzymes does not correlate with any changes in the number of lysosomal granules when these are assessed using acridine orange. With this technique, no significant difference could be seen between the number of granules in macrophages treated with MIF-rich or control fractions. On the other hand, preliminary electron microscopic studies carried out with Dr. Morris Karnovsky showed that there were more granules and vacuoles in MIF-rich treated macrophages than control after 3 days of incubation.

Thus, an explanation for the decrease in the lysosomal enzyme activity observed remains to be found. Possibly, there is a decrease in lysosomal enzyme synthesis in favor of the synthesis of other substances. The decrease in lysosomal enzyme activity that occurs when macrophages are activated by the addition of lymphocytes and antigen directly to the macrophage monolayer is discussed below.

MACROPHAGE ADENYLATE CYCLASE

The activity of this plasma membrane bound enzyme was studied by Remold-O'Donnell and Remold. Specific adenylate cyclase activity was increased at 24 and 48 hr relative to zero-time and decreased at 72 hr in all cultures. Of note, at 24 and 48 hr, the specific activity of adenylate cyclase was 30% greater in macrophages incubated with MIF-rich fractions than in controls (22, 23). Indomethacin (3×10^{-6}M) reduced this difference significantly suggesting a role for prostaglandins (22). The addition of MIF-rich fractions to macrophage homogenates did not increase adenylate cyclase activity. Thus, the action of MIF-rich fractions on adenylate cyclase requires prolonged incubation with intact cells. The change in activity of this enzyme precedes other changes observed in mediator-activated macrophages.

ENHANCED MACROPHAGE BACTERIOSTASIS

Having found that MIF-rich fractions altered the function of normal macrophages in a number of ways, studies were carried out to determine if macrophages activated in this manner would also demonstrate an enhanced yet nonspecific capacity to handle microorganisms such as *Listeria monocytogenes.* The problems encountered in the preliminary studies are discussed elsewhere (24, 25). Fowles et al. found that macrophages incubated for 3 days in MIF-rich fractions exhibited a two- to 10-fold enhanced bacteriostasis compared to controls (25). Further experiments showed that this enhancement was attributable to intrinsic changes in the macrophages and not simply a consequence of the number of macrophages present in the monolayer. Macrophages incubated for only 24 hr with MIF-rich fractions exhibited enhanced bacteriostasis only in one-fourth of the experiments. Others have reported that supernatants from either stimulated lymphoid cells, mixed lymphocyte cultures, or mixed stimulated spleen cells and macrophage cultures enhance resistance to a number of organisms (26–28). A comparison of bacteriostasis by mediator-activated macrophages with macrophage activation by direct contact with lymphocytes and antigen is made below.

TUMOR KILLING BY MACROPHAGES ACTIVATED BY LYMPHOCYTE MEDIATORS

The tumoricidal capacity of macrophages activated by lymphocyte mediators was studied in a syngeneic strain 2 guinea pig tumor system by Piessens et al. (29). Monolayers of normal strain 2 macrophages were incubated for 3 days in unfractionated MIF-rich and control supernatants from OCB–BGG stimulated guinea pig lymphocytes. Tumor cells labeled with ^{3}H-thymidine were then added and cytotoxicity determined after 24 hr of cocultivation by comparing the number of adherent tumor cells remaining in dishes containing similar numbers of activated and control macrophages. The macrophages, which had been preincubated in MIF-rich supernatants were consistently toxic for Line 1 hepatoma cells and for MCA-fibrosarcoma. On the other hand, they did not kill either syngeneic fibroblasts or kidney cells. Tumor cells adhered equally well to both activated and control macrophages when measured after just 2 hr of cocultivation. Activation could be produced by supernatants devoid of lymphotoxin, suggesting that the effect was not due to this mediator adsorbed to macrophages.

The observation that macrophages activated by lymphocyte mediators kill syngeneic tumor cells but not normal cells is consistent with the previous findings of Hibbs et al. (30, 31), who reported that activated macrophages obtained from mice immunized with a number of different microorganisms kill transformed cells but not their normal counterparts, whereas macrophages from nonimmunized mice kill neither cell type.

Since activated macrophages exhibit certain membrane changes from normal macrophages, such as increased ruffled membrane movement, increased spreading, and increased adenylate cyclase activity, as well as other changes (32, 33), it is tempting to speculate that membrane alterations possibly analogous to those found between normal and transformed cells might be present between normal and activated macrophages. Such surface changes might lead activated macrophages to recognize or have a greater affinity for the altered tumor cell membrane leading to interaction and subsequent killing of the tumor cell.

MACROPHAGES ACTIVATED BY CULTURE DIRECTLY WITH LYMPHOCYTES AND ANTIGEN

So far, we have discussed the *in vitro* alteration of macrophage function by lymphocyte mediators, changes which become manifest after 2 to 3 days of culture (changes in adenylate cyclase occur after 24 hr). Can macrophages be activated *in vitro,* as a result of an immunologic stimulus, in a shorter time period? They can when sensitized lymphocytes and antigen are added to macrophages directly.

In their experiments on cellular immunity, Simon and Sheagren first took peritoneal exudates from PPD- or BGG-sensitized guinea pigs (exudates which contained *both* sensitized lymphocytes and macrophages) and incubated them directly with specific antigen for 24 hr. The resultant monolayers of macrophages, when washed and infected with *Listeria monocytogenes,* were bactericidal for the bacteria compared to cultures which had been preincubated without antigen (34). In subsequent experiments, sensitive lymphoctyes obtained from lymph nodes (24, 35) or peritoneal exudates (36) when added to normal macrophages with antigen resulted in macrophage monolayers which exhibited enhanced bactericidal capacity for *Listeria.* The lymphocytes involved in this *in vitro* reaction have recently been shown to be T lymphocytes (37).

In addition to exhibiting enhanced bactericidal activity at 24 hr, such lymphocyte-activated macrophages also exhibit some enhanced adherence and, of special interest, a decrease in the activity of the three lysosomal enzymes which are usually decreased only after 3 days when MIF-rich fractions are used.

The differences between activation of macrophages by the direct presence of lymphocytes and antigen and that brought about by lymphocyte mediators are the following. First, in the presence of lymphocytes and antigen, macrophages show enhanced bactericidal activity, some increased cell adherence, and a decrease in lysosomal enzymes after 24 hr of incubation. The latent period is thus shortened and we have preliminary evidence that it can be shortened even further. Second, the degree of bactericidal activity is greater than the bacteriostasis manifested by macrophages activated by lymphocyte mediators alone. The unexpected finding of enhanced bactericidal activity in the face of lowered lysosomal enzyme activity in this instance is as mysterious as in that previously described.

In conclusion, macrophages can be activated by lymphocyte mediators. It is not known why lymphocytes themselves have a greater influence on macrophages than their mediators. They may produce essential factors which are more labile than mediators such as MIF. Alternatively, direct contact between the lymphocyte and macrophage may be required for more effective bactericidal activity in some cases. Anatomic interaction between lymphocytes and macrophages has been documented (38–42) and further work is required to document whether such a mechanism is operative in enhancement of macrophage function vis-à-vis activation.

ACKNOWLEDGMENTS

The work reported in this chapter was supported in part by U.S. Public Health Service grants AI 07685–09 and AI 10921–02.

REFERENCES

1. Metchnikoff, E.: *Immunity in Infective Diseases.* F. G. Binnie, translator, Cambridge University Press, Londòn, England. 1905.
2. Lurie, M. B.: *Resistance to Tuberculosis: Experimental Studies in Native and Acquired Defensive Mechanisms.* Harvard University Press, Cambridge. 1964.
3. Suter, E., and Ramseier, H.: Cellular reactions in infection. *Adv. Immunol.* 4:117, 1964.
4. Mackaness, G. B.: The immunological basis of acquired cellular resistance. *J. Exp. Med.* 120:105, 1964.
5. Mackaness, G. B.: The influence of immunologically committed lymphoid cells on macrophage activity *in vitro. J. Exp. Med.* 129:973, 1969.
6. Lane, F. C., and Unanue, E. R.: Requirement of thymus T lymphocytes for resistance in Listeriosis. *J. Exp. Med.* 135:1104, 1972.
7. David, J. R.: Delayed hypersensitivity *in vitro:* Its mediation by cell-free substances formed by lymphoid cell-antigen interaction. *Proc. Natl. Acad. Sci.* 56:72, 1966.
8. Bloom, B. R., and Bennett, B.: Mechanism of a reaction *in vitro* associated with delayed-type hypersensitivity. *Science* 153:80, 1966.
9. Dumonde, D. C., Wolstencroft, R. A., Panayi G. S., Matthew, M., Morley, J., and Howson, W. T.: "Lymphokines." Non-antibody mediators of cellular immunity generated by lymphocyte activation. *Nature* 224:38, 1969.
10. Ward, P. A., Remold, H. G., and David, J. R.: The production by antigen-stimulated lymphocytes of a leucotactic factor distinct from migration inhibitory factor. *Cell. Immunol.* 2:162, 1970.
11. Lolekha, S., Dray, S., and Gotoff, S. P.: Macrophage aggregation *in vitro:* A correlate of delayed hypersensitivity. *J. Immunol.* 104:296, 1970.
12. David, J. R., and David, R. A.: Cellular hypersensitivity and immunity: Inhibition of macrophage migration and the lymphocyte mediators. In *Progress in Allergy,* P., Kallos, Waksman, B. H., and de Weck, A. (eds): Vol. 16, S. Karger, Basel, p. 300. 1972.
13. Remold, H. G., Katz, A. B., Haber, E., and David, J. R.: Studies on migration inhibitory factor (MIF): Recovery of MIF activity after purification by gel filtration and disc electrophoresis. *Cell. Immunol.* 1:133, 1970.
14. Remold, H. G., David, R. A., and David, J. R.: Characterization of migration inhibitory factor (MIF) from guinea pig lymphocytes stimulated with concanavalin A. *J. Immunol.* 190:578, 1972.
15. Nathan, C. F., Karnovsky, M. L., and David, J. R.: Alterations of macrophage functions by mediators from lymphocytes. *J. Exp. Med.* 133:1356, 1971.
16. Rocklin, R. E., Winston, C. T., and David, J. R.: Activation of human blood monocytes by products of sensitized lymphocytes. *J. Clin. Invest.* 53:559, 1974.
17. Nathan, C. F., Remold, H. G., and David, J. R.: Characterization of a lymphocyte factor which alters macrophage functions. *J. Exp. Med.* 137:275, 1973.
18. Coyne, J. A., Remold, H. G., Rosenberg, S. A., and David, J. R.: Guinea pig lymphotoxin (LT). II. Physicochemical properties of LT produced by lymphocytes stimulated with antigen or concanavalin A: Its differentiation from migration inhibitory factor (MIF). *J. Immunol.* 110:1630, 1973.
19. Remold, H. G., and David, J. R.: Further studies on migration inhibitory factor (MIF): Evidence for its glycoprotein nature. *J. Immunol.* 107:1090, 1971.
20. David, J. R.: Mediators produced by sensitized lymphocytes. *Fed. Proc.* 30:1730, 1971.

21. Remold, H. G., and Mednis, A.: Alterations of macrophage lysosomal enzyme levels induced by MIF-rich supernatants from lymphocytes. *Fed. Proc. (Abstr.)* 31:753, 1972.
22. Remold-O'Donnell, E., and Remold, H. G.: Changes in macrophage adenylate cyclase (AC) activity induced by lymphocyte mediators. *Fed. Proc. (Abstr.)* 32:878, 1973.
23. Remold-O'Donnell, E., and Remold, H. G.: The enhancement of macrophage adenylate cyclase by products of stimulated lymphocytes. *J. Biol. Chem.* 249:362, 1974.
24. Leibowitch, J. L., and David, J. R.: Lymphocyte-macrophage interaction in resistance to *Listeria monocytogenes. Ann. Immunol.* 124C:441, 1973.
25. Fowles, R. E., Fajardo, I. M., Leibowitch, J. L., and David, J. R.: The enhancement of macrophage bacteriostasis by products of activated lymphocytes. *J. Exp. Med.* 138:952, 1973.
26. Patterson, R. J., and Youmans, G. P.: Demonstration in tissue culture of lymphocyte mediated immunity to tuberculosis. *Infect. Immun.* 1:600, 1970.
27. Godal, T., Rees, R. J. W., and Lamvik, J. O.: Lymphocyte-mediated modification of blood-derived macrophage function *in vitro;* Inhibition of growth of intracellular mycobacteria with lymphokines. *Clin. Exp. Immunol.* 8:625, 1971.
28. Krahenbuhl, J. L., and Remington, J. S.: *In vitro* induction of nonspecific resistance in macrophages by specifically sensitized lymphocytes. *Infect. Immun.* 4:337, 1971.
29. Piessens, W. F., Churchill, W. H., and David, J. R.: Nonspecific tumor killing by macrophages activated *in vitro* with lymphocyte mediators *Fed. Proc. (Abstr.)* 33:781, 1974.
30. Hibbs, J. B., Lambert, L. H., and Remington, J. W.: Control of carcinogenesis: A possible role for activated macrophages. *Science* 177:998, 1972.
31. Hibbs, J. B.: Activated macrophage nonimmunologic recognition: Target cell factors related to contact inhibition. *Science* 180:868, 1972.
32. Dvorak, A. M., Hammond, M. E., Dvorak, H. F., and Karnovsky, M. J.: Loss of cell surface material from peritoneal exudate cells associated with lymphocyte mediated inhibition of macrophage migration from capillary tubes. *Lab. Invest.* 27:561, 1972.
33. Hammond, M. E., and Dvorak, H. F.: Antigen-induced stimulation of glucosamine incorporation by guinea pig peritoneal macrophages in delayed hypersensitivity. *J. Exp. Med.* 136:1518, 1972.
34. Simon, H. B., and Sheagren, J. N.: Cellular immunity *in vitro. J. Exp. Med.* 133:1377, 1971.
35. Leibowitch, J., and David, J. R.: Lymphocyte-macrophage interaction in resistance to *Listeria monocytogenes. Fed. Proc. (Abstr.)* 31:610, 1972.
36. Simon, H. B., and Sheagren, J. N.: Enhancement of macrophage bactericidal capacity by antigenically stimulated immune lymphocytes. *Cell. Immunol.* 4:163, 1972.
37. Krahenbuhl, J. L., Rosenberg, L. T., and Remington, J. S.: The role of thymus-derived lymphocytes in the *in vitro* activation of macrophages to kill *Listeria* monocytogenes. *J. Immunol.* 111:992, 1973.
38. Sharp, J. A., and Burwell, R. G.: Interaction ("Peripolesis") of macrophages and lymphocytes after skin homografting or challenge with soluble antigens. *Nature* 188:474, 1960.
39. Schoenberg, M. D., Mumaw, V. R., Moore, R. D., and Weisberger, A. S.: Cytoplasmic interaction between macrophages and lymphocytic cells in antibody synthesis. *Science* 143:964, 1964.
40. McFarland, W., Heilman, D. H., and Moorhead, J. F.: Functional anatomy of the lymphocyte in immunological reactions *in vitro. J. Exp. Med.* 124:851, 1966.
41. Salvin, S. B., Sell, S., and Nishio, J.: Activity *in vitro* of lymphocytes and macrophages in delayed hypersensitivity. *J. Immunol.* 107:655, 1971.
42. Lipsky, P. E., and Rosenthal, A. S.: Macrophage-lymphocyte interaction. I. Characteristics of the antigen-independent-binding of guinea pig thymocytes and lymphocytes to syngeneic macrophages. *J. Exp. Med.* 138:900, 1973.

DISCUSSION

Bellanti: Does this mediator enhance phagocytosis by polymorphonuclear cells?

David: Dr. Rocklin is about to carry out studies to answer this.

Ward: In your experiments where you have added lymphocytes to the macrophages and induced an increase in the bactericidal activity, do the sensitized lymphocytes *per se* have any ability to do this?

David: No they don't. They are killed when bacteria are added. Further, the mediator-rich fractions do not kill *Listeria* either.

Ward: One of your figures implied (but I don't think you showed any data) that, if lymphoid cells are nonspecifically stimulated with Con A, increased bactericidal activity develops.

David: Yes. You can produce a mediator by stimulation with Con A which activates macrophages to exhibit enhanced bacteriostasis.

Ward: Can you induce the same sort of activity by incubating macrophages with MIF from a mixed lymphocyte culture?

David: Godal et al. reported that media obtained from mixed leukocyte cultures caused macrophage monolayers to inhibit growth of leprosy bacilli; however, the cultures also caused a marked proliferation of the macrophages, and it is difficult to determine whether or not the results are secondary to the increased number of macrophages *per se.*

Kirkpatrick: Can you improve the killing of organisms by MIF-treated macrophages by adding nonimmune lymphocytes?

David: We tried that and it didn't, but we haven't done this in inbred animals and it is possible that receptors such as those described by Lipsky and Rosenthal are involved.

Snyderman: Art Dannenberg did some elegant studies *in vivo* in terms of macrophages and protection against tuberculosis and one *sine qua non* of protection was macrophages with increased lysosomal enzyme content. I wonder how you reconcile your differences.

When you compare the MIF supernatant to control, is it low in MIF because it is possible there is another factor that enhances lysosomal enzymes?

David: The control cultures are not usually very different than media alone. The experiments show that when comparing lysosomal enzymes in MIF compared to control, they are lower at 3 days when MIF-rich supernatants are used, but everything seems speeded up when lymphocytes and antigen are present—then the enzymes are lower at 24 hours. So far, we haven't a good explanation for this. Dr. Dannenberg found differences in lysosomal enzymes in macrophages whether they were at the periphery or more central to the tubercle, but this doesn't explain the findings. The above *in vitro* studies certainly dissociate the quantity of the three lysosomal enzymes studied in the macrophage and the cells' ability to kill *Listeria.*

Spitznagel: This has an interesting correlation with some work that Philip Darcy Hart did a number of years ago. He was studying the protuberculous and antituberculous effects of detergents with macrophages, and to his surprise it turned out that the lysosomal enzymes were reduced in the macrophages that had been rendered more resistant to tubercle bacilli by antituberculous detergent. It was supposed to turn out the other way around.

Karnovsky: Are the guinea pig cells you start with elicited cells and do they incubate for 3 or 4 days?

David: They are elicited by casein and incubated *in vitro* for 1 to 3 days.

Karnovsky: One of the things that bothers me is that when one looks at the metabolism of immediately obtained, elicited cells, it is very high by comparison with that of peritoneal macrophages that you get out by simple washing. I am talking about the mouse, and I wonder if the cells you get from the guinea pigs aren't already activated. If so, they must go through some phase of declining activity while you incubate them, and then the MIF jacks them up again.

David: I can comment, for instance, on glucose oxidation. There is an absolute increase per cell at 3 days as compared to what is present per cell at zero time. You could say that we have selected a certain population to account for this increase. I realize that the problem of using an irritant is that one probably activates some cells. However, one just does not get enough cells that are any good at all if we do not use an irritant in the guinea pig. Further, *in vivo,* the macrophages are attracted to the site of inflammation and in a certain sense one may have started to activate them just by getting them to the site. We are now carrying out studies in mice; with them one doesn't have to use an irritant.

Karnovsky: I noticed in the neuraminidase experiments that the control fractions were considerably diminished in their activity by neuraminidase. This is shown, if I am not mistaken, in the data in which you had MIF-treated cells and those untreated with neuraminidase, control fractions treated and untreated, and MEM. I thought the control fractions on treatment with neuraminidase showed a considerable drop in activity. What is that due to?

David: I hadn't noticed that, but certainly the control fractions do something when compared to tissue culture media in all of these experiments, and it is very possible there may be a small amount of mediator in them.

Karnovsky: And lastly, the cellular cyclic AMP you showed is raised.

David: No, adenylate cyclase.

Karnovsky: I suppose one can't make the assumption that the cyclic AMP is raised?

David: No.

Root: I wonder if you had some insight into the mechanism of enhanced killing by the MIF. Is it oxygen dependent?

David: I don't have any information in terms of how these macrophages kill.

Root: The suggestion would be, if the shunt is increased, H_2O_2 production is increased. Do you have any more direct measurements of H_2O_2 production and its relationships to stimulation by MIF?

David: No.

Gallin: You mentioned MIF increased membrane ruffling. Have you ever looked at the effect of MIF on the random locomotion of macrophages in a Boyden chamber?

David: No. We haven't done studies with large pore filters. You mean using large pore micropore filters?

Gallin: Yes.

David: The macrophages, after several days in MIF, do demonstrate increased motility. Further, examination of time-lapse motion pictures shows an increased motility in cultures that have been incubated 3 days in MIF compared to normal. Macrophages also escape the inhibition from MIF in capillary tubes: in the last 24 hours of a 3-day period they migrate faster.

Hill: Have you looked at the effect of enzyme production on bacteriostatic activity?

David: No.

Cohn: In your experiments in which there is an increase in DNA in the cultures I take it you have free-floating cells in the medium.

David: Yes, but the DNA is all recovered from the monolayers.

Cohn: So there are cells that are continuously attaching to the cover with time?

David: And coming off.

Cohn: You have a net increase?

David: No, you have a decrease in cells, but less decrease in the cultures that contain MIF than in control cultures. In other words, you lose one-half the cells with MIF, and you lose much more with control, or in tissue culture media alone. You don't have the same situation as in a mouse culture where you can keep a steady state. The guinea pig macrophages don't last well in culture and there is a steady decrease in the cells. But the loss is less when MIF is present. In the 3 days observed, there have never been more cells present after 24 hours than were present at zero time.

Bellanti: With regard to adenyl cyclase stimulation, your data suggest that MIF would have a membrane effect, if I understand the data correctly.

David: Yes.

Cohn: Have you had an opportunity to look at agents that have a postmembrane effect such as prostaglandins or histamine, or have you looked at beta blockers, propanolol?

David: William Koopman showed that a number of drugs that increased intracellular cyclic AMP prevented the inhibition of migration of macrophages by MIF. Such drugs have not been used to determine their effect on the more prolonged macrophage activation by MIF-rich mediators in 3 day-cultures.

Bellanti: Will migration increase?

David: There was not a significant increase in migration by the drugs that elevated intracellular cyclic AMP. Terry Higgins has carried out studies to determine if MIF might decrease macrophage cyclic AMP. So far, it does not appear to do so. Drs. Barry Bloom and Chris Henney have also shown that cholera toxin will affect macrophages so that they no longer respond to MIF.

Blaese: Does lipopolysaccharide (LPS) induce MIF production?

David: I don't know.

Snyderman: We will be presenting some data concerning that later.

I would like to make one comment on monocyte chemotactic responsiveness. We looked at the prostaglandin series and drugs that affect cyclic AMP and found no good correlation between levels and monocyte responsiveness. But we found that prostaglandin E-2 enhanced responsiveness and no other did. It also increased the cyclic AMP but it didn't seem to be a direct effect.

I wanted to ask you one question. You mentioned that the MIF fractions increase phagocytosis. . . .

David: In the experiments using dead microbacteria, we were able to measure both the rate and extent of phagocytosis. This is possible only when one can add an excess of antigen. It is not possible to add an excess of antigen when one is using viable *Listeria* since the large amounts of *Listeria* required simply wipe out the monolayer. So, under these circumstances, one cannot actually measure either the rate or extent of phagocytosis. In experiments on comparative bactericidal activity of macrophages, it is very important that the experimental and control monolayers contain an equal amount of macrophages; otherwise, the observations may be simply the result of the number of macrophages present rather than an enhanced intrinsic macrophage capability of handling the microorganism.

Hirsch: Could you say a little about the time course of release of the mediator following antigenic stimulation in the lymphocyte? And the time course of the activation of the macrophage by the mediator?

David: MIF can be detected in a supernatant 4 to 6 hours following lymphocyte stimulation. However, it can be detected earlier in the direct assay. When the migration of peritoneal exudate cells from sensitive guinea pigs is observed, they are sometimes seen to have migrated in 1 to 2 hours in the control cultures. Even at this time, the cultures in which antigen is present are inhibited; it would appear that the lymphocytes start to produce MIF very early. As concerns the time course of activation of macrophages by mediators, we do not usually see changes in enhanced adherence until 48 to 72 hours. Adenylate cyclase activity is enhanced at 24 to 48 hours. Glucose oxidation and bacteriostasis are manifested at 72 hours, although the latter is occasionally seen after 24 hours. The presence of lymphocytes accelerates the rate and extent of activation considerably. Nathan has shown that it is not necessary to have MIF present throughout the 3-day culture. For example, if the macrophages are cultured in medium for 2 days and the MIF is added, enhanced adherence is seen in 24 hours. The macrophages just have to be cultured for 3 days. I am pretty sure that this latent period can be shortened and may be due to some cultural artifact. Certainly, if it took 3 days for activation *in vivo,* it would not be of much use.

The Phagocytic Cell in Host Resistance, edited
by Joseph A. Bellanti and Delbert H. Dayton.
Raven Press, New York © 1975.

The Chemotactic Activity of Dialyzable Transfer Factor: II. Further Characterization of the Activity *In Vivo* and *In Vitro*

Charles H. Kirkpatrick and John I. Gallin

Laboratory of Clinical Investigation, National Institute of Allergy and Infectious Diseases, National Institutes of Health, Bethesda, Maryland 20014

The saga of "transfer factor" began almost 20 years ago when Lawrence (1) reported that it was possible to transfer delayed-type hypersensitivity from skin test positive donors to nonresponsive recipients with nonviable, disrupted blood leukocytes. This observation contrasted sharply with the animal experiments in which successful passive transfer required adequate numbers of viable lymphocytes from strongly reactive donors (2, 3). Passive transfer with transfer factor appeared to be specific for cutaneous reactivities possessed by the donors (4) and the passively acquired responses persisted for many months (5). During the ensuing years, Lawrence and his co-workers reported that the active component of transfer factor was not degraded by treatment of the lysates with pancreatic ribonuclease, deoxyribonuclease, or trypsin (4). Perhaps the most striking observation was the discovery that the skin test-converting property of transfer factor was dialyzable and therefore probably of low molecular weight (6).

It was difficult to propose mechanisms through which molecules with molecular weights of 10,000 daltons or less could provide the information required for recognition of numerous antigens or induction of a large number of specific immune responses. Alternative models suggested that transfer factor might function through less specific pathways, perhaps by amplifying weak, but preexisting, cell-mediated immunity, by acting as an adjuvant, or by participating in formation of highly immunogenic antigen-RNA complexes. Even now the chemical nature of transfer factor remains uncertain, and the controversy over specific and nonspecific properties of transfer factor has not been resolved (7).

Our studies of possible mechanisms of action of transfer factor have revealed that dialyzable transfer factor preparations contain a potent chemotactic substance which is apparently different from previously described chemotactic molecules (8). The material is strongly chemotactic for polymorphonuclear leukocytes but somewhat less chemotactic for mononuclear cells.

In this chapter we review the current status of our studies of the chemotactic activity in dialyzable transfer factor preparations and describe *in vivo* assays for both chemotactic and transfer factor activities in rhesus monkeys.

METHODS AND MATERIALS

Preparation of Transfer Factor

The transfer factor for these experiments was prepared from peripheral blood leukocytes obtained from healthy donors by leukapheresis (9). Ten separate preparations have been studied. The cell suspensions usually contained 80 to 85% lymphocytes, 10 to 20% monocytes, 0 to 5% polymorphonuclear leukocytes, and 0 to 3% basophils.

To determine the cell of origin of the transfer factor and chemotactic activities, leukocyte suspensions are fractionated by the Hypaque-Ficoll technique (10). The bouyant cells contained lymphocytes and monocytes and less than 5% granulocytes. The granulocytes were then separated from the granulocyte-erythrocyte pellet by dextran sedimentation (11), and residual erythrocytes were removed by lysis with Tris-buffered 0.155 M ammonium chloride, pH 7.4. The resulting cells contained more than 95% granulocytes.

Peripheral blood leukocytes were also obtained from two patients with the Sezary syndrome (12) when their peripheral white counts were in excess of 150,000 per mm^3; 98 to 100% of the circulating cells were lymphocytes. The circulating neoplastic cells in this desease have many properties of T lymphocytes (13, 14).

To prepare transfer factor the leukocytes were washed three times with 0.0067 M phosphate-buffered 0.85% saline (PBS) and then disrupted by multiple cycles of freezing at −70°C and thawing at 37°C. The lysates were digested with deoxyribonuclease for 60 min at 37°C and then dialyzed against distilled water for 48 hr at 4°C. The dialysates were lyophilized and then reconstituted in a volume of distilled water so that the extract from 3×10^8 lymphocytes was contained in 1.0 ml (15). Transfer factor was sterilized by Millipore filtration and stored at −30°C. A "reagent blank" was prepared by carrying PBS through the entire procedure including freeze-thawing, enzymatic digestion, dialysis, lyophilization, and reconstitution.

Preparation of Chemotactic Lymphokine

This material (16) was prepared by incubating peripheral blood lymphocytes from healthy donors in serum-free media as described previously (15). The antigens employed in the stimulated cultures were candida, streptokinase-streptodornase (SK–SD), and tuberculin. After 24 hr of incubation at 37°C in an atmosphere of 5% CO_2–95% air, the supernatant fluids were collected, dialyzed against distilled water, lyophilized, and stored at −30°C. For assays of chemotactic activity, the residues were reconstituted to one-half of their original volumes with PBS. Reagent controls were culture fluids to which antigens were added after the cells were removed.

Preparation of C5a

Endotoxin-treated human serum was passed through Sephadex G-75 to partially purify the chemotactic cleavage product of C5, C5a (17). This material was used in a concentration of 10 μg of protein per ml as a reference chemotactic stimulus.

In Vitro Assay of Chemotactic Activity

Granulocyte chemotaxis was measured by the chromium-51 (^{51}Cr, Amersham-Searle, Arlington Heights, Illinois) radioassay of Gallin, Clark, and Kimball (18). For this assay ^{51}Cr-labeled granulocytes were placed in the upper compartment of a double micropore filter (Millipore Corp., Bedford, Massachusetts) chemotactic chamber; the chemotactic stimulus was in the lower compartment. After incubation, the number of granulocytes traversing the upper filter and migrating into the lower filter was proportional to the radioactivity incorporated into the lower filter. After adjusting for variable incorporation of ^{51}Cr by the leukocytes, chemotaxis is expressed as corrected counts per minute lower filter (cor cpm LF). In most experiments the chemotactic stimulus was 100 μl of dialyzable transfer factor diluted to 2.0 ml in Hank's balanced salt solution.

Mononuclear cell chemotaxis was measured by the morphologic assay of Snyderman et al. (19). Mononuclear cells (Hypaque-Ficoll) were placed in the upper compartment of the chemotactic chamber. The upper and lower compartments were separated by a 5.0 μm polycarbonate filter (Nucleopore, Wallabs, Inc., San Rafael, California). After incubation the filter was removed, rinsed in saline, fixed in methanol, and stained as previously described (11). Chemotaxis was expressed as the mean number of cells per high power field that migrated to the lower surface of the filter.

In Vivo Assay of Chemotactic Activity

Fifty and 100 μl of dialyzable transfer factor and 100 μl of reagent blank were injected intradermally into multiple sites on the chest and anterior abdominal walls of rhesus monkeys. With the animals under phencyclidine anesthesia, full thickness punch biopsies were taken from the injection sites and from an uninjected site at 2, 5, and 24 hr. The tissues were fixed in 10% buffered neutral formalin, sectioned at 3 to 4 μm, and stained with hematoxylin and eosin or giemsa. The intensity of the inflammatory responses was scored as the mean number of neutrophils, mononuclear cells, and connective tissue and vascular endothelial cells in 10 oil immersion fields.

Assessment of Delayed Hypersensitivity

The delayed cutaneous hypersensitivity responses of the cell donors were evaluated with intradermal skin tests with intermediate strength tuberculin PPD,

Candida albicans, SK–SD, trichophytin, and mumps (15). The test doses were contained in 0.1 ml and the responses were assessed at 24 hr; positive reactions produced indurations of 0.5 cm or greater.

Skin test-converting activities of the transfer factor preparations were assessed in patients with chronic candidiasis and cellular immune deficiency as described elsewhere (15). To study transfer factor activity in rhesus monkeys, either whole dialyzable transfer factor or sterile fractions from the gel filtration experiments were injected subcutaneously. Five to 7 days later intradermal skin tests were placed on the anterior chest. Full-thickness biopsies of the test sites were taken from the anesthetized animals 24 hr later.

Properties of Transfer Factor

Gel filtration experiments employed Sephadex G-25 and 0.04 M phosphate-buffered saline, pH 7.4. Column dimensions were either 2.5 × 40 cm or 5.0 × 90 cm.

Protein determinations used the method of Lowry et al. (20), and RNA was measured with the orcinol test (21) with a yeast RNA standard. Goat antisera to the third and fifth components of human complement were purchased from Meloy Laboratories, Springfield, Virginia.

Chemotactic activity in the effluent fractions was assayed with the *in vitro* techniques described above. For assays of transfer factor activity, column fractions were pooled according to the optical density profiles, lyophilized, reconstituted in a small volume of distilled water, and sterilized by Millipore filtration. Column fractions were injected subcutaneously into rhesus monkeys. Skin testing was conducted 5 to 7 days later as described above.

RESULTS

In Vitro Chemotactic Activity of Dialyzable Transfer Factor

As shown in Fig. 1, each of the 10 preparations of transfer factor from normal leukocytes was strongly chemotactic for granulocytes. The increases in chemotaxis ranged from 6.3 to 16.6 times the reagent blank. Ten separate preparations of C5a produced approximately 12-fold increases in chemotactic activities. The reagent blank was not stimulatory and therefore excluded the possibility that the chemotactic activity was derived from the reagents or the dialysis membranes.

Experiments with lysates prepared from purified cell populations showed that all of the chemotactic activity was in the lymphocyte-monocyte fraction; the dialyzed granulocyte lysates were inactive. In contrast to the findings with normal lymphocytes, the T cell rich lymphocytes from patients with the Sezary syndrome were poor sources of chemotactic activity.

The possibility that the chemotactic activity in transfer factor preparations was

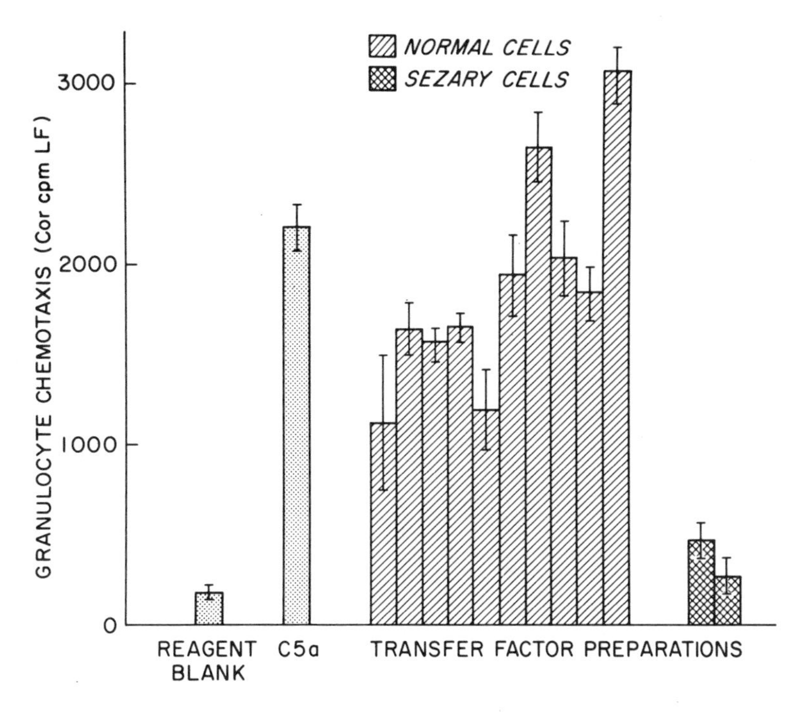

FIG. 1. Comparison of *in vitro* granulocyte chemotactic activities of C5a and dialyzable transfer factor from normal leukocytes and cells from patients with Sezary's syndrome. Note that normal cell dialysates possessed strong chemotactic activity whereas the Sezary cells were poor sources of chemotactic factor.

merely due to increased random motility was ruled out by experiments in which transfer factor was present in both compartments of the chemotactic chamber. Addition of only 5 μl of dialysate to the upper chamber reduced the chemotactic response by 35%.

Dialyzable transfer factor preparations were also chemotactic for blood mononuclear cells although the activity on these cells was considerably less than that of C5a (Fig. 2).

In Vivo Chemotactic Activity of Dialyzable Transfer Factor

Intradermal transfer factor preparations produced intense inflammatory responses in rhesus monkey skin (Fig. 3). A granulocyte response was marked by 2 hr and essentially unchanged at 5 hr. By 24 hr the granulocytic infiltration was less intense. A mononuclear cell infiltration was also apparent at 5 hr and, in contrast to the granulocyte response, was of greater magnitude at 24 hr (Fig. 4). Neither the transfer factor from the Sezary cells nor the reagent blank were chemotactic *in vivo.*

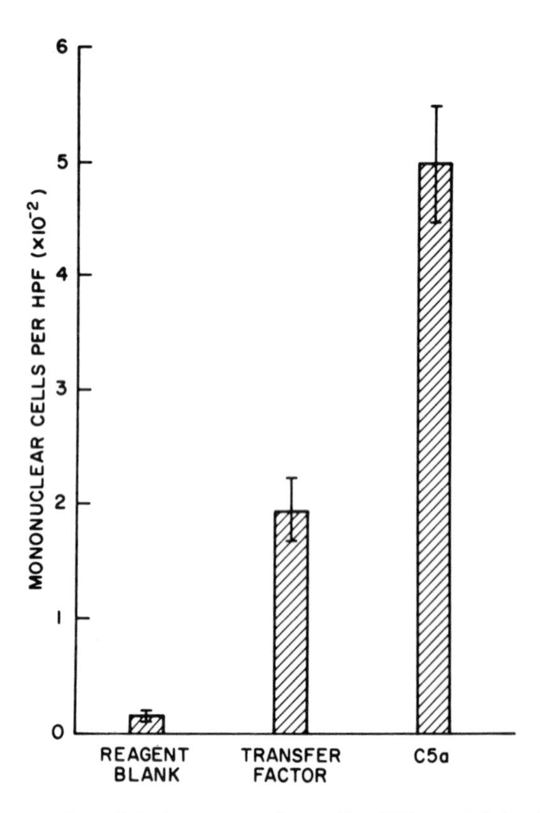

FIG. 2. *In vitro* chemotactic activity for mononuclear cells of C5a and dialyzable transfer factor. After 2 hr of incubation, the transfer factor had 39% of the activity of the C5a.

Properties of the Chemotactic Factor

Comparative time course experiments with transfer factor and C5a showed that the kinetics of granulocyte movement through the micropore membranes were similar for both stimuli (Fig. 5). A dose response curve was linear between 10 and 200 μl of transfer factor.

The chemotactic activity of dialyzable transfer factor was variably sensitive to heating at 56°C for 30 min. Two preparations showed no loss of activity although two others lost as much as 78% of the chemotactic activity (Table 1). C5a was resistant to heat degradation and chemotactic lymphokine was only partially heat labile. The chemotactic activity of dialyzable transfer factor was lost when preparations were stored for 2 weeks at 4°C. Goat antisera to human C3 and C5 did not affect the chemotactic activity of transfer factor, but anti-C5 markedly inhibited the chemotactic activity of C5a.

As summarized in Table 2, all transfer factor preparations from normal donors contained protein by the Lowry reaction and ribose by the orcinol test. However,

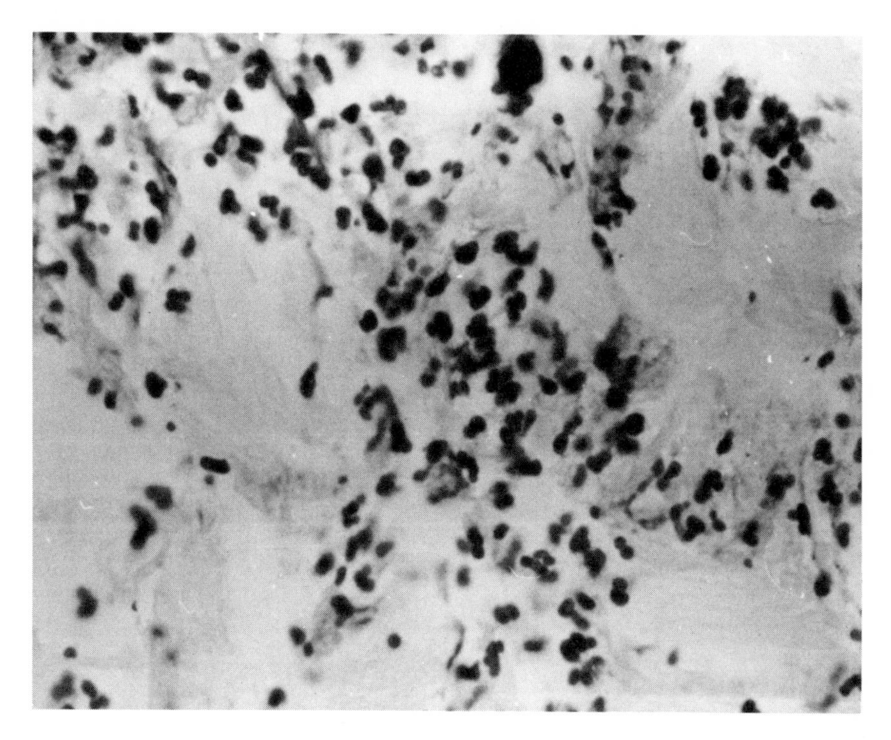

FIG. 3. Biopsy taken 2 hr after injection of 0.1 ml of dialyzable transfer factor from normal leukocytes into rhesus monkey skin. The infiltrate is almost entirely granulocytic. Hematoxylin and eosin stain. Original magnification 520 X.

the dialysates of the Sezary cells were much less reactive in both tests. Transfer factor from normal leukocytes had positive limulus amebacyte lysate tests and this activity was not extractable with chloroform; the material from Sezary cells did not cause gelation of amebacyte lysates (22). Transfer factor did not produce fever after intravenous injection into rabbits.

TABLE 1. *Properties of granulocyte chemotactic factors*

Treatment	Loss of activity (%)		
	Dialyzable transfer factor	C5a	Chemotactic lymphokine
56°C for 30 min	0–78 (4) [a]	0 (12)	40 (3)
4°C for 2 weeks	75 (3)	20 (3)	40 (3)
anti-C5	0 (3)	85 (8)	0 (2)
anti-C3	0 (3)	0 (8)	0 (2)
approximate molecular weight	<5,000	17,500	40,000

[a] Numbers in parentheses indicate number of preparations tested.

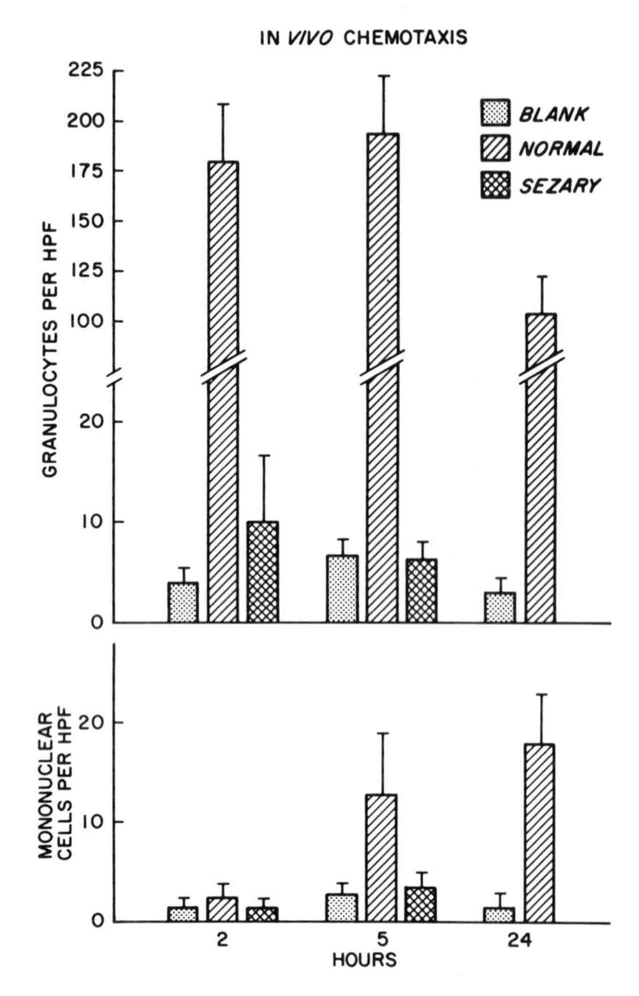

FIG. 4. *In vivo* chemotactic activity of dialyzable transfer factor from normal leukocytes and Sezary cells in rhesus monkey skin. Note that the early infiltration is granulocytic, but a mononuclear cell infiltrate is present at 5 and 24 hr. The dialysate of Sezary cells was essentially inactive *in vivo*.

TABLE 2. *Properties of dialyzable transfer factor*

Lot No.	Protein (mg/ml)	RNA (μg/ml)	Absorbance ratio (255/280 nm)
3	17.0	1,160	1.92
4	10.0	1,220	2.29
6	15.0	1,150	1.86
12 [a]	1.5	310	1.82
13 [a]	1.4	250	1.89
Blank	0.3	0	—

[a] Transfer factor prepared from blood leukocytes of a patient with Sezary's syndrome.

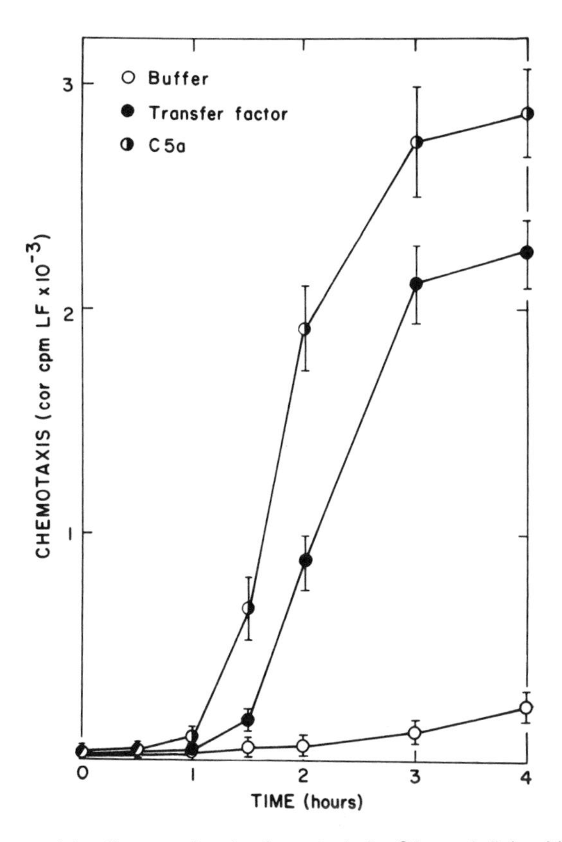

FIG. 5. Time course of *in vitro* granulocyte chemotaxis by C5a and dialyzable transfer factor.

Gel Filtration Experiments

Passage of dialyzable transfer factor through Sephadex G-25 yielded seven peaks of material which absorbed 255-nm ultraviolet light. Four of these peaks appeared after the elution volume of histamine (Fig. 6) and were probably separated by adherence to the gel rather than by molecular size.

Chemotactic Activity in Column Fractions

Figure 6 also shows that the chemotactic activity was present in fractions that eluted shortly after the bacitracin (molecular weight: 1,450 daltons) marker. The chemotactic activity in this peak was labile to 56°C for 30 min and 4°C for 2 weeks but was unaffected by goat antisera to C3 or C5.

Transfer Factor Activity in Column Fractions

The column fractions were then pooled so that one pool contained the chemotactic activity (Fraction II) and the other pools were defined by OD_{255} absorption

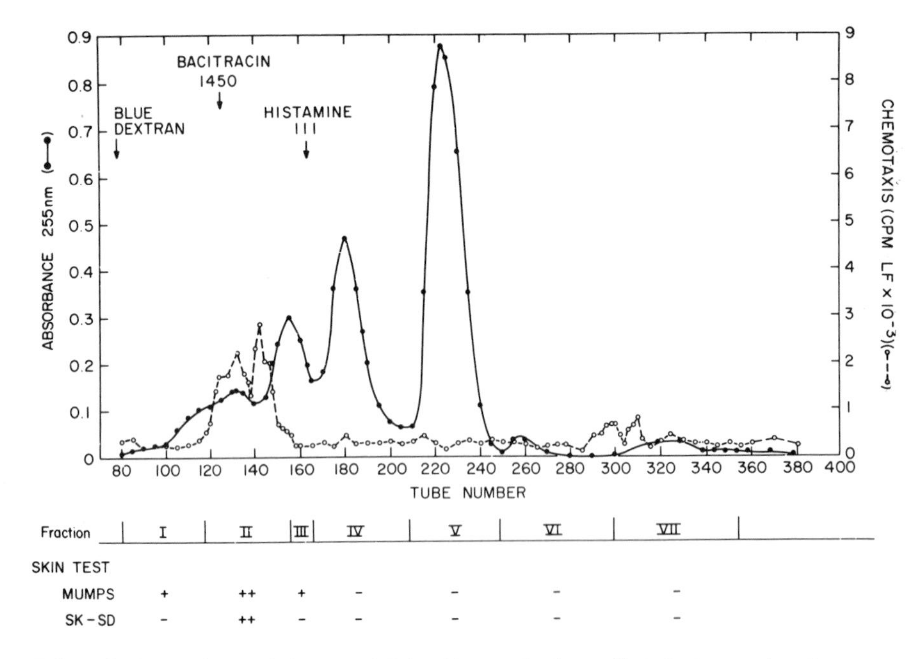

FIG. 6. Sephadex G-25 gel filtration of dialyzable transfer factor. Note that several peaks appear after the histamine molecular weight marker. The chemotactic peak is in fraction II; transfer factor activities appear in fractions I, II, and III.

(Fig. 6). The donor of this transfer factor has a strong delayed reaction to mumps, a moderate response to SK–SD, and negative tests to candida and tuberculin. Fraction II transferred delayed reactivity to both antigens; the adjacent fractions also transferred reactivity to the mumps antigen; other fractions were inactive. Unfractionated transfer factor transferred reactivity to mumps and SK–SD, but no other antigens.

DISCUSSION

The results described in this chapter extend our previously reported observations (8) and demonstrate that dialyzable transfer factor from normal human leukocytes contains a chemotactic substance that is apparently different from previously described chemotactic factors. The chemotactic activity in transfer factor was not affected by goat antiserum to human C3 or C5, and the active material passed through boiled dialysis membranes and eluted from G-25 Sephadex columns in the region of the 1,450 dalton molecular weight marker. In contrast, C3a and C5a have molecular weights of 8,700 and 17,500 respectively (23), and the chemotactic activity of C5a was inhibited by antisera to C5. Thus, it is unlikely that the chemotactic activity in transfer factor was derived from the complement system. The molecular weight data also argue against the presence of the chemotactic enzymes kallikrein or plasminogen activator, which have molecular weights of approximately 130,000 daltons (24, 25), chemotactic lymphokines with molecular weights of 40,000 (16), or the neutrophil-derived chemotactic factor which is nondialyzable (26). The method of preparation of transfer factor mitigates against the presence of chemotactic products of bacterial growth (27). Transfer factor preparations did not produce fever in rabbits, and it is probable that the gelation of limulus amebacyte lysates by transfer factor was due to associated polypeptides or polynucleotides rather than endotoxin (22).

Compared to the reference stimulus C5a, the *in vitro* studies indicated that transfer factor preparations had greater chemotactic activity for granulocytes than mononuclear cells. However, the time course studies in rhesus monkey skin revealed mononuclear cell responses at 5 and 24 hr. It is unclear if this late *in vivo* response was due to a direct effect of the transfer factor preparations or was mediated indirectly by a mononuclear cell chemotactic factor from the granulocytes (28).

The data indicate that both the chemotactic and transfer factor activities are products of lymphocytes or monocytes rather than granulocytes. However, additional experiments will be necessary to absolutely identify the cellular sources of the activities. The lymphocytes from patients with the Sezary syndrome have many properties of T cells (13, 14) and were poor sources of both transfer factor and chemotactic factor. This may be indirect evidence that the activities are derived from B lymphocytes, but the available data are inconclusive. Both the chemotactic and transfer factor activities eluted together from the Sephadex G-25 columns, although adjacent fractions also contained transfer factor activity. These data suggest that both activities are contained in small molecular weight molecules. Previous reports by Lawrence and co-workers (6), Baram, Yuan, and Mosko (29), Arala-Chaves, Lebacq, and Heremans (30) and the recent report by Gottlieb et al. (31) also placed the transfer factor activity in early fractions from similar columns. These observations are in conflict with the report by Neidhart et al. (32), who found the skin test-converting activity in a later peak which corresponded to our peak V (Fig. 6). It is clear that additional studies are necessary to determine if the chemotactic and transfer factor activities are properties of the same molecule.

The role of the chemotactic factor in the biological activity of transfer factor is uncertain. There is evidence that one effect of transfer factor *in vivo* is to induce previously unresponsive lymphoid cells to respond to antigenic stimulation with production of lymphokines, such as, macrophage migration inhibitory factor (15) and chemotactic factor (33), and in one report, transfer factor corrected a cellular defect of monocyte chemotaxis (34). Thus, it is possible that the interaction between antigen and antigen-responsive lymphocytes *in vivo* would cause release of specific transfer factors (35) as well as other lymphokines. In this regard the chemotactic activity of transfer factor could serve as an amplifier of low-intensity immunologic-inflammatory responses and could be responsible for *in vivo* phenomena, such as, local transfer of delayed hypersensitivity with transfer factor in diseases such as sarcoidosis (36).

SUMMARY

Dialyzable transfer factor from human blood leukocytes was found to contain chemotactic activity for granulocytes and monocytes. The chemotactic agent had properties that suggested that it was different from previously recognized chemotactic factors.

Gel filtration experiments showed that the active material entered the bed of a Sephadex G-25 column and eluted just after a 1,450 dalton molecular weight marker. The column fraction with the chemotactic activity also contained the skin test converting activity.

ACKNOWLEDGMENTS

The authors are indebted to Mr. Terrill Smith for his excellent technical assistance and to Dr. D. Lorenz for providing the rhesus monkeys. Dr. Ronald Elin performed the limulus amebacyte lysate tests and the pyrogen assays.

REFERENCES

1. Lawrence, H. S.: The transfer in humans of delayed skin sensitivity to streptococcal M substance and to tuberculin with disrupted leukocytes. *J. Clin. Invest.* 34:219–232, 1955.
2. Landsteiner, K., and Chase, M. W.: Experiments on transfer of cutaneous sensitivity to simple chemical compounds. *Proc. Soc. Exp. Biol. Med.* 49:688–690, 1942.
3. Bloom, B. R., and Chase, M. W.: Transfer of delayed-type hypersensitivity. A critical review and experimental study in the guinea pig. *Prog. Allergy* 10:151–255, 1967.
4. Lawrence, H. S.: Transfer factor. *Adv. Immunol.* 11:195–266, 1969.
5. Rapaport, F. T., Lawrence, H. S., Millar, J. W., Papagianis, D., and Smith, C. E.: Transfer of delayed sensitivity to cocciodioidin in man. *J. Immunol.* 84:358–367, 1960.
6. Lawrence, H. S., Al-Askari, S., David, J., Franklin, E. C., and Zweiman, B.: Transfer of immunological information in humans with dialysates of leukocyte extracts. *Trans. Assoc. Am. Physicians* 76:84–89, 1963.
7. Bloom, B. R.: Does transfer factor act specifically or as an immunologic adjuvant? *N. Engl. J. Med.* 288:908–909, 1973.
8. Gallin, J. I., and Kirkpatrick, C. H.: Chemotactic activity in dialyzable transfer factor. *Proc. Natl. Acad. Sci.* 71:498–502, 1974.
9. Buckner, D., Graw, R. G., Eisel, R. J., Henderson, E. S., and Perry, S.: Leukapheresis by continuous flow centrifugation (CFC) in patients with chronic myelocytic leukemia (CML). *Blood* 33:353–368, 1969.
10. Boyum, A.: Isolation of mononuclear cells and granulocytes from human blood. *Scand. J. Clin. Lab. Invest.* 97 (suppl. 21) 77–89, 1968.
11. Clark, R. A., and Kimball, H. R.: Defective granulocyte chemotaxis in the Chediak-Higashi syndrome. *J. Clin. Invest.* 50:2645–2652, 1971.
12. Crossen, P. E., Mellor, J. E. L., Finley, A. G., Ravich, R. B. M., Vincent, P. C., and Gunz, F. W.: The Sezary syndrome. Cytogenetic studies and identification of the Sezary cell as an abnormal lymphocyte. *Am. J. Med.* 50:24–34, 1970.

13. Brouet, J. C., Flandrin, G., and Seligmann, M.: Indication of the thymus-derived nature of the proliferating cells in six patients with Sezary's syndrome. *N. Engl. J. Med.* 289:341–344, 1973.
14. Edelson, R. L., Kirkpatrick, C. H., Shevach, E. M., Schein, P. B., Smith, R. W., Green, I., and Lutzner, M.: Preferential cutaneous infiltration by neoplastic thymus-derived lymphocytes: Morphologic and functional studies. *Ann. Int. Med.* 80:685–692, 1974.
15. Kirkpatrick, C. H., Rich, R. R., and Smith, T. K.: Effect of transfer factor on lymphocyte function in anergic patients. *J. Clin. Invest.* 51:2948–2958, 1972.
16. Ward, P. A., Remold, H. G., and David, J. R.: The production by antigen-stimulated lymphocytes of a leukotactic factor distinct from migration inhibitory factor. *Cell. Immunol.* 1:162–174, 1970.
17. Shin, H. S., Snyderman, R., Friedman, E., Mellors, A., and Mayer, M. M.: Chemotactic and anaphylatoxic fragment cleaved from the fifth component of guinea pig complement. *Science* 162:361–363, 1968.
18. Gallin, J. I., Clark, R. A., and Kimball, H. R.: Granulocyte chemotaxis: An improved *in vitro* assay employing ^{51}Cr-labeled granulocytes. *J. Immunol.* 110:233–240, 1973.
19. Snyderman, R., Altman, L. C., Hausman, M. S., and Mergenhagen, S. E.: Human mononuclear leukocyte chemotaxis: A quantitative assay for humoral and cellular chemotactic factors. *J. Immunol.* 108:857–860, 1972.
20. Lowry, O. H., Rosebrough, A. L., Farr, A. L., and Randall, R. J.: Protein measurement with the Folin-phenol reagent. *J. Biol. Chem.* 193:265–275, 1951.
21. Schneider, W. C.: Determination of nucleic acids in tissues by pentose analysis. In Colowick, S. P., and Kaplan, N. O. (eds) *Methods in Enzymology,* Vol. 3, Academic Press, New York, pp. 680–684. 1957.
22. Elin, R. J., and Wolff, S. M.: Nonspecificity of the limulus amebacyte lysate test: Positive reactions with polynucleotides and proteins. *J. Infect. Dis.* 128:349–352, 1973.
23. Vallota, E. H., and Müller-Eberhard, H. J.: Formation of C3a and C5a anaphylatoxins in whole human serum after inhibition of the anaphylatoxin inactivator. *J. Exp. Med.* 137:1109–1123, 1973.
24. Kaplan, A. P., Kay, A. B., and Austen, K. F.: A prealbumin activator of prekallikrein. III. Appearance of chemotactic activity for human neutrophils by the conversion of human prekallikrein to kallikrein. *J. Exp. Med.* 135:81–97, 1972.
25. Kaplan, A. P., Goetzl, E. J., and Austen, K. F.: The fibrinolytic pathway of human plasma. II. The generation of chemotactic activity by activation of plasminogen proactivator. *J. Clin. Invest.* 52:2591–2595, 1973.
26. Zigmond, S. H., and Hirsch, J. G.: Leukocyte locomotion and chemotaxis. New methods for evaluation, and demonstration of a cell-derived chemotactic factor. *J. Exp. Med.* 137:387–410, 1973.
27. Ward, P. A., Lepow, I. H., and Newman, L. J.: Bacterial factors chemotactic for polymorphonuclear leukocytes. *Am. J. Pathol.* 52:725–736, 1968.
28. Ward, P. A.: Chemotaxis of mononuclear cells. *J. Exp. Med.* 128:1201–1221, 1968.
29. Baram, P., Yuan, L., and Mosko, M. M.: Studies on the transfer of human delayed-type hypersensitivity. I. Partial purification and characterization of two active components. *J. Immunol.* 97:407–420, 1966.
30. Arala-Chaves, M. P., Lebacq, E. G., and Heremans, J. F.: Fractionation of human leukocyte extracts transferring delayed hypersensitivity to tuberculin. *Int. Arch. Allergy Appl. Immunol.* 31:353–365, 1967.
31. Gottlieb, A. A., Foster, L. G., Waldman, S. R., and Lopez, M.: What is transfer factor? *Lancet* 2:822–823, 1973.
32. Neidhart, J. A., Schwartz, R. S., Hurtubise, P. E., Murphy, S. G., Metz, E. N., Balcerzak, S. P., and LoBuglio, A. F.: Transfer factor: Isolation of a biologically active component. *Cell Immunol.* 9:319–323, 1973.
33. Kirkpatrick, C. H., and Gallin, J. I.: *unpublished observations.*
34. Snyderman, R., Altman, L. C., Frankel, A., and Blaese, R. M.: Defective mononuclear leukocyte chemotaxis: A previously unrecognized immune dysfunction. *Ann. Int. Med.* 78:509–513, 1973.
35. Lawrence, H. S., and Pappenheimer, A. M.: Transfer of delayed hypersensitivity to diphtheria toxin in man. *J. Exp. Med.* 104:321–335, 1956.
36. Lawrence, H. S., and Zweiman, B.: Transfer factor deficiency response—A mechanism of anergy in Boeck's sarcoid. *Trans. Assoc. Am. Physicians* 81:240–247, 1968.

DISCUSSION

Blaese: Is transfer factor chemotactic for lymphocytes?

Kirkpatrick: We have not examined it for lymphocytes.

Ward: You have not looked at the susceptibility of the chemotactic activity in the presence of various proteases such as pronase?

Kirkpatrick: We have not done any enzymatic studies yet. We have worked with some ribonucleases but not very much.

Ward: This material bears many resemblances to the bacterial chemotactic factor of low weight that Drs. Becker, Schiffman, and I have been looking at. It elutes under conditions that are very similar. It has a peculiar behavior in Sephadex columns; it is of very low molecular weight; it is inactivated by pronase, but not by trypsin and other enzymes. We have never really looked to see if there is any comparable material in mammalian tissues, and it is conceivable that such a substance might be extractable.

The other question: Do you have any idea about the relative charge of this material?

Kirkpatrick: We have done only one experiment with isoelectric focusing. We obtained two chemotactic peaks; one was at pH 4.6 and the other was at pH 8.4.

Ward: Because the bacterial factor certainly is anionic. We don't know about the isoelectric part of it, but it certainly would have similar characteristics.

Kirkpatrick: We are concerned about the possibility of a bacteria-like material, and I don't think we have absolutely excluded this. We have some evidence that may be against this. Does your bacterial material contain pyrogen? Have you done a pyrogen test on it?

Ward: We haven't done pyrogen testing. In the limulus tests, our bacterial factor preparation does not induce coagulation.

Kirkpatrick: Our material does not contain pyrogen. It has a positive limulus test but it is known that that test is not specific for endotoxin. The limulus activity is not extracted with chloroform, which is contrary to what one sees with endotoxin.

Ward: When your material is injected, why wouldn't it rapidly diffuse away? One would certainly think that after 24 hours, by simple diffusion, it would have disappeared.

Kirkpatrick: Right. I think that the late mononuclear cell response is probably more akin to something you have described. That is a chemotactic factor for mononuclear cells that is derived from granulocytes. In other words, the granulocytes infiltrate the area as a direct response to the transfer factor and the late mononuclear cell responses may be secondary. I wouldn't want to argue against that at all.

With respect to your comments about diffusion, we thought it would be much easier to do the studies in the skin of other animals. The guinea pig, mouse, and rat were readily available, but we found nothing in these animals, only in the monkey. It may be that the activity is so rapidly diffused away in some of these smaller animals that we don't see it.

Ward: But this would go along with the historical description of the transfer factor preparations, that they have a species specificity.

Kirkpatrick: Yes.

Miller: Are there platelets in these preparations? If so, have you given any consideration to their possible role?

Kirkpatrick: Yes, some of the preparations have had platelets and others have been separated where the platelets have been removed by allowing them to aggregate.

Miller: They are entirely platelet-free?

Kirkpatrick: As platelet-free as we can get them. They are certainly substantially different from being platelet-rich. It doesn't seem to make any difference. There is no difference in a preparation that has a lot of platelets versus a preparation that has a few platelets. But to answer your question, we have not done the one thing that we plan to do and that is take a platelet-rich preparation and lymphocyte-poor preparation and identify the activity.

Miller: The problem is that it is potentially feasible that there are a very, very small number of platelets, so the difference between a platelet-rich and platelet-poor preparation could be above the range where a few platelets could. . . .

Kirkpatrick: I wouldn't dispute that at all. I think the evidence is that we have excluded the granulocyte but it doesn't rule in another cell. For example, we have not yet done the studies with relatively pure preparations of monocytes, which would be equally important.

Snyderman: In regard to the question Dr. Ward brought up, I was struck by the similarity of molecular weight as well. But one of the characteristics of the chemotactic factor we found is that it is remarkably heat stable. It can actually be boiled for fairly long periods of time and not lose its chemotactic activity. I don't remember what you said about the stability of the factor you are talking about.

Kirkpatrick: We have not done experiments with boiled material. The heat stability at 56 degrees for 30 minutes is variable, with some preparations being absolutely resistant to degradation by heating and others being very sensitive.

Snyderman: The other thing is if you just fractionate normal human serum you always find very small amounts of chemotactic activity eluting at the little bump where amino acids come out, and sometimes you see high levels of activity there. Do you think what you are seeing in those molecular weight areas is similar to what you are finding from the lymphocytes?

Kirkpatrick: The cells are washed to reduce the likelihood of serum contaminants. One can't absolutely exclude the number of molecules that are adherent to cells. The cells haven't been through any procedure that would activate something that is latent in the serum. I think that we likely minimize the possibility of serum contamination.

David: You mentioned that pure polys didn't have a chemotactic activity?

Kirkpatrick: That is correct.

Bellanti: I am a little confused. You show transfer factor being produced following antigen stimulation. It has been my understanding that transfer factor exists preformed in lymphocytes. Did you mean it to be produced following antigen stimulation?

Kirkpatrick: There was a report many years ago by Lawrence and Pappenheimer which showed that an antigen-specific transfer factor was released as one of the lymphokines from cells stimulated with antigen. The supernatants from these cells would transfer activity to that antigen while the cells themselves lost the ability to transfer reactivity to that antigen. That is the evidence for transfer factor being one of the lymphokines.

David: I think there is a difference. Transfer factor can be released without antigen stimulation, whereas all the other mediators require antigen or mitogen stimulation for their production.

Bellanti: This is precisely the point. The chemotactic factors that have been described for polymorphonuclear leukocytes require active proliferation and differentiation. Is it the transfer factor which has the chemotactic activity, or is it another substance that is the preformed equivalent of this chemotactic factor?

Kirkpatrick: The preparations that I have described today have not been stimulated with any antigens prior to preparation. And the two properties thus far go together. In other words, they haven't been separated. I wouldn't want to say they are absolutely one and the same, however. I think we probably have not done the essential experiments to separate them. For example, we know there are a host of substances in the lysates. If one considers purity, by passing something through a dialysis membrane you are accomplishing an enormous step toward purification. You eliminate a lot of large molecules. To have it from a column is still more purification. Yet, there is a large amount of material residing in one of those peaks.

Bellanti: Yes. It is entirely conceivable that this could be.

Kirkpatrick: I think there are two types of transfer factors, one which is released from cells by just disrupting the cell, and another which requires antigenic stimulation.

Cohn: Whenever you are dealing with a molecule of this size, you wonder if it is a product of enzymatic cleavage during preparation. If you incubate disrupted cells, do you modify the amount of transfer factor you find in such dialysates?

Kirkpatrick: It is very hard to quantitate this sort of thing but the answer is probably no. I don't think we have done a rigorous experiment that would really answer the question the way you'd like. The cells are disrupted by freezing and thawing at 37 degrees. In a sense, that is a brief incubation. The question then is: Could something occur during this brief time as a cleavage?

Cohn: You have a long period for dialysis to occur also.

Kirkpatrick: That is at 4 degrees, but that doesn't mean that enzymes can't work at 4 degrees.

Snyderman: Do you think the factor is a B cell product?

Kirkpatrick: I don't know yet. I don't think one can derive any conclusions from the Sezary cell data. Those are abnormal cells both in morphology and function. And I don't think one can make any conclusions unless the leukemia cells are rich sources of this material. Then you could make some inferences.

David: You use DNAase to prepare your transfer factor?

Kirkpatrick: Yes.

David: Do you also get this material if you don't use DNAase?

Kirkpatrick: Yes, no difference.

The Phagocytic Cell in Host Resistance, edited
by Joseph A. Bellanti and Delbert H. Dayton.
Raven Press, New York © 1975.

The Growth and Development of Our Understanding of Chronic Granulomatous Disease

Robert L. Baehner

Division of Pediatric Hematology-Oncology, Department of Pediatrics, Indiana University School of Medicine, Indianapolis, Indiana 46202

INTRODUCTION

It seems appropriate in a volume sponsored by the National Institute of Child Health and Human Development to consider the growth and development of our understanding of disorders of phagocytic function of leukocytes since 1966. In that year Holmes, Quie, Windhorst, and Good published their initial and important observations on the phagocytizing leukocytes from the blood of children with chronic granulomatous disease (CGD) (1). I will point out the related events that preceded their discovery and then sketch the developmental milestones that have contributed to our understanding of this disease. After nearly a decade of growth, the final development is far from complete since there remain many unanswered questions, gaps in our knowledge, and areas of dispute related to both basic mechanisms of action and clinical treatment of these children.

STUDY OF CHILDREN WITH RECURRENT INFECTION

Clinical Features

Physicians caring for male children with primary immune deficiency soon realized that there still remained another group of boys with normal or elevated levels of serum immunoglobulins who suffered episodes of recurrent pyogenic infections similar to those with agammaglobulinemia. In 1954 Janeway and co-workers (2) called attention to this fact and in 1957 Berendes, Bridges, and Good (3) defined the condition as a distinct clinical entity and coined the term fatal granulomatous disease of childhood to describe its clinical severity as well as the histopathology of the involved organs. They also pointed out that these organs were most frequently infected by *Staphylococcus aureus* or *Serratia marcescens* and contained peculiar granulomata which were often surrounded or infiltrated by pigmented lipid histiocytes. In that same year Landing and Shirkey (4) provided the first definitive series of pathologic studies of the disease. In 1968 Carson and co-workers (5) documented the genetic transmission to be X-linked. A review of the clinical features of almost a score of these patients with CGD appeared in 1971 (6) and the frequency of their signs and symptoms is listed in Table 1. The lymphadenopathy is most prominent in the cervical and submandibular region and these nodes frequently suppurate and require incision and drainage. Pneumonia or an infectious eczematoid rash of the skin is usually evident by 1 year of age. Unfortunately as many as one-third of these children die before 7 years of age.

TABLE 1. *Frequency of signs and symptoms in 92 patients with CGD*

Finding	Number of patients
Marked lymphadenopathy	87
Pneumonitis	80
Male sex	80
Suppuration of nodes	79
Hepatomegaly	77
Dermatitis	77
Onset by 1 year	72
Splenomegaly	68
Hepatic-perihepatic abscess	41
Death before 7 years old	34
Osteomyelitis	30
Onset with dermatitis	28
Onset with lymphadenitis	28
Persistent rhinitis	23
Facial periorificial dermatitis	22
Conjunctivitis	21
Death from pneumonitis	21
Persistent diarrhea	20
Perianal abscess	17
Ulcerative stomatitis	15

Data previously published by Johnston and Baehner (6).

Laboratory Features

Until 1966 little was understood about the pathogenesis of this disease. The total white blood count, differential, serum immunoglobulin levels, and delayed hypersensitivity mechanisms were intact in these affected children. But in 1966 and 1967 Holmes and Quie reported that the leukocytes of CGD patients could ingest but could not kill the bacteria which infected them (1, 7). The species specificity of this intracellular microbicidal defect was pointed out by Kaplan and co-workers (8) in 1968 when they showed that CGD leukocytes could kill ingested streptococci and *Escherichia coli.* These findings correlated with the results of Klebanoff and White (9), who showed that iodination and presumed peroxidation of catalase positive bacteria, such as, *S. aureus* and other microorganisms that infect these patients, did not occur in CGD cells whereas catalase negative bacteria, such as, lactobacilli that did not cause infection, were indeed iodinated and killed. The biochemical groundwork that enabled proper interpretation of Klebanoff's findings began more than a decade earlier.

MORPHOLOGIC AND METABOLIC STUDIES OF PHAGOCYTOSIS

Basic Studies of Phagocyte Function

The pioneer studies by Sbarra and Karnovsky (10, 11) on the metabolic basis of phagocytosis in polymorphonuclear leukocytes (PMN) as well as the morphologic studies of PMN during phagocytosis by Cohn and Hirsch (12, 13) have provided the clinical investigator with a clearer understanding of these events. Figure 1 is an oversimplified schematic summary of the phagocytic process in PMN. First, a particle or an opsonized bacteria makes contact with the phagocytic surface. Pseudopodia from the PMN form around the particle that is subsequently engulfed into a phagocytic vacuole. The lysosomal granules within the PMN apply to the surface of the phagocytic vacuole and discharge their contents, which include hydrolases, myeloperoxidases, and cationic proteins in the case of the neutrophilic granulocyte. If the particle is a live bacteria, it no longer can proliferate within the phagocytic vacuole and is ultimately killed and digested.

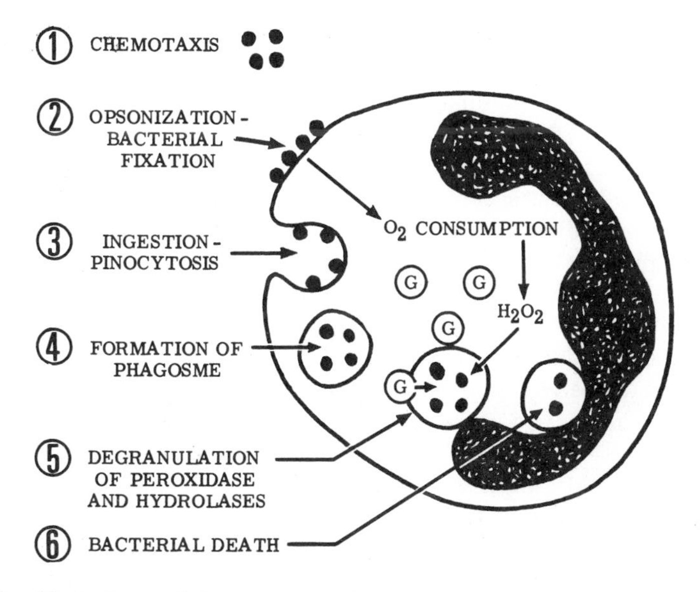

FIG. 1. Simplified schema of phagocytosis by PMN. Phagocytic cells accumulate at the site of infection mediated by a variety of chemotactic factors, 1. Bacteria require opsonization for their binding to the membrane of the PMN, 2. The particle is then ingested, 3, and entrapped within a phagocytic vacuole, 4. The granules of the PMN discharge their contents into the phagocytic vacuole, 5. There is an associated increase in oxygen consumption, hydrogen peroxide (H_2O_2) production, hexose monophosphate shunt stimulation, and iodination of ingested particles by PMN. Finally, bacteria are killed and digested in the phagocytic vacuole, 6.

Biochemical Aspects of Phagocytosis

Shortly after particles are added to a suspension of phagocytes, there is increase in glucose consumption and lactate production by the PMN. Metabolic inhibitors of anaerobic glycolysis, i.e., fluoride, 2-deoxyglucose, and iodoacetate, markedly decrease the uptake of particles by PMN whereas inhibitors of oxidative phosphorylation, such as, cyanide, antimycin, and dinitrophenol, have no such effect. Thus, the phagocytic process in PMN requires ATP derived principally from glycolysis. Another series of metabolic reactions is also observed; these are stimulated by particle contact with the PMN. They include increased oxygen consumption and oxidation of glucose-1-^{14}C to $^{14}CO_2$; a much smaller oxidation of glucose-6-^{14}C to $^{14}CO_2$ also occurs. The so-called respiratory burst and stimulation of the hexose monophosphate shunt (HMP) are not depressed by cyanide. As we shall see later, the respiratory increment and a great increase in the HMP are key observations to further understanding of metabolic dysfunctions observed in the PMN of patients with recurrent infection. In addition, Quastel and his collaborators (14) noted some years ago that the conversion of ^{14}C-formate to $^{14}CO_2$ was also markedly stimulated during phagocytosis and correctly inferred that this was due to increased hydrogen peroxide production by PMN which converted ^{14}C-formate to $^{14}CO_2$ in the presence of cellular catalase. Further documentation of increased hydrogen peroxide formation by PMN during phagocytosis was by Paul and Sbarra (15), who placed cells in a dialysis sac and quantitated the hydrogen peroxide that diffused out. The amount of additional peroxide which they detected during phagocytosis was about 1% of that formed in the respiratory burst, if all the oxygen consumed led to hydrogen peroxide production. We calculated that 3% of the peroxide produced by the respiratory burst was available for the intracellular oxidation of ^{14}C-formate by catalase (16). In another series of studies (17) we observed the rate of reduced glutathione (GSH) oxidation in glucose-6-phosphate dehydrogenase (G6PD) deficient red blood cells by juxtaposed phagocytizing PMN was 10 to 15% of the peroxide generated during the respiratory burst. These studies inferred that the additional hydrogen peroxide generated during phagocytosis may be utilized by other routes.

The enzymatic basis for some of the metabolic perturbations in the phagocytizing PMN remains the subject of considerable discussion and investigation. One unifying hypothesis to explain the increased oxygen uptake, hydrogen peroxide production, and HMP activity is presented in the scheme shown in Fig. 2. In this scheme, ATP for particle uptake is generated by breakdown of glucose to lactate (Reaction 1); there is a 20% increase in anaerobic glycolysis during phagocytosis. Glycolysis also provides reduced nicotinamide adenine dinucleotide (NADH) from nicotinamide adenine dinucleotide (NAD^+) (Reaction 2). NADH and oxygen, catalyzed by NADH oxidase (Reaction 3), react to form hydrogen peroxide. Although there is debate about this point, we believe that the reaction primarily responsible for the increased oxygen consumption by neu-

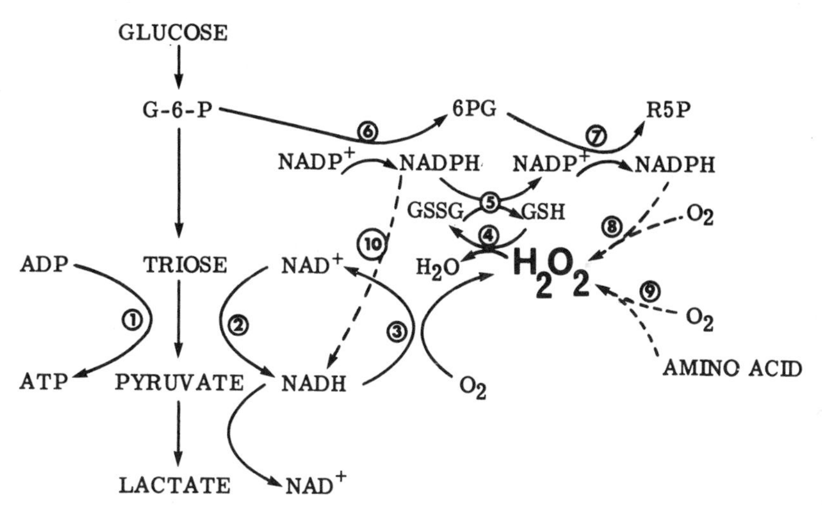

FIG. 2. Metabolic reactions by PMN during phagocytosis. See text for details and explanation of the 10 numbered reactions.

trophils during phagocytosis involves NADH oxidase. Hydrogen peroxide stimulates the HMP by oxidizing GSH in a reaction catalyzed by glutathione peroxidase (Reaction 4); the oxidized glutathione is in turn reduced during the oxidation of reduced nicotinamide dinucleotide phosphate (NADPH) catalyzed by glutathione reductase (Reaction 5). The flow of glucose through the HMP, catalyzed by G6PD (Reaction 6) and 6-phosphogluconate dehydrogenase (Reaction 7), generates NADPH from $NADP^+$. Other sources of hydrogen peroxide are from NADPH oxidase (Reaction 8) and amino acid oxidase catalyzed reactions (Reaction 9). Data obtained from G6PD-deficient PMN (18) support the operation of a transhydrogenase which catalyzes the reaction between the pyridine nucleotides (Reaction 10).

The importance of hydrogen peroxide for adequate bacterial killing by PMN was inferred by the observation of Sbarra and co-workers (19), who noted diminished microbicidal activity by PMN placed in nitrogen. Clearer insight into this mechanism has been provided by the elegant work of Klebanoff and his colleagues (20, 21), who demonstrated that myeloperoxidase, an anion, particularly a halide, and hydrogen peroxide constituted a potent bactericidal system. Iodide was shown to be the most potent halide in this system and iodination of bacteria occurred concomitantly with their killing. Figure 3 is a schematic summary of the known metabolic reactions of hydrogen peroxide within the normal PMN. A variable amount of peroxide is destroyed by soluble catalase which also catalyzes the oxidation of ^{14}C-formate; it also stimulates the HMP and contributes to the potent intracellular bactericidal system in concert with granule myeloperoxidase and halide ion (22).

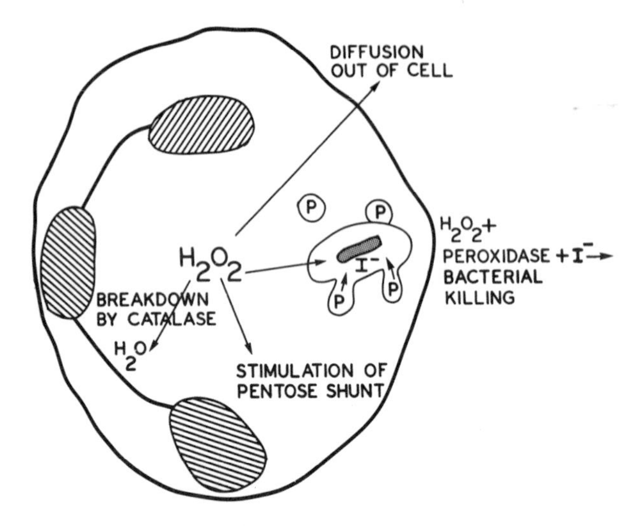

FIG. 3. Disposition of hydrogen peroxide in PMN during phagocytosis. A variable amount is converted to water and oxygen by intracellular catalase. As much as 15% of the H_2O_2 formed during the respiratory burst leaks out of the PMN. Stimulation of the hexose monophosphate shunt, iodination of particles, and bactericidal killing are other important functions of H_2O_2 (see text for further details).

THE CGD LEUKOCYTE

Studies of Degranulation

Holmes and co-workers noted in 1966 (1) that the morphology of CGD granulocytes during ingestion of bacteria differed from that of normal cells. Following normal ingestion, these PMN did not become as distorted nor did they develop the very large phagocytic vacuoles which so grossly alter the morphology of normal granulocytes. White (7) extended these studies to electron microscopic analysis and reported that the vacuoles in CGD cells phagocytizing staphylococci were neither as prominent nor as distorting as were the vacuoles in normal PMN that ingested the same organisms. These morphologic observations suggested that the CGD leukocyte may be defective in the delivery of lysosomal granules to the phagocytic vacuole. This concept implied a failure of either migration, fusion, or transmission of lysosomal enzymes. However, quantitative chemical analysis of the subcellular distribution patterns for acid and alkaline phosphatase, beta glucuronidase, and peroxidase was measured in PMN after 30 and 60 min incubation with a variety of particles (23). The PMN from four patients with CGD and five young adults with acute infection showed no difference in the quantitative shift of these enzymes from the granule to the soluble fraction (Fig. 4) after phagocytosis. However, these studies suffered from the lack of kinetic analysis over the first 30 min of phagocytosis. Both Kauder et al. (24) and Nathan et al. (25) performed histochemical studies of degranulation on CGD and normal

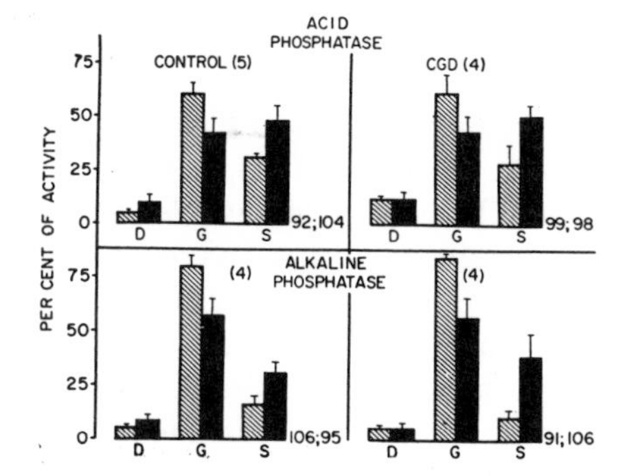

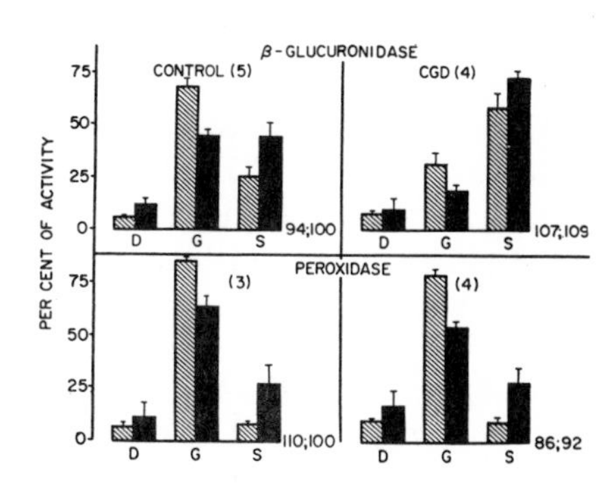

FIG. 4. Subcellular distribution of acid phosphatase and alkaline phosphatase (left) and β-glucuronidase and peroxidase (right). The hatched bars represent resting cells and the solid bars represent phagocytizing cells. The number of subjects studied is indicated at the top of each graph. Measurements on three controls and three CGD patients were carried out after 30 min incubation. Starch particles or heat killed *E. coli* were used for phagocytosis. No differences were noted with respect to release of enzymes from the granules. The percentage of enzyme activity recovered from the subcellular fractions compared to the whole homogenate is indicated at the right of each bar graph; resting cells on the left and phagocytizing cells on the right. The SEM is indicated above each bar. For further details consult (23).

leukocytes ingesting either microorganisms or zymosan particles but failed to produce any evidence for a defect in the release of granule enzymes during phagocytosis in CGD cells. The electron micrograph studies by Żucker-Franklin et al. (26) and Morris Karnovsky's (23) electron micrographs demonstrated peroxidase around zymosan particles in phagocytic vacuoles of CGD cells. Mandell and Hook (27) performed quantitative analysis of degranulation and observed no abnormality.

Stossel (28) has developed a method to isolate phagolysosomes which has overcome some of the prior technical difficulties in assessment of degranulation because it directly measures the enzyme activity in phagolysosomes themselves. In his studies on CGD leukocytes he could observe no defect in either the ingestion of emulsified paraffin oil containing Oil Red O or the activity of acid phosphatase, beta glucuronidase, and peroxide in the phagocytic vesicles isolated 15 and 45 min after phagocytosis (29). However, Gold and co-workers (30) have recently reported that PMN granules are exotosed and sequentially released into the surrounding media after the cell membrane is stimulated by a noningestable surface-coated aggregated IgG. They found impaired release of enzyme 5 and 15 min after stimulation, but by 30 min there was no difference in quantities of lysosomal enzyme released.

In support of studies which showed no defect in the uptake of particles by CGD cells, their lactate production and glucose consumption were found to be normal (31, 32). The bulk of the evidence suggests that, although there may be an initial alteration in the rate of release of granule enzymes into the media in CGD cells, their transfer into the phagocytic vesicle appears to be normal beyond 15 min after phagocytosis.

Studies of Oxidative Metabolism

The clinical significance of the respiratory burst in PMN became clarified after metabolic studies on CGD PMN began. Holmes, Page, and Good (32) and our own studies (31) reported that the leukocytes of children with this disorder lacked the respiratory burst and did not evoke the stimulation of glucose-1-^{14}C oxidation during phagocytosis. In addition, we (31) found that there was no intrinsic defect of the HMP in CGD cells since the addition of methylene blue produced a marked stimulation of glucose-1-^{14}C oxidation; this is in marked contrast to PMN with total deficiency of G6PD which lacked this response as evident in Fig. 5. Although Bellanti and co-workers (33) have found that the rate of decay of G6PD in CGD PMN homogenates is accelerated, there is no reduction of this enzyme in fresh cytolysates.

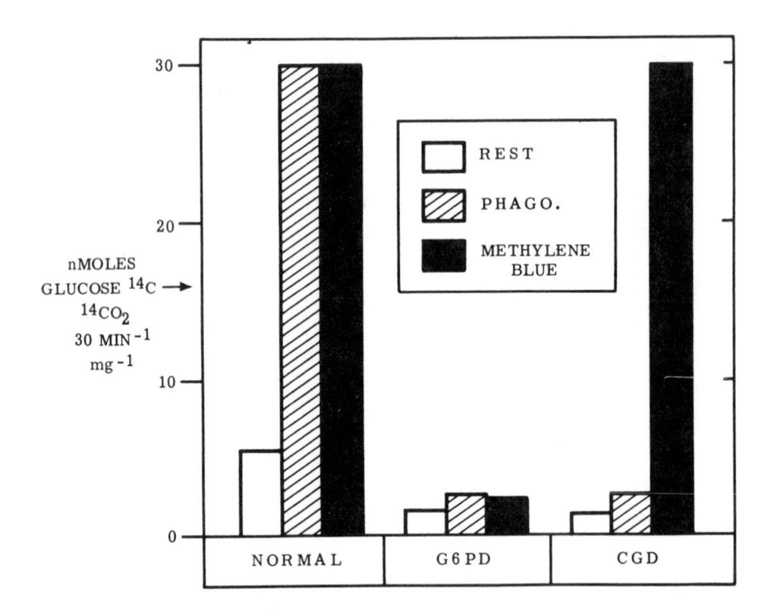

FIG. 5. The differential effect of methylene blue on hexose monophosphate shunt activity of normal, glucose-6-phosphate dehydrogenase deficient, and CGD PMN. Incubations were for 30 min at 37°C in closed Kontes flasks. Phagocytosis was with 0.81 micron latex particles and final concentration of methylene blue was 2 mM. For further details consult (18).

The report in 1967 by Holmes et al. (32) that hydrogen peroxide-dependent formate oxidation was also impaired in CGD PMN led us and others to investigate enzymes that could qualify as the respiratory enzyme. We reasoned that the enzyme must be insensitive to cyanide, must catalyze a reaction between oxygen and a hydrogen donor to produce peroxide, and must be present in sufficient activity to cover the amount of oxygen consumed during phagocytosis. For this reason, we performed studies on resting and phagocytizing human leukocytes to determine the quantity of oxygen consumed during phagocytosis of 0.81 micron latex beads. As noted in Table 2, about 60 nanomoles of oxygen was consumed per milligram of cell protein per hour. Leukocyte granule NADPH oxidase was insufficient to explain this respiratory burst (5 nanomoles) whereas the soluble NADH oxidase was present in adequate amounts to cover this response (60 nanomoles). At the pH optimum of 5 the level of NADH oxidase was much greater than the respiratory burst (120 nanomoles). In Fig. 6 it was noted that, if alkaline isotonic KCl solution was used as the homogenization medium, NADH oxidase was completely solubilized. In contrast, when 0.34 molar sucrose solution was used for homogenization, one-half of the NADH oxidase has shifted to the granule fraction and could be washed off the granules with alkaline isotonic KCl. This suggested to us that NADH oxidase may be a membrane-associated enzyme.

TABLE 2. *Correlation of the respiratory burst by PMN to the activities of NADH and NADPH oxidase*

		Human leukocytes (4)	
	pH	Rest	Phagocytosis
QO_2 [a]		1.1	2.5
Δ Respiration [b]		63	
NADPH oxidase [b]	7.0	5	
NADH oxidase [b]	7.0	60	
	5.0 [c]	120	

[a] μl mg^{-1} total cell protein hr^{-1}.
[b] nmoles oxygen mg^{-1} total cell protein hr^{-1}.
[c] based on pH optimum curve for guinea pig enzyme.

Respirometry was performed in micro Warburg flasks with air as the gas phase and a total fluid volume of 1.1 ml at 37°C. All enzyme assays were at 37°C pH 7.0 with 1 mM KCN. NADPH oxidase was measured by the rate of decrease in PO_2 at a final NADPH concentration of 7.0×10^{-4} mole/liter. NADH oxidase was measured in 1 mm light path cuvettes by the decrease in absorbance at 340 nm of NADH.

Data previously published by Baehner, Gilman, and Karnovsky (16).

We found that alkaline isotonic KCl extracts of PMN from five cases of CGD were deficient in NADH oxidase compared to six infected controls. However, Holmes and co-workers found normal activity of both NADH and NADPH oxidase in their patients' leukocyte cytolysates (32). In their cases, noninfected individuals were used as controls. Further studies have clearly shown that NADH oxidase increases during infection in subjects without CGD. Figure 7 compares NADH oxidase activity in granulocytes of normal uninfected controls, infected controls, and patients with CGD. Group 1 represents data provided by Dr. Holmes-Gray. The data for Group 2 were obtained jointly by Drs. Holmes-

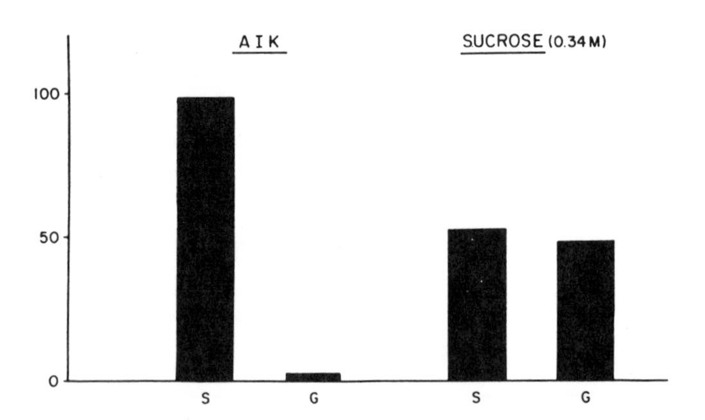

FIG. 6. Distribution of NADH oxidase activity in homogenates of leukocytes. The data is expressed as total activity in nanomoles O_2 hr^{-1}. S indicates soluble fraction, G indicates granule fraction. AIK means alkaline isotonic KCl. For further details consult (16).

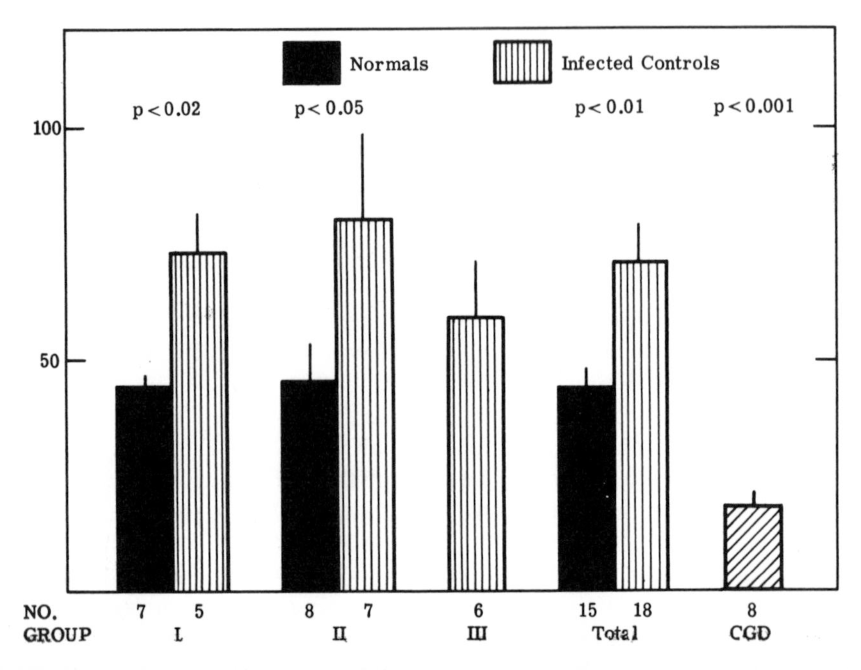

FIG. 7. Comparison of NADH oxidase in PMN of normal uninfected controls, infected controls, and patients with CGD. Group I represents data kindly provided by Dr. B. Holmes-Gray. The data for Group II were obtained jointly with Drs. Gray and Karnovsky in Boston; Group III are data previously published (60) and three more observations. The ordinate is nanomoles mg^{-1} cell protein hr^{-1} of NADH oxidized. Previously reported data (60) were given per atom of oxygen rather than per mole.

Gray, Karnovsky, and myself in Boston. Group 3 are data previously reported which were given per atom of oxygen rather than per mole of oxygen (60). The CGD patients are five patients previously studied by us and three additional observations. These studies indicate that alkalinized isotonic KCl cytolysates of PMN from CGD were significantly different from those obtained from normal controls and infected controls. It should be emphasized that these studies were done on resting PMN and that similar studies are lacking in phagocytizing PMN. In that context, studies of NADPH oxidase by Rossi and his colleagues (34, 35) have noted that phagocytosis stimulates the activity of NADPH and decreases the K_m 10-fold. If activation of a membrane oxidase is the real basis for the respiratory burst, then our study of resting PMN may be irrelevant.

Another line of inquiry into the role of oxidase activity as the basic enzymatic defect in CGD has been pursued. If lack of an oxidase system that generated hydrogen peroxide intracellularly during phagocytosis is the primary abnormality in CGD PMN, introduction of such a system into these cells might normalize their metabolic and bactericidal activity. Toward this end, we (36) bound hydrogen peroxide producing glucose oxidase to latex particles and allowed these particles to be ingested by CGD PMN. Coating of latex particles with protein has a depressant effect on their capacity to be ingested by PMN. We assessed the rate of uptake of plain latex and latex coated with glucose oxidase by normal PMN by quantitative estimation of the ingested latex after extraction and solubilization with dioxane. As noted in Fig. 8, both the rate and extent of uptake of latex by PMN were markedly diminished. Therefore, the extent of stimulation

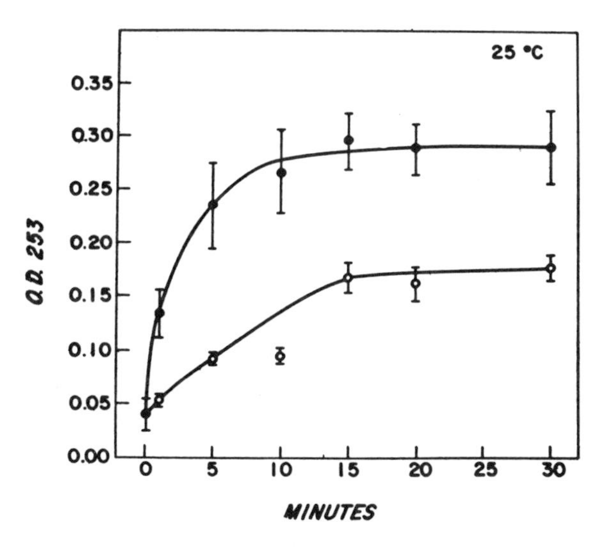

FIG. 8. Uptake of plain latex (solid circles) and latex coated with glucose oxidase (open circles) by normal human leukocytes. The bars indicate the standard error of the mean. The ordinate is absorbence of the solubilized latex read at 253 mm. For further details consult (36).

of ^{14}C-formate oxidation and glucose-1-^{14}C oxidation was less in normal PMN phagocytizing latex coated with glucose oxidase compared to the response observed with uncoated latex. However, as noted in Fig. 9, the oxidative responses were almost similar when CGD and normal cells ingested the enzyme-coated latex. Thus, insertion of hydrogen peroxide producing glucose oxidase into phagocytic vacuoles of CGD PMN improved the metabolic deficiencies in these cells since hydrogen peroxide-dependent ^{14}C-formate oxidation and glucose-1-^{14}C

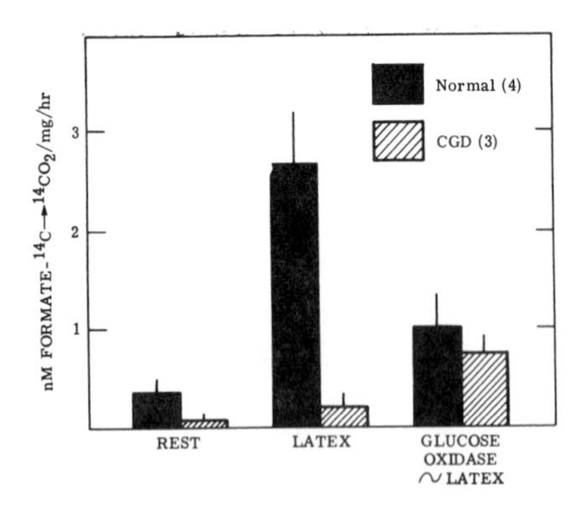

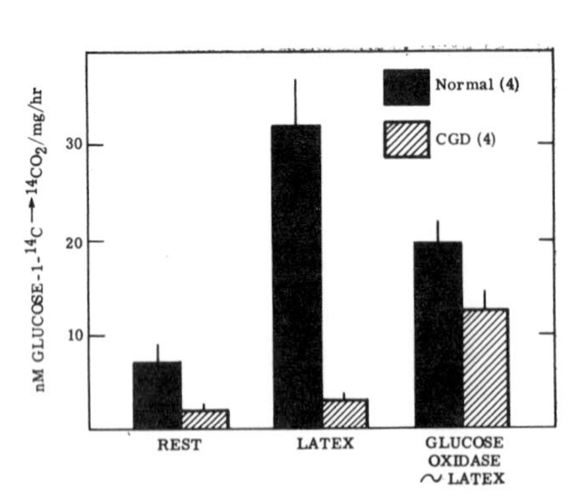

FIG. 9. Rate of formate-^{14}C oxidation (left) and glucose-1-^{14}C oxidation by control and CGD leukocytes at rest, during phagocytosis of plain latex, and during phagocytosis of latex coated with glucose oxidase. For further details consult (36).

oxidation by the HMP were normalized. Similar studies also showed improvement of the CGD PMN in killing *S. aureus* and *S. marcescens* (37). These data strengthen the evidence that the fundamental metabolic lesion in CGD cells during phagocytosis is indeed deficient production of hydrogen peroxide, probably due to diminished oxidase activity.

Studies of Bacterial Killing

The early observations by the Minnesota group (Fig. 10) that CGD PMN could kill streptococci and the recognition of the role of hydrogen peroxide in bacterial killing added greatly to our present understanding of the unique bactericidal defect in CGD. In that regard, Mandell and Hook (38) showed that CGD leukocytes were able to kill catalase negative bacteria that produce hydrogen peroxide, i.e., *Lactobacillus acidophilous.* Klebanoff's (39) observation that iodination of live *L. acidophilous* and *Streptococcus faecalis* is greater than that of dead organisms would offer a rational explanation for the selective killing lesion observed in these patients' leukocytes. Holmes and co-workers (40) and Pitt and co-workers (41) have utilized mutant strains of bacteria to emphasize that catalase positive strains of the same species are not killed whereas catalase negative mutants are killed normally by CGD PMN. This fact is also apparent when one

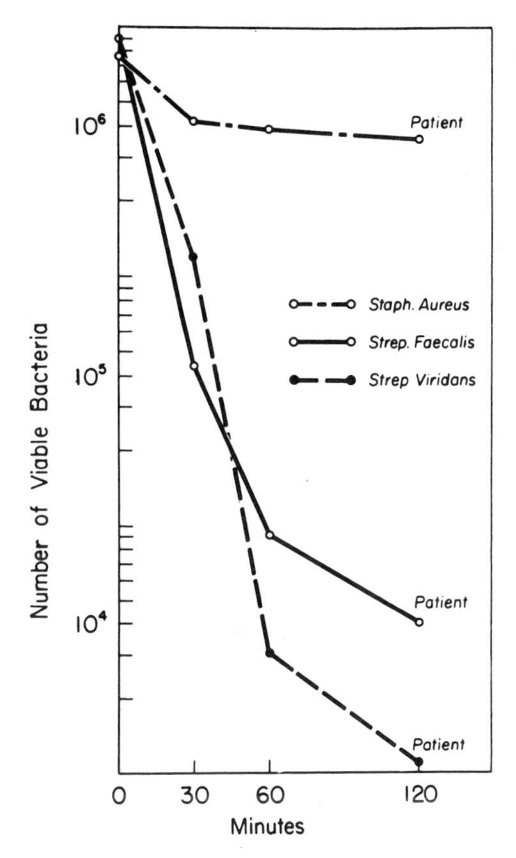

FIG. 10. The results of killing of three separate species of bacteria by CGD PMN noted that the catalase negative streptococci were killed normally but that there was an inability to kill the catalase positive staphylococci. For further details consult (8). Graph printed by permission of authors.

observes the list of microorganisms commonly cultured from infected foci in these patients (Table 3). Hydrogen peroxide producing catalase negative bacteria such as pneumococci, enteric streptococci, and *Hemophilus influenzae* which are common pathogens in childhood do not cause serious infections in these patients. Thus, the *in vivo* information clearly supports the conclusion based on *in vitro* studies that CGD PMN can kill microorganisms provided that adequate peroxide generated from any source is available in the cell (probably in the phagocytic vacuole).

Genetic Studies

During our studies of CGD, we added nitroblue tetrazolium (NBT) to CGD and normal PMN at rest and during phagocytosis (31). This approach was based

TABLE 3. *Microbials most commonly cultured from purulent foci in children with CGD*

Organism	Number of patients[a]
Staphylococcus aureus	58
Klebsiella-Aerobacter organisms	22
E. coli	19
Staphylococcus albus	10
Serratia marcescens	9
Candida albicans	7
Pseudomonas organisms	7
Aspergillus organisms	6
Proteus organisms	5
Salmonella organisms	4
Paracolobactrum organisms	4
Streptococci	3
Other enteric bacteria	6
Other organisms[b]	3

[a] Refers to number of different patients from whom that organism was cultured.
[b] *Nocardia* organisms, two; *Actinomyces israelii*, one.
Data previously published by Johnston and Baehner (6).

on the concept that the oxidative perturbations that occur during phagocytosis might be associated with transfer of electrons to the tetrazolium dye. We found a marked increase in NBT reduction in normal PMN during ingestion of latex particles and that this reaction had a pH optimum of 7.0 and a temperature optimum of 37°C (42). We utilized a simple incubation system involving a known number of latex spherules, NBT and PMN at standard concentration and volume, and incubated the suspension for 15 min; the reaction was stopped with acid, the leukocytes were pelleted by centrifugation, and the purple formazan within the cells was extracted with pyridine. This established a quantitative determination of reduction of NBT as shown in Fig. 11. Male and female CGD patients had deficient reduction of their PMN both at rest and during phagocytosis. The mothers of male patients had intermediate reduction of NBT supporting the theory that the disease was due to a genetic defect on the X-chromosome. Studies by Quie and co-workers (7) and Macfarlane and co-workers (43) indicated that the X-linked carrier state could be detected by an intermediate degree of bacterial killing as well as intermediate abnormalities in oxygen consumption and the HMP. Windhorst and her co-workers (44) adopted the quantitative NBT test as a cytologic tool and demonstrated that between 30 to 70% of the PMN of female carriers reduced NBT whereas the remainder did not. This histochemical test provided excellent evidence of X-inactivation and the Lyon hypothesis in the carrier situation. Further studies by Klebanoff and White (9) using autoradiographic techniques showed that one population of PMN's from carriers iodinate ingested bacteria whereas another equal population did not iodinate them.

It was also noted that the mothers of affected female patients had normal

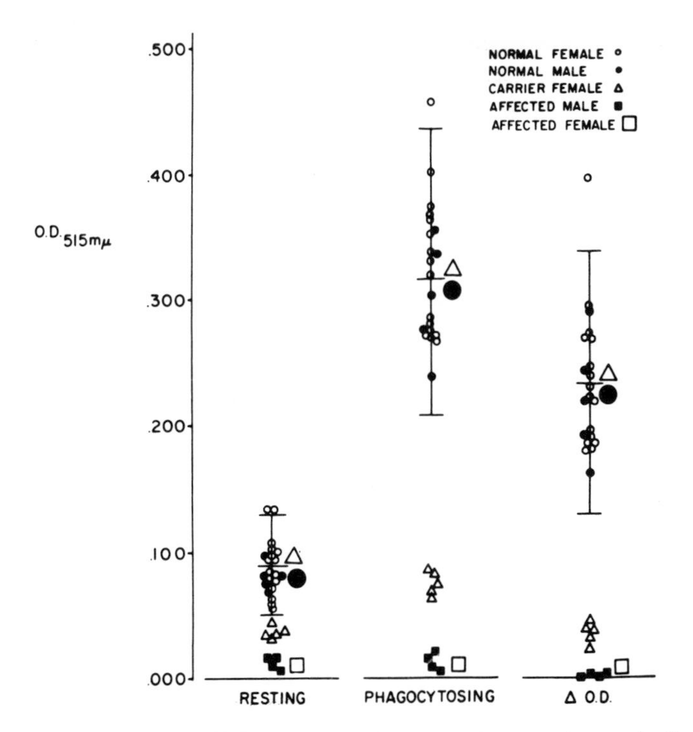

FIG. 11. Results of quantitative NBT dye test performed on 21 normal controls, five mothers of affected males, and four affected males. The results obtained in the affected female and her parents are indicated by the larger symbols. For additional details consult (42).

quantitative reduction of NBT and normal bactericidal activity; in one case the parents were first cousins which suggested an autosomal recessive inheritance pattern (42). Other female patients have been reported by Quie and co-workers (45) and Azimi et al. (46); more than a dozen female patients with CGD have now been reported (6). The suggestion by Soothill and co-workers (47) that all cases of CGD involve sex-modified autosomal inheritance was based on the presence of a microbicidal defect in the PMN of their fathers, but Barnes and co-workers studied the same father and could not confirm this finding (48). Holmes and co-workers (49) reported a deficiency of glutathione peroxidase in the PMN of female patients; it is not clear how this might relate to decreased hydrogen peroxide bactericidal activity in these cells.

Additional Studies on NBT

The metabolic and morphologic aspects of the NBT test in PMN has been under investigation since 1966. Nathan (25) studied the morphologic basis of formazan production in PMN and monocytes and observed that during zymosan ingestion NBT reduction occurred in the region of the phagocytic vacuole. Dye reduction was initially evident at the point of contact between the particle and the cell membrane, which suggested a relationship to activation of an oxidative membrane enzyme. He also showed that NBT does not enter fresh PMN in suspension, probably because the charge prevents it from transversing the membrane of the cell. NBT may enter PMN that are spread on glass slides since the cell membrane is altered by this maneuver. This fact has been utilized by Gifford and Malawista (50) for a microadaptation of the NBT test using PMN adherent glass slides. Park (51) has demonstrated an increase in the spontaneous reduction of NBT by resting PMN in patients with acute bacterial infection. This has been confirmed by Feigin and others (52) and does provide a useful method to help differentiate bacterial from nonbacterial infection in the early phases of the illness and prior to use of antibiotic therapy.

Matola and Patterson (53) have shown that exposure of PMN in whole blood to endotoxin will produce the identical response seen in the early phase of acute bacterial infection. Since NBT is reduced in the region of phagocytic vacuoles, it apparently substitutes for oxygen as a hydrogen acceptor. This is shown in Fig. 12, which is a polarographic determination of oxygen consumption in human

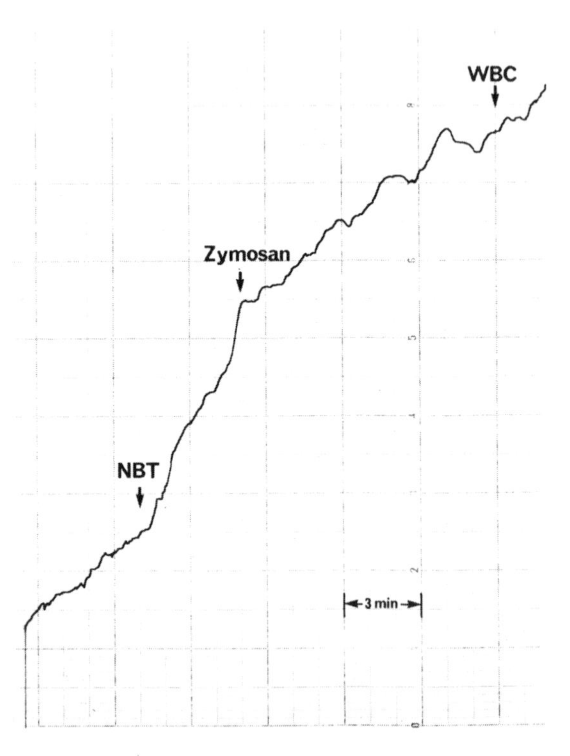

FIG. 12. Effect of NBT reduction to formazan on oxygen consumption by phagocytizing PMN. Polarographic estimation of oxygen consumption was obtained using the oxygen electrode (Yellow Springs Instrument Co., Ohio) and a 3-ml suspension of PMN at a final concentration of 1.0×10^7 ml^{-1}. Note the diminished oxygen consumption during reduction of NBT by PMN.

PMN and indicates that the respiratory burst during phagocytosis is decreased upon addition of NBT to the suspension; as the NBT is reduced to formazan, oxygen consumption decreases. The hydrogen donor for this reaction in PMN could be either reduced pyridine nucleotides; NADH or NADPH both will reduce NBT to purple formazan in the presence of cell cytolysates.

ROLE OF SUPEROXIDE IN NORMAL AND CGD PMN

The recent studies by Fridovich and McCord (54, 55) have demonstrated that hydrogen peroxide producing oxidases generate unstable highly reactive intermediate radicals; the two best characterized being the hydroperoxyl ($HO_2^{\cdot}$) radical and the superoxide anion ($O_2^{\cdot}$). Since ground state oxygen contains two unpaired electrons, oxidation-reduction reactions involving oxygen usually proceed by one electron steps, thus creating these free radical intermediates. Both $O_2^{\cdot}$ and $HO_2^{\cdot}$ radicals undergo spontaneous dismutation to yield $O_2 + H_2O_2$ at a pH optimum of 4.8. At physiologic pH, low levels of $O_2^{\cdot}$ could accumulate and be toxic for living cells. It is reasonable that a dismutating enzyme, superoxide dismutase (SOD) which catalyzes the reaction $O_2^{\cdot} + O_2^{\cdot} + 2H^{+} \rightarrow O_2 + H_2O_2$, was found and that it was widely distributed within mammalian organisms in aerobic cells. This enzyme contains copper and zinc, which are required for its activity, and was first purified from bovine erythrocytes.

Fridovich observed that xanthine oxidase which catalyzes the oxidation of xanthine to urate also reduced cytochrome C (Cyto-C) and NBT. This reduction could be abolished by addition of SOD. This observation led to an assay for $O_2^{\cdot}$ which involves the inhibition of the $O_2^{\cdot}$ mediated reduction of either Cyto-C or NBT by SOD.

Babior, Kipnes, and Curnutte (56) have documented that human PMN generate $O_2^{\cdot}$ since the observed reduction of Cyto-C by phagocytizing PMN could be completely inhibited by SOD. They (57) have also reported that CGD PMN fail to reduce Cyto-C, which suggests that the superoxide anion is not generated by these defective cells. As noted in Table 4, we have performed similar studies on PMN from four patients with CGD (three with the X-linked form and one female with the autosomal recessive form) confirmed by the quantitative NBT test. None of the CGD PMN reduced Cyto-C at rest or during phagocytosis. The carrier state could not be identified since only one of four carriers previously detected by the NBT test had PMN which did not reduce Cyto-C normally. These data

TABLE 4. *Superoxide ($O_2^{\cdot}$) production by PMN from patients and carriers of CGD*

	$\Delta OD_{553}/3 \times 10^6$ PMN/60 min
Controls (4)	0.217 ± 0.010
Carriers (4)	0.198 ± 0.031
Patients (4)	0.026 ± 0.007

The method was that of Babior et a (56).

support the concept that O_2^- generating oxidase activity is defective or absent in CGD PMN.

Similar to our previous studies with glucose oxidase, the binding of SOD to latex particles provides a simple convenient system to deplete phagocytizing PMN phagocytic vesicles of superoxide. Using this system, Johnston and co-workers (58) have found that bacterial killing was inhibited in PMN that were simultaneously phagocytizing bacteria and latex coated with SOD compared to PMN phagocytizing bacteria and latex coated with bovine serum albumin (BSA). The rate of ingestion of bacteria and latex was similar for the SOD and BSA samples. These data suggest that superoxide may play a role in bacterial killing in phagocytizing PMN.

Since SOD rapidly depletes the phagocytic vacuole of O_2^- in the above system, the rate of hydrogen peroxide production from the reduction of O_2^- should likely be increased. We have utilized this system to gain further insight into the relative contribution of O_2^- and hydrogen peroxide to stimulation of the HMP and to ^{125}I fixation of ingested particles. As noted in Fig. 13, the rate of oxygen consumption

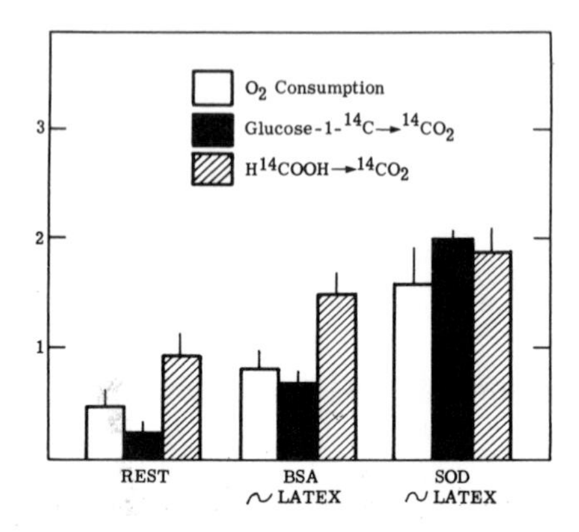

FIG. 13. Effect of addition of SOD-coated latex particles and BSA-coated latex particles to PMN. The ingestion rate of both particles was similar. The influence of SOD on increased oxygen consumption, glucose-1-^{14}C oxidation, and formate-^{14}C oxidation by PMN can be noted. Data are expressed as a ratio and not in absolute values.

and ^{14}C-formate oxidation was increased confirming that SOD stimulates both the rate of the respiratory burst and hydrogen peroxide production. As expected, the rate of glucose-1-^{14}C oxidation was also increased presumably because of the added stimulation by hydrogen peroxide. Similarly, the rate of iodination of zymosan particles was increased in PMN ingesting latex coated with SOD compared to latex coated with BSA (Table 5). Under similar conditions, NBT reduction was decreased but not completely inhibited by SOD (Table 6). These studies suggest that glucose-1-^{14}C oxidation and ^{125}I fixation of ingested particles are dependent upon hydrogen peroxide whereas NBT reduction by PMN is due in part to O_2^- generation, which is lacking in PMN from patients with CGD.

TABLE 5. *Effect of SOD on iodination of zymosan particles by phagocytizing PMN*

Time (sec)	cpm/10^7 PMN	
	Latex ~ BSA (8)	Latex ~ SOD (8)
0	81 ± 2[a]	102 ± 12
15	706 ± 106	1,059 ± 129
30	1,423 ± 136	2,886 ± 379
60	2,077 ± 237	4,063 ± 404

[a] x ± SE.
Latex ~ BSA means latex coated with 0.1 mg BSA.
Latex ~ SOD means latex coated with 0.1 mg SOD.

TABLE 6. *Effect of SOD on NBT reduction by PMN*

	OD_{515}/15 min/10^7 cells	
	(5) +.1 mg BSA	(5) +.1 mg SOD
Rest	.139 ± .005	.055 ± .006
Phago	.337 ± .018	.129 ± .012

Method used was that of Baehner and Nathan (42). Numbers in parentheses refer to number of studies performed.

TREATMENT OF CGD

Effective treatment of CGD is still inadequate. If a deficiency of hydrogen peroxide generation is central to defective bactericidal activity in these phagocytes, then we must find a way to restore a continuous supply of hydrogen peroxide to the phagocytic vacuoles of the PMN. The rapid hourly turnover of PMN in the circulation demands a continuously available system producing hydrogen peroxide in PMN just emerging into the bloodstream. The presence of soluble catalase in each PMN serves as a molecular sponge to prevent hydrogen peroxide transfer between phagocytic vacuoles. Therefore, it would seem likely that the "generator" of hydrogen peroxide must be closely associated with most, if not all, phagocytic vacuoles containing viable bacteria. The bacteria ingested by the CGD PMN are shielded by the membrane of the phagocytic vacuole which protects the bacteria from the lethal effects of antibiotics. Holmes (59) has clearly demonstrated this effect *in vitro.*

The search for treatment of CGD patients has included the use of a variety of drugs that are nontoxic but provide an adequate and continuous source of peroxide. In that regard, certain oxidant drugs such as methylene blue, sulfanamides, and quinone compounds have been tried with limited success *in vivo*. The evaluation of any of these therapies must be on a continuous and long-term basis since the clinical course of affected patients is quite variable. Even without treatment, some patients do very well and live into young adult life despite repeated visceral and cutaneous infection. It seems that patients with CGD are always infected to some extent. Once the diagnosis is established, acute flare-ups of infection can be treated by long-term parenteral high dosage antibiotics. This approach seems to have decreased the need for surgical drainage in the majority of instances as evident in Fig. 14 (61). The question of whether these patients

OPERATIVE INTERVENTION (11 Patients)

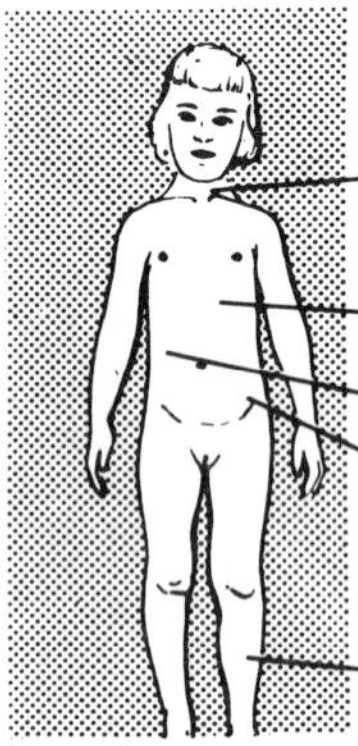

PROCEDURE	BEFORE Dx	AFTER Dx
I & D Node biopsy	~67/9	0
Thoracotomy	2/2	0
Drainage, RUQ	11/5	2/2
Drainage, Retroperitoneum	4/1	0
Drainage, Osteo	7/3	0

FIG. 14. Operative procedures performed in 11 patients. The contrast is between the number of procedures performed on each patient before and after the diagnosis of CGD was established. For further details consult (61).

should receive continuous antibiotic therapy between bouts of obvious infection remains unanswered. Our preliminary studies in a small group of patients suggest that such an approach may be of benefit. As noted in Table 7, five of six such children have spent fewer days in the hospital since they were placed on this therapy (62).

We still look forward to better methods of treatment designed to improve the basic biochemical lesion in these cells. Hopefully, children now afflicted with CGD will soon receive therapy that will correct completely their inherited susceptibility to recurrent chronic infection. Through the continued and coordinated efforts of basic science and clinical science, this final goal will be achieved.

ACKNOWLEDGMENTS

Part of the work reported in this chapter was supported by the Riley Memorial Association and National Institutes of Health grant AI 10892–01.

TABLE 7. *Comparison of number of days patient spent in hospital before and after continuous nafcillin therapy*[a]

Case	Age (yr)	Duration therapy (yr)	Hospital days/year	
			before treatment	after treatment
L.D.	21	5	40	41
M.D.	10	4	79	18
C.G.	27	3	47	0
P.L.	17	2	49	0
P.L.	17	2	42	0
T.L.	9	2	25	0

[a] Requirements for hospitalization expressed as hospital days per year before and after initiation of continuous nafcillin therapy. Years were calculated from time of onset of disease in sites other than lymph nodes.
Data previously published by Philippart, Colodny, and Baehner (61).

REFERENCES

1. Holmes, B., Quie, P. G., Windhorst, D. B., and Good, R. A.: Fatal granulomatous disease of childhood: An inborn abnormality of phagocytic function. *Lancet* 1:1225, 1966.
2. Janeway, C. A., Craig, J., Davidson, M., Downey, W., Gitlin, D., and Sullivan, J. C.: Hypergammaglobulinemia associated with severe recurrent and chronic nonspecific infection. *Am. J. Dis. Child.* 88:388, 1954.
3. Berendes, H., Bridges, R. A., and Good, R. A.: Fatal granulomatous of childhood: Clinical study of a new syndrome. *Minn. Med.* 40:309, 1957.
4. Landing, B. H., and Shirkey, H. S.: A syndrome of recurrent infection and infiltration of viscera by pigmented lipid histiocytes. *Pediatrics* 20:431, 1957.
5. Carson, M. J., Chadwick, D. L., Brubaker, C. A., Cleland, R. S., and Landing, B. H.: Thirteen boys with progressive septic granulomatosis. *Pediatrics* 35:405, 1968.
6. Johnston, R. B., Jr., and Baehner, R. L.: Chronic granulomatous disease: Correlation between pathogenesis and clinical findings. *Pediatrics* 48:730, 1971.
7. Quie, P. G., White, J. G., Holmes, B., and Good, R. A.: *In vitro* bactericidal capacity of human polymorphonuclear leukocytes: Diminished activity in chronic granulomatous disease of childhood. *J. Clin. Invest.* 46:668, 1967.
8. Kaplan, E. L., Laxdal, T., and Quie, P. G.: Studies of polymorphonuclear leukocytes from patients with chronic granulomatous disease of childhood: Bactericidal capacity for streptococci. *Pediatrics* 41:591, 1968.
9. Klebanoff, S. J., and White, L. R.: Iodinating defect in the leukocytes of a patient with chronic granulomatous disease of childhood. *N. Engl. J. Med.* 280:460, 1969.
10. Sbarra, A. J., and Karnovsky, M. L.: The biochemical basis of phagocytosis. I. Metabolic changes during the ingestion of particles by polymorphonuclear leukocytes. *J. Biol. Chem.* 234:1355, 1959.
11. Karnovsky, M. L.: Metabolic basis of phagocytic activity. *Physiol. Rev.* 42:143, 1962.
12. Cohn, Z. A., and Hirsch, J. G.: The influence of phagocytosis on the intracellular distribution of granule-associated components of polymorphonuclear leukocytes. *J. Exp. Med.* 112:983, 1960.
13. Hirsch, J. G.: Cinemicrophotographic observation of granule lysis in polymorphonuclear leukocytes during phagocytosis. *J. Exp. Med.* 116:827, 1962.

14. Iyer, G. Y., Islam, M. F., and Quastel, J. H.: Biochemical aspects of phagocytosis. *Nature* 192:535, 1961.
15. Paul, B., and Sbarra, A. J.: The role of phagocyte in host-parasite interactions. XIII. The direct quantitative estimation of H_2O_2 in phagocytizing cells. *Biochim. Biophys. Acta* 156:168, 1968.
16. Baehner, R. L., Gilman, N., and Karnovsky, M. L.: Respiration and glucose oxidation in human and guinea pig leukocytes—Comparative studies. *J. Clin. Invest.* 49:692, 1970.
17. Baehner, R. L., Nathan, D. G., and Castle, W. B.: Oxidant injury of caucasian glucose-6-phosphate dehydrogenase-deficient red blood cells by phagocytizing leukocytes during infection. *J. Clin. Invest.* 50:2466, 1971.
18. Baehner, R. L., Johnston, R. B., Jr., and Nathan, D. G.: Comparative study of the metabolic and bactericidal characteristics of severe glucose-6-phosphate dehydrogenase deficient polymorphonuclear leukocytes and leukocytes from children with chronic granulomatous disease. *J. Reticuloendothel. Soc.* 12:150, 1972.
19. McRipley, R. J., and Sbarra, A. J.: Role of the phagocyte in host parasite interactions. XI. Relationship between stimulated oxidative metabolism and hydrogen peroxide formation and intracellular killing. *J. Bacteriol.* 94:1417, 1967.
20. Klebanoff, S. J., Clem, W. H., and Luebke, R. G.: The peroxidase-thiocyanate-hydrogen peroxide antimicrobial system. *Biochim. Biophys. Acta* 117:63, 1966.
21. Klebanoff, S. J.: Myeloperoxidase-halide-hydrogen peroxide antibacterial system. *J. Bacteriol.* 95:2131, 1968.
22. Klebanoff, S. J.: Myeloperoxidase: Contribution to the microbicidal activity of intact leukocytes. *Science* 169:1095, 1970.
23. Baehner, R. L., Karnovsky, M. T., and Karnovsky, M. L.: Degranulation of leukocytes in chronic granulomatous disease. *J. Clin. Invest.* 47:187, 1969.
24. Kauder, E., Kahle, L. L., Morene, H., and Partin, J. C.: Leukocyte degranulation and vacuole formation in patients with chronic granulomatous disease of childhood. *J. Clin. Invest.* 47:1753, 1968.
25. Nathan, D. G., Baehner, R. L., and Weaver, D. K.: Failure of nitroblue tetrazolium reduction in the phagocytic vacuoles of leukocytes in chronic granulomatous disease. *J. Clin. Invest.* 48:1895, 1969.
26. Elsbach, P., Zucker-Franklin, D., and Sansarioq, C.: Increased lecithin synthesis during phagocytosis by normal leukocytes and by leukocytes in chronic granulomatous diseases. *N. Engl. J. Med.* 280:1319, 1969.
27. Mandell, G. L., and Hook, E. W.: Leukocyte function in chronic granulomatous disease of childhood. *Am. J. Med.* 47:473, 1969.
28. Stossel, T. P., Pollard, T. D., Mason, R. J., and Vaughan, M.: Isolation and properties of phagocytic vesicles from polymorphonuclear leukocytes. *J. Clin. Invest.* 51:604, 1972.
29. Stossel, T. P., Root, R. K., and Vaughan, M.: Phagocytosis in chronic granulomatous disease and the Chediak-Higashi syndrome. *N. Engl. J. Med.* 286:120, 1972.
30. Gold, S. B., Hanes, D. M., Stites, D. P., Ponce, B., and Fudenberg, H. H.: Abnormal kinetics of polymorphonuclear leukocyte (PMN) degranulation in chronic granulomatous disease (CGD). *Blood* 42:982a, 1973.
31. Baehner, R. L., and Nathan, D. G.: Leukocyte oxidase: Defective activity in chronic granulomatous disease. *Science* 155:835, 1967.
32. Holmes, B., Page, A. R., and Good, R. A.: Studies of the metabolic activity of leukocytes from patients with a genetic abnormality of phagocytic function. *J. Clin. Invest.* 46:1422, 1967.
33. Bellanti, J. A., Cantz, B. E., and Schlegel, R. J.: Accelerated decay of glucose-6-phosphate dehydrogenase activity in chronic granulomatous disease. *Pediatr. Res.* 4:405, 1970.
34. Patriarca, P., Cramer, R., Marussi, S., Rossi, F., and Romeo, D.: Mode of activation of granule-bound NADPH oxidase in leukocytes during phagocytosis. *Biochim. Biophys. Acta* 237:335, 1971.
35. Patriarca, P., Cramer, R., Moncalvo, S., Rossi, F., and Romeo, D.: Enzymatic basis of metabolic stimulation in leukocytes during phagocytosis: The role of activated NADPH oxidase. *Arch. Biochem. Biophys.* 145:255, 1971.
36. Baehner, R. L., Nathan, D. G., and Karnovsky, M. L.: Correction of metabolic deficiencies in the leukocytes of patients with chronic granulomatous disease. *J. Clin. Invest.* 49:865, 1970.
37. Johnston, R. B., Jr., and Baehner, R. L.: Improvement of leukocyte bactericidal activity in chronic granulomatous disease. *Blood* 35:350, 1970.

38. Mandell, G. L., and Hook, E. W.: Leukocyte bactericidal activity in chronic granulomatous disease: Correlation of bacterial hydrogen peroxide production and susceptibility to intracellular killing. *J. Bacteriol.* 100:531, 1969.
39. Pincus, S. H., and Klebanoff, S. J.: Quantitative leukocyte iodination. *N. Engl. J. Med.* 284:744, 1971.
40. Holmes, B., and Good, R. A.: Laboratory models of chronic granulomatous disease. *J. Reticuloendothel. Soc.* 12:216, 1972.
41. Shohet, S., Pitt, J., Baehner, R. L., and Poplack, D.: Lipid changes and bacterial killing in phagocytes of peroxide and non-peroxide producing pneumococci. *J. Clin. Invest.* 51:89a, 1972.
42. Baehner, R. L., and Nathan, D. G.: Quantitative nitroblue tetrazolium test in chronic granulomatous disease. *N. Engl. J. Med.* 278:971, 1968.
43. Macfarlane, P. S., Speirs, A. L., and Sommerville, R. G.: Fatal granulomatous disease of childhood and benign lymphocytic infiltration of the skin (congenital dysphagocytosis). *Lancet* 1:408, 1967.
44. Windhorst, D. B., Holmes, B., and Good, R. A.: A newly diagnosed X-linked trait in man with demonstration of the Lyon effect in carrier females. *Lancet* 1:737, 1967.
45. Quie, P. G., Kaplan, E. L., Page, A. R., Grusky, F. L., and Malawista, S. F.: Defective polymorphonuclear-leukocyte function and chronic granulomatous disease in two female children. *N. Engl. J. Med.* 278:976, 1968.
46. Azimi, P., Bodenbender, J. G., Hintz, R. L., and Kontras, S. B.: Chronic granulomatous disease in three sisters. *Lancet* 1:208, 1968.
47. Chandra, R. K., Cope, W. A., and Soothill, J. F.: Chronic granulomatous disease. Evidence for an autosomal mode of inheritance. *Lancet* 2:71, 1969.
48. Barnes, R. D., Bishun, N. P., and Holliday, J.: Impaired lymphocyte transformation and chromosomal abnormalities in fatal granulomatous disease of childhood. *Acta Paediatr. Scand.* 59:403, 1970.
49. Holmes, B., Park, B. H., Malawista, S. E., Quie, P. G., Nelson, D. L., and Good, R. A.: Chronic granulomatous disease in females: Deficiency of leukocyte glutathione peroxidase. *N. Engl. J. Med.* 283:217, 1970.
50. Gifford, R. H., and Malawista, S. E.: A simple rapid micromethod for detecting chronic granulomatous disease of childhood. *J. Lab. Clin. Med.* 75:511, 1970.
51. Park, B. H., Fikrig, S. M., and Smithwick, E. M.: Infection and nitroblue tetrazolium reduction by neutrophils. *Lancet* 2:532, 1968.
52. Feigin, R. D., Shackelford, P. G., Choi, S. C., Flake, K. K., Franklin, F. A., Jr., and Eisenberg, C. S.: Nitroblue tetrazolium dye test as an aid in the differential diagnosis of febrile disorders. *Pediatrics* 78:230, 1971.
53. Matola, G., and Patterson, P. Y.: Reduction of nitroblue tetrazolium by neutrophils of adults with infection. *N. Engl. J. Med.* 285:311, 1971.
54. McCord, J. M., and Fridovich, I.: Superoxide dismutase: An enzymatic function for erythrocuprein (hemocuprein). *J. Biol. Chem.* 244:6049, 1969.
55. Fridovich, I.: Superoxide radical and superoxide dismutase. *Accounts Chem. Res.* 5:321, 1972.
56. Babior, B. M., Kipnes, R. S., and Curnutte, J. T.: Biological defense mechanisms. The production by leukocytes of superoxide, a potential bactericidal agent. *J. Clin. Invest.* 52:741, 1973.
57. Curnutte, J. T., Whitten, D. M., and Babior, B. M.: Defective superoxide production by granulocytes from patients with chronic granulomatous disease. *N. Engl. J. Med.* 290:593–597, 1974.
58. Johnston, R. B., Jr., Keele, B., Webb, L., Kessler, D., and Rajagopalan, K. V.: Inhibition of phagocytic bactericial activity by superoxide dismutase: A possible role for superoxide anion in the killing of phagocytized bacteria. Presented to the American Society for Clinical Investigation, Atlantic City, April 30, 1973.
59. Holmes, B., Quie, P. G., Windhorst, D. B., Pollara, B., and Good, R. A.: Protection of phagocytized bacteria from the killing action of antibiotics. *Nature* 210:1131, 1966.
60. Baehner, R. L., and Karnovsky, M. L.: Deficiency of reduced nicotinamide adenine dinucleotide oxidase in chronic granulomatous disease. *Science* 162:1277, 1968.
61. Philippart, A. I., Colodny, A. H., and Baehner, R. L.: Chronic granulomatous disease of childhood. *J. Ped. Surg.* 4:85, 1969.
62. Philippart, A. I., Colodny, A. H., and Baehner, R. L.: Continuous antibiotic therapy in chronic granulomatous disease: Preliminary communication. *Pediatrics* 50:923, 1972.

DISCUSSION

Ward: Is it really fair, in looking at the question of whether or not lysosomal granule fusion and discharge is defective in these leukocytes, to use things like zymosan? What is the situation if one uses the organisms that these patients get into trouble with? Do you find normal fusion and enzyme release under those conditions?

Baehner: We used a variety of particles in our degranulation studies including one microorganism that does produce infection in these children, i.e., *E. coli.* But I think your point is well taken. Perhaps one should look at a large number of microorganisms that infect these patients in order to answer your question very completely. Another point to be emphasized is the sensitivity of methods to study the rate of degranulation especially in the early phases of phagocytosis. Dr. Stossel's study was performed with emulsified paraffin oil and looked at shift of granule enzyme into the phagocytic vacuole at 15 minutes.

Stossel: I could amplify that. There is really no evidence that the problem in these patients has to do with getting the bacteria into the cell, and the epidemiology of infections and the studies Jane Pitt did with the peroxide positive and negative mutants really suggest the trouble is after, in the killing. But just in terms of the ingestion, I think the degranulation rate is very much tied up in the ingestion rate. And looking carefully at a large number of patients with rate of ingestion, we found that although they were all in the normal range they were clustered at the lower end of normal. And there is that interesting patient Ward described who had CGD but also had a chemotactic defect. We have seen a similar patient who had CGD by the usual criteria. One wonders whether some of the patients have circulating immune complexes that paralyze the cell and whether some of the controversy around degranulation really revolves around secondary phenomena.

Sbarra: Were there any differences in superoxide concentration in the three populations that you studied? Perhaps you gave differences between resting and phagocytizing, but I missed that fact.

Baehner: I didn't show the resting and phagocytizing values of the groups. In that regard, the one female carrier had a normal resting level but a low phagocytic value. The other three female carriers had normal resting and phagocytic values.

Sbarra: There was an actual decrease?

Baehner: Yes. In the one female carrier. Of course the patients with chronic granulomatous disease had profound depression of their phagocytic responses as I already indicated.

Karnovsky: In view of what Dr. Spitznagel said about phosphatases and their localization in human PMN, how are we going to reconcile what you say—and what I say, too—concerning the release of this enzyme from a granule fraction and the appearance of soluble enzyme during phagocytosis? He said, I think, that the alkaline phosphatase is not a granule enzyme.

The second point is that when one adds NBT to the cells one is doing a very odd thing. We are offering a chance to decrease oxygen consumption by simply dumping hydrogen electrons via diaphorases onto the NBT. We are essentially blocking some of the formation of superoxide because I don't think there is any evidence that the reduction of NBT *per se* produces any superoxide. On the one hand you are siphoning off hydrogen onto NBT which then is not available for terminal oxidation to form your O_2-minus which again would reduce NBT. I think we have a very complicated, funny balance in which we are striking into the enzyme sequence and siphoning off the hydrogen and also preventing by that maneuver the formation of a second NBT-reducing substance.

Baehner: Although alkaline phosphatase may be somewhat atypical as a prototype lysosomal granule enzyme, it does shift from the granule into phagocytic vacuoles. Furthermore, alkaline phosphatase activity is observed in the soluble fraction of subcellular components obtained from leukocyte homogenates after phagocytosis.

My explanation of the NBT response is that two mechanisms are simultaneously in operation in the phagocytizing PMN. As you know, in a cell free system, such as the system which generates superoxide from xanthine catalyzed by xanthine oxidase, NBT is reduced to formazan. The proof that superoxide is responsible for NBT reduction lies in the additional observation that depletion of superoxide from the system by superoxide dismutase (SOD) results in the inhibition of NBT reduction to formazan. Since we have observed inhibition of NBT reduction by PMN ingesting latex coated with SOD, we conclude that superoxide is available for NBT reduction in PMN. As you point out, the depression in oxygen consumption during NBT reduction clearly indicates that NBT reduction can also be due to the direct transfer of hydrogen ion from hydrogen donors, i.e., NADH and NADPH to NBT.

Karnovsky: But my point is that you would actually be interfering with superoxide production if the NBT were sopping up the reduced nucleotides.

Baehner: That is right but still some superoxide must be formed since we can inhibit NBT reduction appreciably by addition of superoxide dismutase.

Karnovsky: I think that the effect is really at the primary step. And you felt adding superoxide dismutase should increase oxygen consumption which you showed, and that indicated that whatever it is that is the oxidative step, the main step for oxidizing reduced pyridine nucleotides is not rate-limiting in these cells. This is very surprising to me.

Baehner: Why would you be surprised at that?

Karnovsky: Because you and I found only an adequate minimal amount of oxidase. And therefore I would have assumed it might be limiting unless it works at a pH far below 7, like about 6 or 5.5. I think we would be unjust not to stress the fact that the Italian group, Rossi et al., have a completely different enzyme sequence and seem to be able to justify a TPNH oxidase on the basis of adequate enzyme levels which you and I couldn't detect. Marion Stubbs in our laboratory made a really Herculean effort to find enough of this and was unable to. Dr. Rossi and I have had numerous long talks and have come to the conclusion that if I went to his laboratory I would get his results, and if anybody from his laboratory came to us they'd get our results; we can't solve the problem by talking.

Baehner: One of the problems in our studies was that they were performed on resting polymorphonuclear cells and not on phagocytic polymorphonuclear cells.

Karnovsky: We have studied phagocytic cells since.

Sbarra: I haven't seen the data.

Karnovsky: I am not surprised since we haven't published those data. Your criticism was quite a reasonable one, but it doesn't affect the issue. The DPNH oxidase is raised maybe 20 percent.

Sbarra: You have shown a defect in oxidase and also a defect in superoxide production. On the basis of these two findings, would you expect to find other deficiencies? In other words, are these specific or is there a general defect in all activities in these cells?

Baehner: I think we can explain the failure of superoxide generation in CGD polys by the lack of NADH oxidase. As you know, superoxide is an intermediate unstable radical generated by many oxidases which then form hydrogen peroxide.

Sbarra: I meant supposing you measured another unrelated soluble enzyme in the cell. Would that be decreased in CGD as opposed to normal?

Baehner: I don't know the answer to that.

Klebanoff: Why would you believe that it would be?

Sbarra: I don't necessarily believe that. I simply wondered if there is a general decrease in enzyme activity in the CGD cell or is this a specific decrease?

Holmes-Gray: In the studies done on degranulation with aggregated gamma-globulin, LDH was the marker and cells from CGD patients had normal activity.

Snyderman: Did they have a normal lysosomal pattern?

Holmes-Gray: Yes.

Snyderman: In terms of electrophoretic gradient, this might be expected to act differently.

Bellanti: We have also looked at lactic acid dehydrogenase levels in our laboratory in three cases of the X-linked variety of CGD and found them to be normal. But I'd like to raise the question that has never been adequately answered of an observation which we made a few years ago of an accelerated rate of decay of G-6-PD in the polymorphonuclear leukocytes of CGD patients (Bellanti, J. A., Cantz, B. E., and Schlegel, R. J.: Accelerated decay of glucose-6-PO_4 dehydrogenase activity in CGD. *Pediatr. Res.* 4:405, 1970). We have reason to believe this is related in some way to a lack of availability in NADP. What is the current thinking along the lines of enzymes which keep that system in the oxidized state? We feel this might be why we were observing the increased rate of decay.

Baehner: Since G-6-PD stability is in part due to its substrate binding to NADP, we were interested in the levels of reduced and nonreduced pyridine nucleotides in CGD and G-6-PD-deficient PMN. We found normal levels of all pyridine nucleotides in CGD PMN including NADP. As expected, in the patient with total deficiency of G-6-PD in her PMN, NADP and NADPH were low.

However, there may be some molecular alteration of the enzyme *per se* which could account for its instability in CGD PMN homogenates. I think Dr. Spitznagel mentioned some data to me in this regard on the G-6-PD decay in the cytolysates from patients with CGD.

Spitznagel: Yes, Neil Kirkman in the Department of Pediatrics at the University of North Carolina has studied polys from several patients with CGD. Dr. Holmes from Minnesota kindly sent us some of the material. We confirmed that there was a rapid destruction of G-6-PD activity. Dr. Kirkman took an A-mutant G-6-PD which is electrophoretically distinct from the normal G-6-PD and added it to the lysates of the polys in which the degradation of the G-6-PD was being observed. After the incubation period, the material was separated electrophoretically and both the G-6-PD's were observed. The mutant enzyme which was added to these lysates was degraded just as rapidly as the G-6-PD of the patient. This suggested to Dr. Kirkman that the patient's enzyme was probably normally stabile, but that some substance in the lysates destroyed both the A-mutant and the patient's G-6-PD more rapidly than did the lysates of normal cells.

Klebanoff: Our own experience with a family with severe leukocytic G-6-PD deficiency (Gray et al. *Lancet* 2:530, 1973) would support what has been found with other patients with this condition; that is, that despite severe deficiency of G-6-PD, as demonstrated immunologically and by enzyme assay, the patients were relatively well as compared to classical CGD. One of the boys had chronic granulomatous lymphadenitis but it started late (age 12) and infections were not a major problem in the other two boys. All suffered from nonspherocytic hemolytic anemia. Although the biochemical parameters were all CGD-like, they were not as low as we see in infants with CGD.

Johnston: This falls in the realm of anecdote swapping, but I believe it worth stating that Rebecca Buckley has experience with long-term sulfonamide therapy in CGD that compares favorably with the nafcillin experience. In 17 total patient years (five patients) there have been something like 11 days of hospitalization. We need controlled studies to prove whether sulfa or nafcillin makes a difference. However, I would like to submit that we not exclude the possibility that sulfonamide or a molecule like sulfonamide might have a stimulatory effect on the CGD phagocyte *in vivo.* A good chemist might come up with an analogue that would do even better.

Sbarra: Would it be possible to look at this defective killing in these patients from a completely different viewpoint? We have been looking at spleen lymphocyte killing in AKR mice, leukemic and nonleukemic, and we found that spleen lymphocytes from the nonleukemic mice are able to kill bacteria very efficiently. In contrast, spleen lymphocytes from leukemic AKR mice cannot kill bacteria to any great extent. We studied some of the biochemical activities of the spleen lymphocytes in the two sets of mice, leukemic and nonleukemic, and found that the leukemics' lymphocytes did not have any peroxidase activity. This meant that either there is a deficiency in peroxidase activity in these cells or perhaps maybe there could be an inhibitor that is not permitting us to detect peroxidase activity in the cell. In order to explore this point, we took spleen lymphocytes from the leukemic mice and added them to normal spleen lymphocytes and found that we could inhibit the peroxidase activity. From this it would appear that a peroxidase inhibitor is present in AKR leukemic lymphocytes. Similarly, could there be an enzyme inhibitor which would effect H_2O_2 production in CGD leukocytes? I am not certain if that is a good point.

Baehner: Would you expect the peroxidase activity to be low?

Sbarra: I don't know. We do know, however, that you get a decrease in peroxide production in CGD leukocytes. The search for an inhibitor would seem to me to be a reasonable approach to study the nature of the defect. This would be a most fundamental thing to do.

Snyderman: In a kind of simplistic way, one of the things I never understood is if you look at the spectrum of infections they seem to be what we think are handled by cellular immune systems. What can you tell me about macrophage or monocyte killing in these patients?

Baehner: Dr. Quie, do you have any data?

Quie: I really don't have any information from my own laboratory on the monocyte killing in patients with CGD primarily because in my hands monocytes from controls frequently do a poor job of killing staphylococci. It is safe to say, however, that monocytes from CGD patients are defective in intercellular bacterial killing. In a study done by Mandell and Hook (*Am. J. Med.* 47:473, 1969), however, it was shown that macrophages that had been fixed on glass showed similar bactericidal activity, when macrophages from a boy with CGD were compared with normal macrophages. More definitive studies on monocyte function have been done recently in Dr. Remington's laboratory, and it has been shown that monocytes normally engulf bacteria much more slowly than polymorphs. There is good evidence that both CGD monocytes and polymorphs have abnormal metabolic responses to phagocytosis. Both types of phagocytes fail to reduce NBT. A deficiency of intracellular bactericidal activity although not completely satisfactorily documented would be one logical explanation for persistence of microbial species requiring cell-mediated immunity.

Holmes-Gray: I don't think anyone has ever really adequately tested skin reactions for delayed hypersensitivity with extracts of the bugs that infect these patients. They have done skin tests with crude extracts in the very early days of separating this disease. But it has not been extensively studied, and I think it is very important to see if they do have normal delayed hypersensitivity.

Hirsch: What organisms did you have in mind?

Snyderman: I was thinking in terms of the *Aspergillus* as well. I was thinking more about the fungi.

Mandell: Those are the same organisms granulocytopenic leukemics get, so it's hard to say.

The Phagocytic Cell in Host Resistance, edited
by Joseph A. Bellanti and Delbert H. Dayton.
Raven Press, New York © 1975.

Comparison of Other Defects of Granulocyte Oxidative Killing Mechanisms with Chronic Granulomatous Disease

Richard K. Root

Infectious Disease Section, Department of Medicine, University of Pennsylvania School of Medicine, Philadelphia, Pennsylvania 19104

INTRODUCTION

In the preceding chapter Dr. Baehner has historically summarized the manifestations and definition of defects in granulocyte H_2O_2 formation that result in impaired killing and repeated infection with catalase-positive microorganisms. In this chapter I compare and contrast the clinical and laboratory features of these patients with those of individuals who have defects in other areas of function of their oxidative killing mechanisms. It is in part through studies of these patients that the role of myeloperoxidase and its delivery into the phagocytic vacuole in the normal killing processes of granulocytes has been defined. Furthermore, examination of the metabolic processes of these cells has provided insight into the pathways of utilization of H_2O_2 by granulocytes. As I shall demonstrate, such information can be employed to correct deficiencies in the function of cells which are incapable of normal H_2O_2 formation.

CLINICAL AND LABORATORY FEATURES OF PATIENTS WITH MYEOLPEROXIDASE DEFICIENCY AND THE CHEDIAK-HIGASHI SYNDROME

In 1969 Lehrer and Cline reported findings on a patient with a total deficiency of antigenically and functionally definable neutrophil myeloperoxidase (MPO) (1). Since then approximately a dozen individuals with acquired or congenital MPO deficiency have been identified in several areas of the world and their functional defects characterized (2). In striking contrast to patients with absent H_2O_2 formation MPO-deficient patients are for the most part clinically well and free of recurrent infections. Microbicidal assays have revealed a *delay* in killing of a variety of bacteria, both catalase negative and positive, but no absolute defect has been demonstrated as seen in individuals with absent formation of the substrate for MPO, H_2O_2 (3). Metabolic studies have shown that granulocytes from patients with MPO deficiency have exaggerated oxidative activities including oxygen consumption and the oxidation of ^{14}C-1-glucose and ^{14}C-formate, all of which are related to H_2O_2 formation and utilization by these cells (4). It has been suggested that the absence of a major catabolic enzyme for H_2O_2 allows greater than normal amounts to accumulate during phagocytosis, which may be sufficient to produce adequate killing of microorganisms despite the lack of MPO (4). MPO-deficient leukocytes show impaired killing under anerobic conditions which supports the idea that H_2O_2 is used by these cells for killing. On the other hand it does not fully explain why MPO-deficient cells perform better in bactericidal assays than normal cells that have been treated with azide to inactivate MPO (5), since the latter also produces increased amounts of H_2O_2.

In contrast to MPO-deficient patients, individuals with the Chediak-Higashi syndrome (CHS) do suffer with repeated infections, particularly with staphylococci (6). CHS granulocytes contain abnormal giant primary lysosomes, apparently due to aberrant formation from the Golgi apparatus during cellular maturation in the bone marrow (7) (Fig. 1). As shown in Table 1 several functional impairments involving granulocytopoesis, as well as the responses of granulocytes and monocytes to inflammatory stimuli and their bactericidal capabilities, have been defined that may be instrumental in increasing susceptibility to bacterial infection. Granulocyte maturation is disordered and the demonstration of high circulating levels of muramidase has suggested the occurrence of intramedullary destruction of maturing forms to account for the varying degrees of neutropenia present in this syndrome (8). Patients with the CHS exhibit diminished responses *in vivo* to inflammatory stimuli, as tested by the Rebuck skin window technique, which are disproportionate to their neutropenia (9). *In vitro* they display a cellular defect in the chemotactic responsiveness of both granulocytes and monocytes (9, 10). Similar findings have been reported using cells from animals with the CHS (10).

In studies of the bactericidal capabilities of CHS cells, two facts have emerged. First, the phagocytic activity of CHS granulocytes and monocytes for bacteria is normal. In fact, certain inert particles (e.g., paraffin oil emulsion) are ingested at rates which are significantly greater than normal (11). Second, when bacterial killing is assessed, CHS granulocytes and monocytes exhibit delays in killing of intracellular bacteria that are not unlike those seen for MPO-deficient cells. Both catalase-positive and -negative organisms are involved (12).

Analysis of the mechanisms responsible for this delay in killing has demonstrated by both morphological and biochemical means that degranulation of the peroxidase-containing abnormal primary lysosomes is aberrant (11, 12). The MPO activity present in the giant lysosomes and CHS cells is within normal limits; however they are relatively few in number when compared to normal cells. Presumably because of this low number many phagocytic vacuoles do not receive myeloperoxidase after phagocytosis until relatively late, when MPO-free vesicles fuse with those containing the contents of degranulated giant lysosomes (Fig. 2).

Treatment of CHS leukocytes with 1 mM sodium azide to inhibit MPO resulted in less inhibition of killing than by normal cells, although an effect was seen at each time interval examined (Table 2). Azide-treated normal and CHS cells exhibited comparable killing rates suggesting that the nonperoxidase-mediated

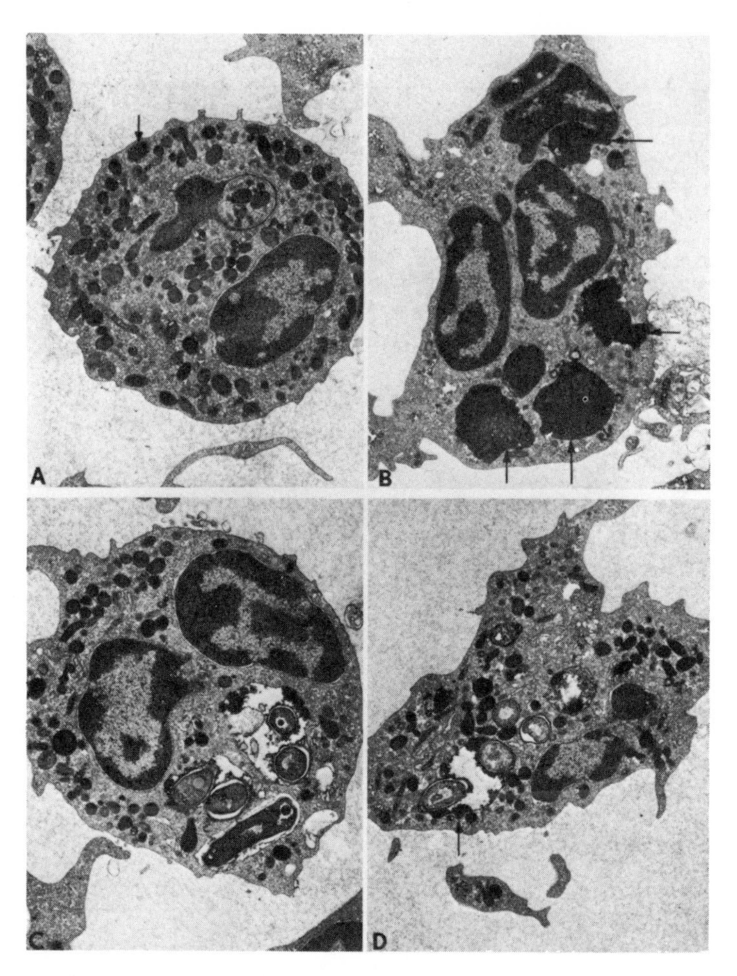

FIG. 1. Electron micrographs of granulocytes histochemically stained for peroxidase activity. A is a normal and B a CHS granulocyte without ingested particles. Arrows point to peroxidase-positive lysosomes. C and D are representative sections of normal granulocytes 15 min after mixing with *S. aureus.* Note the dark staining peroxidase activity in phagosomes surrounding bacteria and evidence of active degranulation (arrow, D) (24).

killing mechanisms in the two cell types are functionally equivalent. Both of these observations serve to distinguish further the functional mechanisms of cells that lack MPO as opposed to those with an impaired intraphagosomal "delivery" system as seen with the CHS. No studies of killing by CHS cells in an anaerobic environment have been performed to assess the contribution of H_2O_2 to their total killing mechanism.

Studies of the metabolism of CHS granulocytes during phagocytosis indicate normal activities of the hexose monophosphate shunt (^{14}C-1-glucose oxidation) and the oxidation of ^{14}C-formate. On the other hand, protein iodination was found

TABLE 1. *Functional properties of granulocytes from patients with different defects in the H_2O_2–MPO antimicrobial system*

	CGD	Myeloperox-idase deficiency	Chediak-Higashi syndrome
I. *Inflammatory responses*			
Granulocytopoiesis	normal	normal	reduced
Granulocytosis	normal	normal	reduced
Skin window response	normal	normal	reduced
Chemotaxis	usually normal	?	reduced
II. *Microbicidal activities*			
Phagocytosis	normal	normal	normal to increased
Killing of:			
Catalase-positive organisms	impaired	delayed	delayed
Catalase-negative organisms	slight delay	slight delay?	delayed
Effect of azide on killing	none	none	mild impairment
III. *Metabolic activities during phagocytosis*			
O_2 consumption	reduced	increased	increased
^{14}C-1-glucose oxidation	reduced	increased	normal
Formate oxidation	reduced	increased	normal
Protein iodination	reduced	reduced	increased
H_2O_2 release	absent	?	?
Under basal conditions			
O_2 consumption	reduced	?	increased
^{14}C-1-glucose oxidation	reduced	?	increased
Formate oxidation	reduced	?	increased
Protein iodination	reduced	?	increased

to be greater than normal and was over 95% inhibited in the presence of 1 mM azide (12). In resting cells all three oxidative activities were greater than normal. ^{14}C-1-glucose oxidation was increased two-fold, formate iodination 1.5-fold, and iodination five-fold. Furthermore both resting and phagocytizing cells exhibited increased oxygen consumption when compared to normal controls. These observations suggest that CHS leukocytes form greater than normal amounts of H_2O_2 at rest with normal increments in production occurring during phagocytosis. Again a distinction between CHS- and MPO-deficient cells is observed in that the latter exhibit oxidative hyperactivity during phagocytosis rather than under resting conditions, and iodination is markedly depressed because of absent MPO (4) (Table 1). Not only is H_2O_2 utilization by MPO and the other pathways high in CHS cells at rest, but also there may be some preferential utilization by MPO during phagocytosis as measured by a greater than normal increment in iodination. On the other hand, the morphological and biochemical information on degranulation, as well as the bactericidal data, indicates that much of this utiliza-

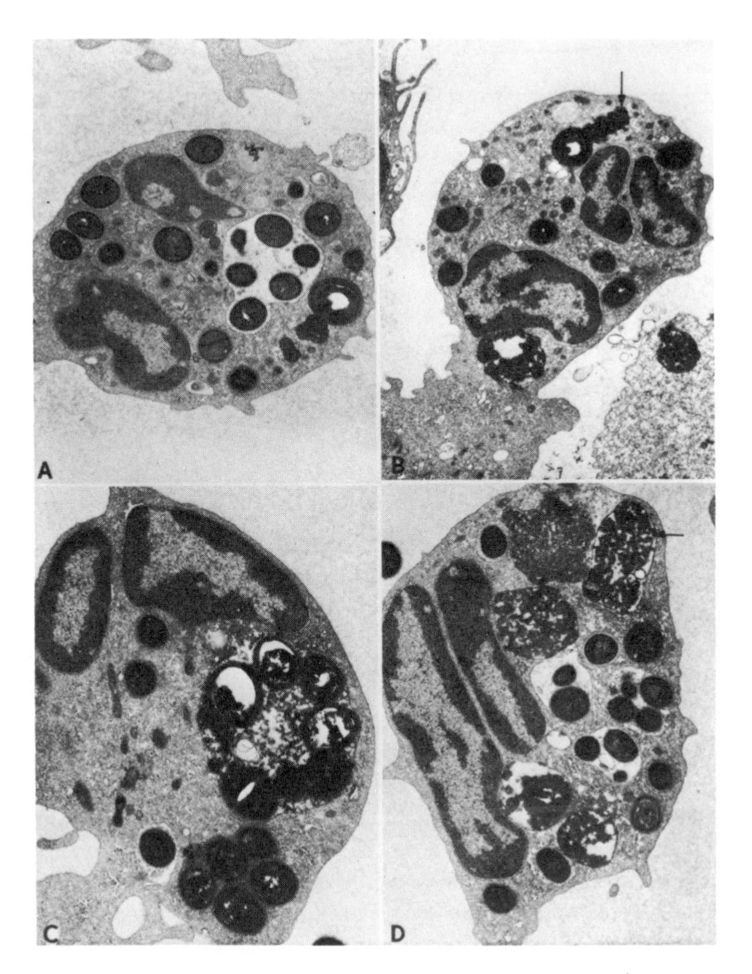

FIG. 2. Electron micrographs of granulocytes that have phagocytized *S. aureus* and are histochemically stained for peroxidase. A and B depict sections of CHS granulocytes taken 15 min after mixing with staphylococci. Note the lack of peroxidase activity around most phagosomes with the exception of those into which giant lysosomes (arrows) appear to be discharging their contents. C is a normal granulocyte 60 min after mixing with staphylococci showing phagosomal fusion with peroxidase activity in the phagosomes and a lack of peroxidase-positive granules in the cytoplasm. D is a CHS granulocyte at the same time interval, which depicts the persistence of structurally intact peroxidase-positive giant lysosomes (arrows). Peroxidase activity can be in some, but not all, phagosomes. (24).

tion must occur within the confines of the giant lysosomes where it cannot contribute to the microbicidal efficacy of the cell.

Evidence indicates that in normal cells the majority of iodination occurs in phagocytic vacuoles (13) whereas the enzymes for the hexose monophosphate shunt and catalase (which mediates formate oxidation) are in the cell cytoplasm. A general conclusion that can be derived from these observations is that H_2O_2,

TABLE 2. *Effect of sodium azide (1mM) on killing of* S. AUREUS *by CHS and normal phagocytes*

Subject	% Survival at different times (min)		
	20	60	120
Normal (2)	14.8 (14.2–15.4)	4.4 (3.4–5.3)	1.6 (1.4–1.8)
+ Azide	58.3 (54.8–61.7)	34.3 (23.4–45.2)	22.1 (22.0–22.1)
Inhibition of killing (%)	51.6 (47.8–55.4)	31.4 (20.7–42.1)	20.8 (20.7–20.8)
CHS (2)	40.7 (31.7–49.6)	15.1 (12.5–17.7)	6.2 (5.6–6.8)
+ Azide	60.3 (58.2–62.5)	29.0 (26.2–31.7)	15.0 (14.4–15.6)
Inhibition of killing (%)	30.1 (15.1–45.1)	16.1 (10.3–21.9)	9.4 (8.2–10.6)

Dextran sedimented cells with a mean distribution of phagocytes as follows: Normal—91.9% PMN, 2.1% monocytes, 6.9% eosinophils; CHS—81.8% PMN, 11.9% monocytes, 6.3% eosinophils.

by virtue of its high diffusability, must be able to cross cell and organelle membranes to stimulate several metabolic activities simultaneously. Other data indicate that phagocytizing granulocytes may release a certain proportion of H_2O_2 to the extracellular medium, which may have implications for microorganisms or other cells that are in the immediate environment (14). Finally, other studies with CHS leukocytes have indicated that their turnover of membrane lipids under nonphagocytizing conditions is also increased above normal by about fivefold (15), a figure which closely approximates the enhancement of iodination by these cells. A body of information suggest a role for the plasma membrane in the regulation of H_2O_2 formation by granulocytes (16). Thus there might be a direct relationship between membrane turnover and H_2O_2 formation and utilization in CHS leukocytes to tie together the observations on their metabolic activities.

Some recent studies from our laboratory provide further evidence that H_2O_2 is formed and released promptly from normal human granulocytes during the membrane changes induced by phagocytosis and that it can move freely within cellular compartments even when introduced exogenously. As will be shown, such information can be employed to correct metabolic and functional abnormalities in CGD granulocytes.

TIME COURSE OF H_2O_2 FORMATION AND RELEASE BY HUMAN PMN'S

Recently, with the advice and assistance of Drs. Britton Chance and Nazumo Oshino of the Johnson Foundation, University of Pennsylvania, we have adapted a highly sensitive assay for the detection of 10^{-7}M concentrations of H_2O_2 in solution in studies with intact phagocytizing human PMN's. This technique derives its specificity for H_2O_2 by making its detection dependent upon its utilization as a specific substrate for the peroxidase-mediated oxidation of the fluorescent coumarin derivative scopoletin. As initially described by Andreae in 1955 (17), scopoletin fluoresces at 460 nm when activated by light of 350nm. The fluorescence of scopoletin in aqueous solutions is directly proportional to its concentration through a 5 μM range. H_2O_2 alone will not oxidize scopoletin but in the presence of horseradish peroxidase (HPO) the compound is rapidly oxidized with resultant loss of fluorescence. The stoichiometry of the reaction is such that for every mole of available H_2O_2, 1 mole of scopoletin is oxidized, provided HPO is present in excess. Any substance that competes with scopoletin for the H_2O_2-HPO enzyme-substrate complex will reduce the extinction of fluorescence, a fact that must be taken into consideration when working with intact cells or with other substrates that can be oxidized by HPO and H_2O_2.

Table 3 indicates how the scopoletin technique has been utilized to measure H_2O_2 release from cells during phagocytosis. The optimum cell concentration was

TABLE 3. *Methods for measuring H_2O_2 release from granulocytes by the HPO-mediated quenching of scopoletin fluorescence*

1. PMNs (2.5 × 10^6/ml) are suspended in KRB buffer pH 7.4 with 5.5 mM glucose.
2. Scopoletin added (final concentration 2 to 4 μM).
3. Exciting wavelength set at 350 nm, detecting at 460 nm.
4. HPO added (final concentration 20 to 40 μM) and basal quenching of fluorescence recorded.
5. Particles added and measurements continued.
6. System is standardized by adding known amounts of ethyl H_2O_2 or glucose oxidase.

found to be 2.5 × 10^6/ml since higher numbers caused significant quenching of fluorescence. By using very high particle to cell multiplicities it was possible to stimulate phagocytosis sufficiently at 37°C to run the assays in a nonagitated system. After suspending the cells in Krebs-Ringer-bicarbonate buffer at pH 7.4 containing 5.5 mM glucose, scopoletin was added to a final concentration of 2 to 4 μM and the emission slits set at OD_{460} to read 100% transmittance. HPO in excess (20 μM) was added and base line change in scopoletin fluorescence recorded. Various particles were then used to stimulate phagocytosis. The system was standardized using known amounts of H_2O_2 (provided as ethyl-H_2O_2 or generated from glucose oxidase of known activity). Figure 3 displays recordings from a representative experiment in which H_2O_2 was added as ethyl-H_2O_2 or generated from glucose by glucose oxidase and compared to that after the addition of opsonized staphylococci to cells. The sharp decrease in fluorescence followed a latency of only 10 sec, indicative of the rapid release of H_2O_2 into the medium from the phagocytizing cells. Qualitatively similar results have been obtained using opsonized yeast or latex spherules as phagocytic particles, both

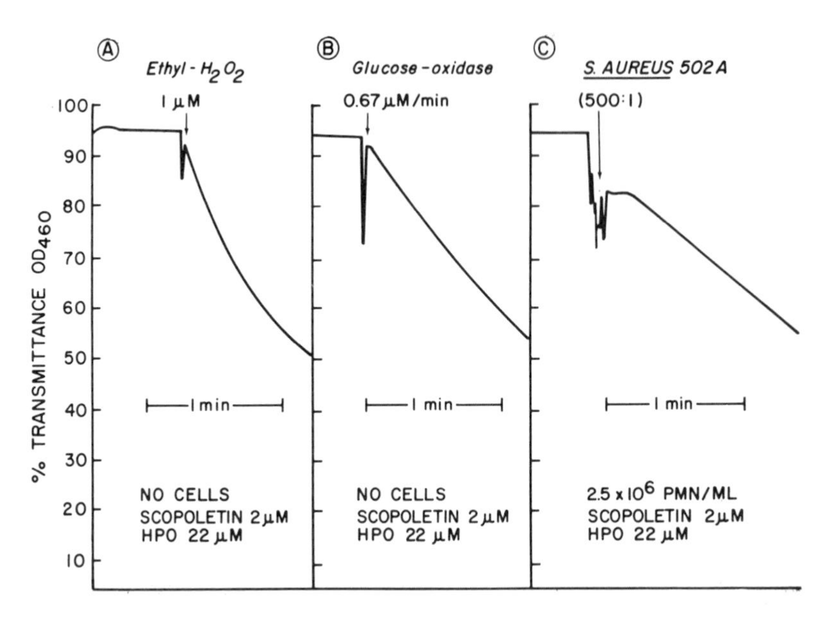

FIG. 3. Effect of adding different sources of H_2O_2 on the flourescence of scopoletin at 460 nm when horseradish peroxidase (22 μM) is in the medium. A indicates the loss of fluorescence by oxidation of the scopoletin after addition of 1 μM (final concentration) ethyl-H_2O_2; B gives the same data using glucose-oxidase to generate H_2O_2 from glucose in the medium with a resulting increase in H_2O_2 concentrations of 0.67 μM/min; C represents the release of H_2O_2 into the medium from human granulocytes phagocytizing opsonized staphylococci which were added to the cells in a bacteria to cell ratio of 500 : 1. All tracings were taken with a constant recording Hitachi Perkin Elmer spectrophoto-fluorometer.

of which stimulate H_2O_2 formation and release after a similar short latency. Nonopsonized staphylococci or yeast did not stimulate H_2O_2 formation presumably because of a failure of phagocytosis. Furthermore, when the assay was run in the presence of serum in the medium, no change of scopoletin fluorescence occurred, presumably because of factors in serum competing with scopoletin for H_2O_2 (e.g., catalase) or for oxidation by HPO–H_2O_2 (e.g., thiol groups).

Evidence that the principal reaction occurs in the extracellular location is indicated in Fig. 4. In the absence of added HPO little change in fluorescence of scopoletin occurs during phagocytosis. Since the cells are not permeable to HPO, the sharp drop-off in fluorescence at that point represents the utilization by HPO of H_2O_2 that accumulated in the medium. Further support for this concept was obtained when catalase was added to the medium and the extinction of fluorescence was inhibited by competition of catalase with HOP for the H_2O_2 accumulating in the medium. Table 4 summarizes results of H_2O_2 release, measured under different conditions. When H_2O_2 formation by normal cells was prevented by using noningestible particles, or when cells from CGD patients were employed, no H_2O_2 release occurred, indicating the dependency of this phenomenon upon the formation of H_2O_2 in increased amounts during particle ingestion.

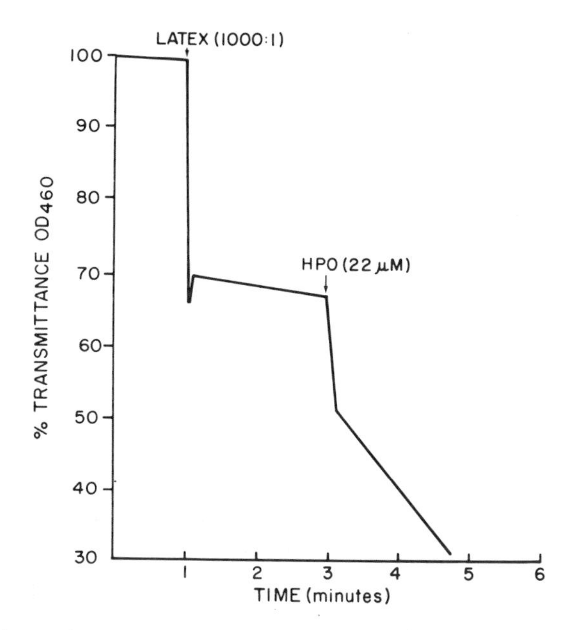

FIG. 4. Effect of reversing the addition of phagocytic particles (latex at a 1,000 : 1 particle to cell ratio) and HPO to granulocytes (5.0 X 10^6ml) suspended in KRB-containing 2 μM scopoletin.

TABLE 4. *Detection of H_2O_2 released from human granulocytes under different conditions*

Additions	No. subjects	H_2O_2 detected nmoles/2.5 X 10^6 PMN/min
None	8	0.012 ± 0.003
Latex		0.445 ± 0.064
Opsonized yeast	3	0.283 ± 0.08
Opsonized *S. aureus* 502 A	3	0.395 ± 0.089
Nonopsonized yeast	2	0
Nonopsonized yeast + 10% serum	2	0
Nonopsonized *S. aureus*	2	0
Latex + catalase [a]	2	0.025 ± 0.015
Latex + 10% serum	2	0
Latex	2	0

The last addition was made to CGD cells; all other cells were normal.
Results are expressed as the mean ± SE of the maximal rates of H_2O_2 production detected by scopoletin oxidation. The particle to cell ratios were as follows: latex 1,000:1, yeast 40:1, and *S. aureus* 500:1.
[a] Catalase concentrations varied between 40 and 1,000 U.

With increasing multiplicities of particles to cells, H_2O_2 formation and release were progressively increased until a plateau was reached under conditions of maximal phagocytosis (Fig. 5). Depending upon the particle employed, H_2O_2 production and release rates by PMN's were stimulated up to 50-fold after a

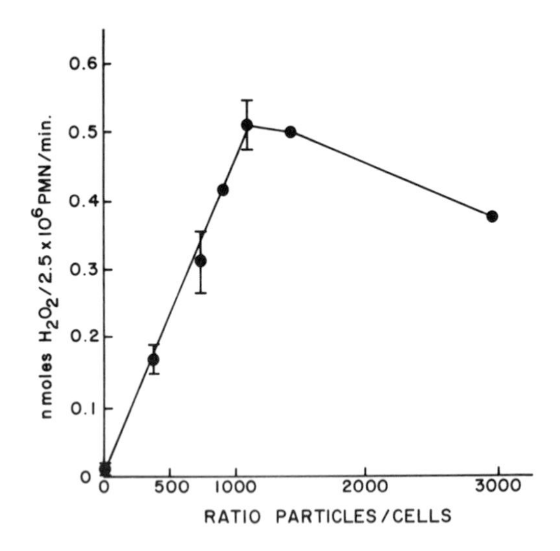

FIG. 5. Relationship between the number of latex particles added to granulocytes and mean maximal rates of H_2O_2 release. Brackets indicate standard errors of the mean of duplicate determinations obtained in three experiments. Mean values of duplicate determinations in a single experiment are displayed without brackets.

latency of only 10 sec. The marked rapidity of this phenomenon and its dependency upon particles that are presumably capable of using specified membrane receptors for phagocytosis is compatible with a role for certain areas in the plasma membrane in stimulating H_2O_2 formation.

RELATIONSHIP OF H_2O_2 FORMATION AND RELEASE TO OTHER OXIDATIVE ACTIVITIES OF HUMAN PMN'S

A series of experiments were then performed to compare rates of H_2O_2 release to other oxidative activities of PMN's during conditions of maximal phagocytosis. Comparative results for cells ingesting either latex or opsonized yeast are shown in Fig. 6. H_2O_2 release rates paralleled those of O_2 consumption and were followed by ^{14}C-1-glucose oxidation and, after a several minute latency, by myeloperoxidase-mediated protein iodination. This latency is presumably due to a need for the delivery of MPO into phagocytic vacuoles from degranulating lysosomes, the site of this reaction as determined in previous studies conducted with Stossel (13).

The degree of stimulation of the various activities was dependent upon the particle employed, and opsonized yeast or staphylococci produced significantly greater metabolic effects than did latex phagocytosis. Regardless of the particle employed, the amount of H_2O_2 released was similar (4 to 6 nmoles/2.5 $\times$ 10^6 PMN/30 min). Using O_2 consumption as an index of H_2O_2 formation and correcting data for different phagocytic rates it was calculated that from 5 to 15% of H_2O_2 formed was released into the medium. The lowest fraction was observed

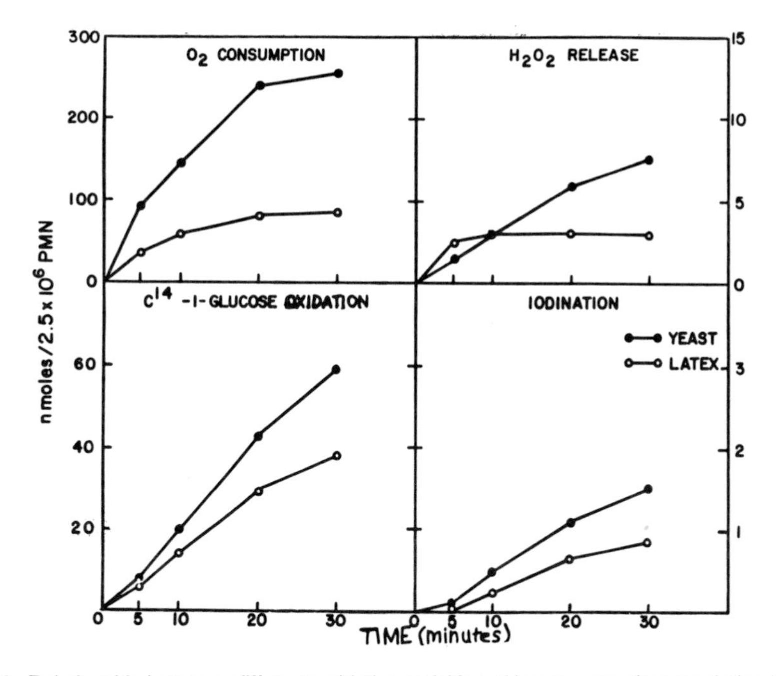

FIG. 6. Relationship between different oxidative activities of human granulocytes during ingestion of opsonized yeast or latex added to the cells in quantities sufficient to produce maximal phagocytic rates (particle to cell ratio yeast = 40 : 1, latex = 1,000 : 1). O_2 consumption was measured with a Clark oxygen electrode ^{14}C-1-glucose oxidation by trapping and liquid scintillation counting of $^{14}CO_2$ released from ^{14}C-1-glucose. Iodination refers to the fixation of inorganic iodide to a trichloracetic acid precipitable form using $Na^{125}I$ as a marker.

during yeast ingestion and the highest during latex ingestion. The simultaneous stimulation of all of the oxidative activities is consistent with the rapid entry of H_2O_2 into a common intracellular pool after its formation. The stoichiometric relationships between iodination and O_2 consumption suggest that only 3% of H_2O_2 formed is utilized by MPO in this reaction. On the other hand the relationship between O_2 consumption and ^{14}C-1-glucose oxidation at different time points after the initiation of phagocytosis ($>2:1$ within the first 5 min versus $1:1$ after 10 min) suggests that NADPH, generated from pentose shunt and coupled glutathione peroxidase activities, does not serve as a major substrate for H_2O_2 formation until relatively late in the course of phagocytosis. Such comparisons are in part hampered by an artifact introduced by the contribution of catalase activity to the amount of O_2 available to the cells late in phagocytosis by decomposition of H_2O_2. Thus the measured consumption of O_2 from the medium is diminished by O_2 generated through catalase. Further proof for this was obtained when the studies were run in the presence of small quantities (1 to 10 μM) of azide which inhibit catalase. Initial rates of O_2 consumption were not altered over 30 min incubation. However, total O_2 consumption increased in the presence of azide due to a prolongation of the high rates seen during initial particle ingestion.

H_2O_2 ABSORPTION BY HUMAN PMN's

Through the use of the scopoletin technique it soon became apparent that H_2O_2 is diffusible not only through intracellular compartments of PMN's and is released from the cells during phagocytosis, but also that H_2O_2 generated in the medium could enter the cell and stimulate metabolic and functional activities. Figure 7 compares the detection of H_2O_2 generated from glucose by glucose oxidase in the absence and presence of cells. When cells were in the medium,

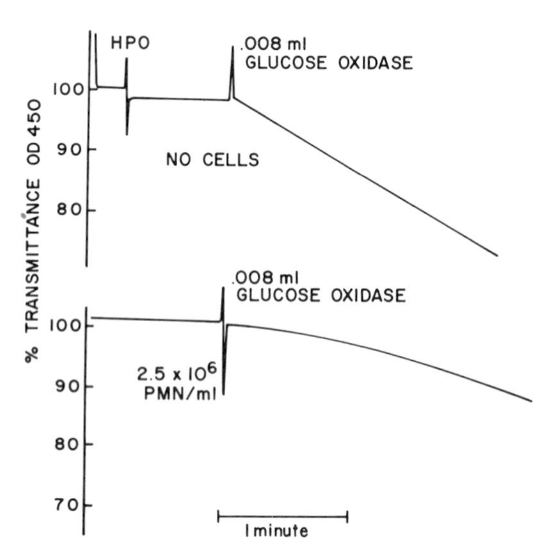

FIG. 7. Comparison of the detection of H_2O_2 generated at a rate of 0.3μM/min from glucose (5.5 mM) by glucose oxidase in the absence (upper panel) and presence of granulocytes (lower panel). Shown are tracings from a representative experiment in which the fluorescence of scopoletin at 460nm was monitored continuously.

decreased amounts of H_2O_2 were detected, particularly in the initial phases after adding glucose oxidase. Similar to rat leukocytes (19), H_2O_2 generated under these conditions could enter the cells and stimulate intracellular metabolic events, including ^{14}C-1-glucose oxidation (Fig. 8) and MPO-mediated protein iodination (Fig. 9). As noted, a plateau of stimulation for each was reached at rates of H_2O_2 formation above 2 μM/min. Below this plateau the molar ratio of ^{14}C-1-glucose oxidation to H_2O_2 formation was 1 : 2, compatible with catabolism of the compound through the HMS presumably by a link to the glutathione cycle. On the other hand, the relationship between iodination and H_2O_2 formation over the same concentration ranges was 1 : 30. Levels of iodination achieved were equivalent to those occurring during maximal latex phagocytosis. This suggests that the recipients for iodination under the latter circumstance are probably tyrosine residues on endogenous proteins (20). In contrast, phagocytosis of protein-containing particles, such as, opsonized yeast and staphylococci, stimulated more

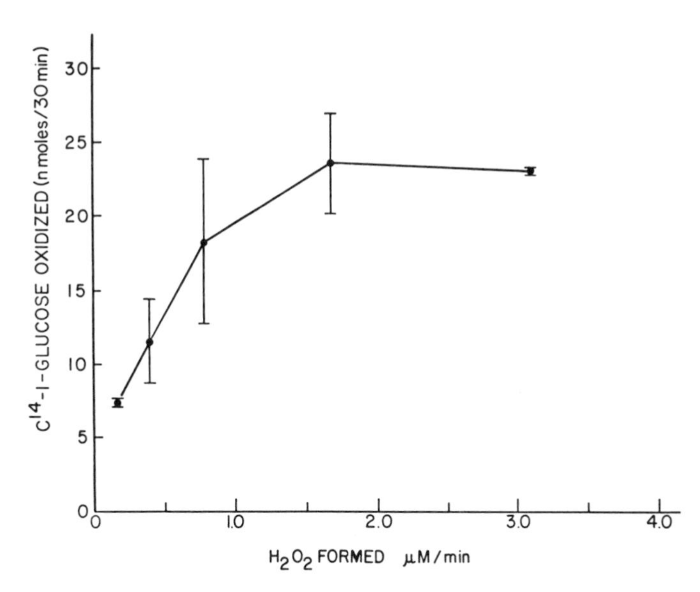

FIG. 8. Relationship between ^{14}C-1-glucose oxidation by granulocytes suspended in KRB buffer and increasing amounts of exogenous H_2O_2 generated in the extracellular medium from glucose by glucose oxidase. The activities of increasing amounts of glucose oxidase are noted on the abscissa in terms of their ability to change H_2O_2 concentration (μM) per minute. Shown are the mean and range of experiments performed with cells from three normal subjects.

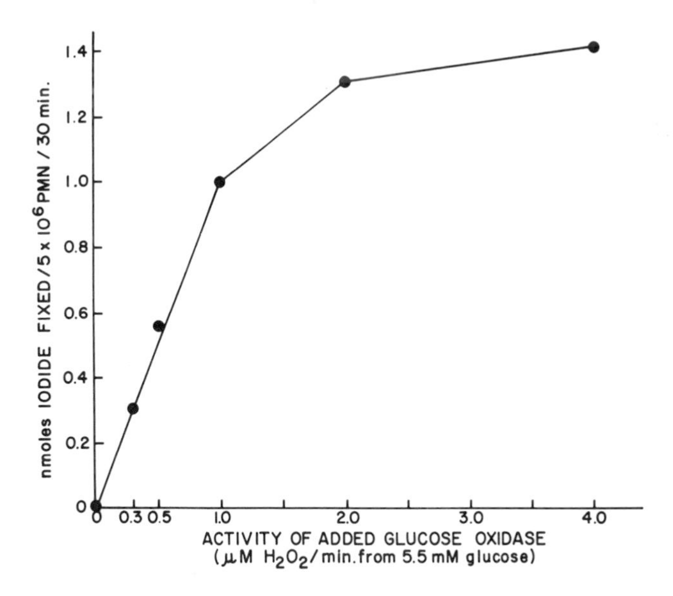

FIG. 9. Relationship between the fixation of inorganic iodide to a TCA-precipitable form by granulocytes suspended in KRB buffer and increasing amounts of H_2O_2 produced exogenously from glucose by glucose oxidase. Shown is the mean of duplicate determinations from a single representative experiment. Addition of 1 mM sodium azide to the suspensions abolished this activity, indicating its dependence upon the interaction of intracellular myeloperoxidase and H_2O_2.

O_2 consumption and iodination. The latter occurred presumably because of increased H_2O_2 formation as well as increased numbers of intracellular tyrosine residues provided by the phagocytosis of protein-rich compounds.

Why different particles induce different amounts of H_2O_2 formation remains a problem for further elucidation. Different rates and quantities of membrane internalization during phagocytosis may play a regulating role in this respect as suggested by the data of Stossel et al. (20).

These observations suggest that the high basal oxidative rates seen in CHS cells are due to high spontaneous H_2O_2 formation. Furthermore the correlation of these activities with high membrane lipid turnover in these cells is also consistent with a role for cell membranes in H_2O_2 formation by granulocytes.

CORRECTION OF THE DEFICIENCIES OF CGD GRANULOCYTES WITH EXOGENOUS H_2O_2

The documentation that human granulocytes can absorb exogenous H_2O_2 led to a series of experiments with leukocytes from CGD patients in which their metabolic and functional deficiencies were corrected by H_2O_2 generated in the medium by glucose oxidase. As shown in Table 5, both ^{14}C-1-glucose oxidation and iodination in the nonphagocytizing CGD cells were stimulated to levels

TABLE 5. *Stimulation of PMN oxidative metabolism by phagocytosis and exogenous H_2O_2*

	Conditions			
Subject (No.)	Basal	Phagocytizing	Basal + H_2O_2 [a]	Phagocytizing + H_2O_2
^{14}C-1-glucose oxidation				
Normal (2)	17.6 [b]	131	40.3	—
	(14.5–20.8)	(112–149)	(33.3–40.3)	
CGD (2)	13.1	15.8	25.8	—
	(1.1–25.1)	(2.2–29.3)	(21.5–30.1)	
Protein Iodination				
Normal (2)	0.094 [b]	2.85	1.24	3.67
	(0.06–0.127)	(1.85–3.85)	(1.08–1.40)	(3.26–4.07)
CGD (2)	.001	0.0027	1.20	2.50
	(0–0.002)	(0.0014–0.004)	(1.12–1.27)	(2.37–2.64)

[a] Provided from glucose oxidase generating 2.0 to 5.0 μM H_2O_2/min.
[b] Mean (range) nmoles/30 min/2.5 × 10^6 PMN.

equivalent to that seen with normal cells by exogenous H_2O_2. When this was coupled with phagocytosis of opsonized yeast, a further stimulation of iodination but not ^{14}C-1-glucose oxidation was observed. Two conclusions can be derived from these findings: (a) the enhanced stimulation of iodination during phagocytosis in the presence of exogenous H_2O_2 is probably due to the provision of additional tyrosine receptors for this process by the yeast; and (b) the failure of

^{14}C-1-glucose oxidation to be similarly further enhanced under the same conditions is consistent with an inability of these cells to utilize NADPH as substrate for H_2O_2 formation even when generated in greater amounts by stimulation of the pentose shunt by the added H_2O_2. Whether this is due in these cells to a deficiency of an NADPH oxidase, an implied absolute requirement for NADH oxidase for H_2O_2 formation, or simply "faulty" compartmentalization (e.g., NADPH oxidase located in lysosomes and phagocytic vesicles cannot utilize cytoplasmic NADPH generated from pentose shunt activity to make H_2O_2 because of membrane barriers) remains to be determined.

The last observation derived from these studies is that the phagocytic vesicle membranes, like the plasma membranes on the exterior of the cell, are freely permeable to H_2O_2. This was demonstrated by showing that intracellular staphylococci in CGD cells could be killed normally in the presence of exogenous H_2O_2. After a 20-min period for phagocytosis, lysostaphin was utilized to lyse noningested organisms, then glucose oxidase was added to generate H_2O_2. At the end of a 2-hr incubation, killing of intracellular organisms was equivalent to normal in CGD cells exposed to H_2O_2 (Table 6). Appropriate controls have shown that

TABLE 6. *Effect of exogenous H_2O_2 on PMN bactericidal activity*

Subject	Glucose oxidase added at 30 min	% Intracellular staphylococci killed (min) 60	120
Normal (4)	no	89.1 ± 4.1	94.6 ± 0.7
	yes	89.1 ± 4.7	95.3 ± 2.1
CGD RM (3)	no	70.7 ± 5.5	73.6 ± 6.4[a]
	yes	72.3 ± 5.6	95.1 ± 1.7
CGD LG (1)	no	69.5	76.8[a]
	yes	85.3	98.3

[a] $p < 0.01$ for CGD vs. normal.

these results cannot be explained by lysis of the cells and release of the organisms into the medium. Furthermore the amount of H_2O_2 generated by the glucose oxidase was insufficient to kill the bacteria in the absence of cells.

CONCLUSIONS AND SUMMARY

I have presented a brief review of some of the more salient biochemical features of granulocytes that lack MPO or fail to deliver it normally into the phagocytic vacuole and have suggested ways in which information gained from studies on these cells and normal human granulocytes might be employed to correct disorders of the H_2O_2–MPO antimicrobial system when H_2O_2 synthesis is impaired. By way of summary, a few additional interpretive comments are in order.

First, the almost normal ability of MPO-deficient granulocytes to kill intracellular bacteria is of great interest and is indicative of the operation of adaptive mechanisms when a major enzyme in the oxidative killing system is deleted. Since MPO-deficient cells perform significantly better in microbicidal assays than cells in which H_2O_2 formation is absent, this implies that H_2O_2 generated by the MPO-deficient leukocytes is utilized to kill intracellular bacteria although far less efficiently than when it can serve as substrate for MPO.

The impairment of bactericidal activity of MPO-deficient cells under anerobic conditions is consistent with a role for H_2O_2 in this process. The failure of azide or cyanide to further inhibit killing suggests that they do not utilize a heme-containing enzyme, such as, catalase, in the peroxidative fashion to accomplish this. The precise nature of their adaptive mechanisms remains to be defined, however, and may be more than that mediated by greater than normal formation and accumulation of H_2O_2 since azide-treated MPO-deficient leukocytes perform better in bactericidal assays than azide-treated normal cells, despite almost equivalent H_2O_2 formation.

Second, the fact that CHS patients who have a functional deficiency in the operation of the MPO–H_2O_2 microbicidal mechanisms of their granulocytes have more clinical infections than MPO-deficient leukocytes is explained by the complex nature of their disorder. Not only is killing delayed in their granulocytes but they also have impaired granulocyte formation leading to neutropenia and diminished chemotactic responses as well. All of these undoubtedly play a role in the pathogenesis of their recurrent infections.

Regarding the bactericidal mechanisms used by CHS granulocytes, results of azide treatment of CHS granulocytes indicate that there is a definite contribution of MPO to intracellular killing throughout all time periods after phagocytosis, although this is quantitatively less than that in normal cells. This can be explained by the fact that some, but not all, phagocytic vacuoles containing bacteria receive MPO from degranulating giant lysosomes early in the post-ingestion phase. Studies of the enzyme content of phagocytic vesicles derived from CHS leukocytes suggest that there is not only a qualitative abnormality in degranulation by primary lysosomes but that enzyme delivery is quantitatively depressed as well (11).

Third, both MPO-deficient and CHS granulocytes display increased oxidative metabolism compatible with the formation and accumulation of greater than normal amounts of H_2O_2. MPO-deficient leukocytes exhibit this phenomenon principally during phagocytosis, and the absence of a major enzyme for H_2O_2 catabolism has been suggested as the mechanism responsible. This would lead to increased utilization of H_2O_2 by pathways other than MPO, such as, the glutathione link to the hexose monophosphate shunt and catalase. This does not explain why O_2 consumption and presumably H_2O_2 formation are increased in these cells, however. In contrast to MPO-deficient cells, CHS leukocytes exhibit most of their metabolic hyperactivity under nonphagocytozing conditions. Increments during phagocytosis are normal to below normal so that ^{14}C-1-glucose and ^{14}C-formate oxidation are both equivalent to that shown by normal cells, whereas iodination and oxygen consumption are increased above normal.

Fourth, the oxidative hyperactivity shown by resting CHS leukocytes is parallelled by an increased synthesis and breakdown of membrane lipids and suggests a relationship between alterations in membrane structure and H_2O_2 formation. In studies with normal cells using the scopoletin technique it was possible to show that H_2O_2 formation and release into the medium is an extremely rapid event and is stimulated only by those particles that are presumably able to interact with phagocytic receptors on the cell surface. Such findings imply a role for these specialized areas of the cell membrane in triggering H_2O_2 synthesis.

Fifth, the simultaneous stimulation of H_2O_2-dependent metabolic activities in different intracellular compartments, as well as its prompt release from cells during phagocytosis, is consistent with the concept that newly synthesized H_2O_2 rapidly enters a common intracellular pool by diffusion through cellular and subcellular membranes. Support for this point was gained by the observation that H_2O_2 generated in an extracellular location could stimulate several intracellular activities in human granulocytes as had been demonstrated earlier by Reed for rat leukocytes (19). Furthermore this fact could be taken advantage of to correct functional and metabolic abnormalities in cells which are incapable of generating normal amounts of H_2O_2 during phagocytosis. Thus it is not necessary to deliver a hydrogen peroxide generating system into the phagocytic vacuoles of CGD leukocytes to achieve this (22), but merely to place them in an environment which contains adequate amounts of H_2O_2. In dose response assays of the correction of abnormal killing of intracellular staphylococci by CHD cells, a requirement for >1 mM/min quantities of H_2O_2 was found to be necessary for this purpose.

The therapeutic implications of these findings are obvious but so are the difficulties since H_2O_2 is a powerful oxidant and many enzymatic systems exist within and without cells to catabolize it. For instance, it was found that as little as 10% concentrations of serum could inhibit the bactericidal effect when present in the medium along with the glucose oxidase. At the very least, our observations lend some weight to the argument that H_2O_2, rather than its possible precursor in human granulocytes, superoxide anions (23), acts as the key substrate in the oxidative bactericidal reaction in these cells.

Finally, little attention has been paid in this discussion to the role played by the nonoxidative killing mechanisms of human granulocytes. It is becoming clear that these mechansms are highly important for the destruction of some intracellular organisms, particularly certain fungal species (24). Undoubtedly clinical examples of defects in these mechanisms will become increasingly recognized. Furthermore, the application of these studies in elucidating the functional mechanisms of other phagocytic cells, particularly macrophages, will prove to be an interesting and highly important exercise.

ACKNOWLEDGMENTS

The work reported in this chapter was supported in part by U.S. Public Health Service grants AI 70600 and AI 08713.

REFERENCES

1. Lehrer, R. I., and Cline, M. J.: Leukocyte myeloperoxidase deficiency and disseminated candidiasis: The role of myeloperoxidase in resistance to Candida infection. *J. Clin. Invest.* 48:1478, 1969.
2. Klebanoff, S. J.: Intraleukocytic microbicidal defects. *Ann. Rev. Med.* 22:39, 1971.
3. Johnston, R. B., and Baehner, R. L.: Chronic granulomatous disease: Correlation between pathogenesis and clinical findings. *Pediatrics* 48:730, 1971.
4. Klebanoff, S. J., and Hamon, C. B.: Role of myeloperoxidase-mediated antimicrobial systems in intact leukocytes. *J. Reticuloendothel. Soc.* 12:170, 1972.
5. Klebanoff, S. J.: Myeloperoxidase: Contribution to the microbicidal activity of intact leukocytes. *Science* 169:1095, 1970.
6. Blume, R. S., and Wolff, S. M.: The Chediak-Higashi syndrome: Studies in four patients and a review of the literature. *Medicine* 51:247, 1972.
7. Douglas, S. P., Rosenthal, A. S., and Wolff, S. M.: *Personal communication.*
8. Blume, R. S., Bennett, J. M., Yankee, R. A., and Wolff, S. M.: Defective granulocyte regulation in the Chediak-Higashi syndrome. *N. Engl. J. Med.* 279:1009, 1968.
9. Clark, R. A., and Kimball, H. R.: Defective granulocyte chemotaxis in the Chediak-Higashi syndrome. *J. Clin. Invest.* 50:2645, 1971.
10. Gallin, J. I., Klimerman, J. A., Padgett, G. A., and Wolff, S. M.: Defective mononuclear cell chemotaxis in the Chediak-Higashi syndrome (CHS) of humans, mink, and cattle. *Clin. Res. (to be published).*
11. Stossel, T. P., Root, R. K., and Vaughn, M.: Phagocytosis in chronic granulomatous disease and the Chediak-Higashi syndrome. *N. Engl. J. Med.* 286:120, 1972.
12. Root, R. K., Rosenthal, A. S., and Balestra, D. J.: Abnormal bactericidal, metabolic and lysosomal functions of Chediak-Higashi syndrome leukocytes. *J. Clin. Invest.* 51:649, 1972.
13. Root, R. K., and Stossel, T. P.: Myeloperoxidase-mediated iodination by granulocytes: Intracellular site of operation and some regulating factors. *J. Clin. Invest.* 53:1207, 1974.
14. Baehner, R. L., Nathan, D. G., and Castle, W. B.: Oxidant injury of caucasian glucose-6-phosphate dehydrogenase-deficient red blood cells by phagocytosing leukocytes during infection. *J. Clin. Invest.* 50:2466, 1971.
15. Kanfer, J. N., Blume, R. S., Yankee, R. A., and Wolff, S. M.: Alteration of sphingolipid metabolism in leukocytes from patients with the Chediak-Higashi syndrome. *N. Engl. J. Med.* 279:410, 1968.
16. Rossi, F., Romeo, D., and Patriarca, P.: Mechanism of phagocytosis-associated oxidative metabolism in polymorphonuclear leucocytes and macrophages. *J. Reticuloendothel. Soc.* 12:127, 1972.
17. Andreae, W. A.: Sensitive method for the estimation of hydrogen peroxide in biological materials. *Nature* 175:859, 1955.
18. Reed, P. W.: Glutathione and the hexose monophosphate shunt in phagocytizing and hydrogen peroxide treated rat leukocytes. *J. Biol. Chem.* 244:2459, 1969.
19. Hubbard, A. I., and Cohn, Z. A.: The enzymatic iodination of the red cell membrane. *J. Cell Biol.* 55:390, 1972.
20. Stossel, T. P., Mason, R. J., Hartwig, J., and Vaughan, M.: Quantitative studies of phagocytosis by polymorphonuclear leukocytes: Use of emulsions to measure the initial rate of phagocytosis. *J. Clin. Invest.* 51:615, 1972.
21. Johnston, R. B., Jr., and Baehner, R. L.: Improvement of leukocyte bactericidal activity in chronic granulomatous disease. *Blood* 35:350, 1970.
22. Babior, B. M., Kipnes, R. S., and Curnutte, J. T.: Biological defense mechanisms: The production of leukocytes of superoxide, a potential bactericidal agent. *J. Clin. Invest.* 52:741, 1973.

23. Lehrer, R. I.: Functional aspects of a second mechanism of candidacidal activity by human neutrophils. *J. Clin. Invest.* 51:2566, 1972.
24. Root, R. K., Rosenthal, A. S., and Balestra, D. J.: Abnormal bactericidal, metabolic, and lysosomal functions of Chediak-Higashi syndrome leukocytes. *J. Clin. Invest.* 51:649, 1972.

DISCUSSION

Quie: Does the glucose oxidase system for generating peroxide act in the presence of serum?

Root: I am glad you brought that point up. It is only when I use greater than 2-micromolar-per-minute amounts of H_2O_2 production that I can get the cell to do this. If the dose is below that, presumably there is enough competition for H_2O_2 by other pathways so that sufficient amounts don't get into the vacuole to produce killing. If you use serum in the medium, it doesn't work, presumably because of competition with the cell for H_2O_2.

Cohn: Do you reach a point when you add glucose oxidase in which you get toxicity to the poly?

Root: I haven't carried the dosage up to that which produces measurable toxicity. I can tell you that with up to 5 micromolar H_2O_2 per minute dosages polys survive well as described.

Bellanti: Have you measured the levels of NADP following the addition of glucose oxidase?

Root: No, I have not.

Bellanti: You really don't know if the shunt is activated through that mechanism?

Root: No, but there is a presumption it would be. I haven't specifically looked at that.

Karnovsky: I think that what you have said regarding the peroxide, particularly with the assistance of the CGD data, does a great deal to help answer at least one question. That is: Is the key NADH oxidase that which produces peroxide and, in a roundabout way, stimulates the hexose monophosphate pathway via the gluathione cycle, or is it NADPH oxidase which produces peroxide but stimulates the shunt before the peroxide is produced? Your data would suggest that really it is the peroxide that is driving the shunt.

Root: Right. I think it may be even more complicated than that. What happens when you sequence these various events using two particles, latex and yeast; namely, the stimulation of oxygen consumption and peroxide release as it relates to the shunt and iodination with time? As I mentioned, peroxide is released with a latent period of 10 to 15 seconds. O_2 consumption is about 20 seconds. I think they are probably identical but the O_2 electrode isn't sufficiently sensitive to detect the early consumption of small amounts of O_2. Glucose oxidation through the shunt does not increase until after a minute's latent period, suggesting that this follows the initial events of O_2 consumption and peroxide production. And, of course, there is an even longer latency with iodination under these conditions

(2 minutes). I think this is because of the need for degranulation and delivery of myeloperoxidase into the vacuole to stimulate this event in addition to H_2O_2 formation. If you do RQ's for O_2 consumption, the early ratio between O_2 consumption and shunt is at least five-to-one with any particle. Later the ratio becomes one-to-one. Part of this is artifact because we haven't poisoned catalase in the system and that is accounting for some of the fall-off in O_2 consumption with time. But this would suggest to me that NADPH is not being used until later as a source for peroxide and that the initial formation of H_2O_2 depends upon another hydrogen ion donor, perhaps NADH.

Karnovsky: Could I continue this for a minute to say that Marion Stubbs measured the RQ's, and it turns out that by the DPNH oxidase pathway one could expect an RQ in early periods approaching 0.5 for the actual phagocytic increment in metabolism. For the TPNH oxidase-mediated pathway it should approach 1 starting from 0.5. We found 0.59 ± 0.08 (five measurements) in the first 20 minutes, and 0.97 ± 0.03 in 45 minutes. Unfortunately, this does not really resolve the question of DPNH-oxidase or TPNH-oxidase as the source of H_2O_2. One thing that bothers me a bit is: Are you sure scopoletin doesn't get into the cells at all?

Root: No, I am not. If you look at the molecule, it's got to get through membranes. I am using the arguments that by adding extracellular enzymes, which probably don't get in, we can change the kinetics of the reaction significantly and it's almost an immediate change, suggesting it's too fast for transport to take place. But I can't tell you there isn't any scopoletin inside the cell.

Karnovsky: You are heavily leaning on the peroxidase that you add not getting in. What was its molecular weight? Forty thousand? Is that horseradish peroxidase?

Root: Yes, horseradish.

Cohn: No appreciable amount gets in.

Klebanoff: Does the superoxide anion oxidize scopoletin?

Root: I haven't done that. Incidentally, I have run these reactions using monocytes and macrophages and it's interesting how their latencies differ from polys. For instance, using alveolar macrophages from the rabbit, there is a latency of about 2.5 to 3 minutes before you see H_2O_2 release and cells from BCG-treated animals have a shorter period.

Cohn: Have you carried your multiplicity studies on peroxide release down to lower levels? You started with latex at 500-to-1.

Root: Yes, I have carried the latex all the way down to about 5-to-1 multiplicity. We pick up a small amount of release under those conditions. Incidentally, both the staphylococci and yeast are much more potent stimulators of H_2O_2 formation and release.

Baehner: Is the monitoring of the fluorescence continuous?

Root: My figures were actually taken directly off the recorder strip.

Hirsch: Can you see this fluorescence under the fluorescence microscope? What wave length is it?

Root: 460.

Hirsch: You should be able to see it.

Root: Yes.

Hirsch: Can you load the cells and demonstrate disappearance of the fluorescence?

Root: I would think you might be able to do that. I haven't done it.

Baehner: I think it would be important to determine the site on the cell surface or on the cell at which fluorescence is occurring.

Root: I'd like to know the nature of the relation between the cell surface and the production of the whole phenomenon of H_2O_2 formation and release because I am struck by the differences obtained with opsonized and nonopsonized yeast. For example, it really suggests to me that the membrane is playing a crucial role in at least regulating peroxide formation perhaps through the action of receptors for phagocytosis. In this regard, I have run the same assay using a noningestible particle, IgG-coated red cells with monocytes. I did not see any release of peroxide under these conditions. But I didn't really form very good rosettes in suspension and there was a great deal of quenching by the hemoglobin.

Johnston: In regard to Dr. Klebanoff's point about enzyme substrates, Hara Misra showed when he was in Irwin Fridovich's laboratory that some superoxide anion is generated by the reaction of glucose oxidase on its substrate. How much I don't know. I haven't seen the data.

Root: I think what really needs to be done is to put scavengers of superoxide anion into my system, such as superoxide dismutase, to measure killing. If it is unchanged or augmented, then this would further support the concept that H_2O_2 is the final bactericidal substrate.

Klebanoff: I think the point has to be made that H_2O_2 formation by oxidases can occur without an apparent superoxide intermediate, and in some instances this is the rule. Even with xanthine oxidase, a high proportion of the hydrogen peroxide formed cannot be accounted for by a superoxide intermediate (Fridovich, *J. Biol. Chem.* 245:4053, 1970). In the glucose oxidase system a much greater proportion of the hydrogen peroxide is formed by the direct divalent reduction of oxygen.

Karnovsky: Does any go through superoxide?

Johnston: I was told by Hara Misra that some does go through superoxide. I don't know how much.

Karnovsky: It is very, very little because we recently did measure it and it's extremely little compared with xanthine oxidase.

Just a comment on these crevasses Dr. Hirsch was talking about yesterday, and the question of whether the peroxide is really coming out of your cells through the membrane by diffusion. Dr. Baehner spoke of diffusion and I think you implied diffusion of peroxide out of the cells. I have a photograph of a polymorphonuclear leukocyte that has been ingesting polystyrene which is incompletely dissolved away. But all we did—this is work of Dick Briggs in my brother's laboratory—was simply put diaminobenzidine on the outside. There is no additional peroxidase. What is in the crevasse, in the unsealed phagosome, is simply the visualization of the peroxide that the cell is making and the myeloperoxidase that is leaking to the outside. And, of course, Dr. Sbarra showed long ago that peroxide leaks out. You have just adequately shown how *much* comes out. I wonder whether your scopoletin gets into these crevasses, but Dr. Stossel says it may be like a waterfall: it is difficult to swim up stream.

Root: I have the prejudice—and I think there are data to support it—that the enzymes for H_2O_2 production are intimately related to receptors on the cell surface for phagocytosis. The receptors appear to be triggering or maybe even contain the enzymes for peroxide formation. Indeed, what we are seeing when we measure other activities such as glucose oxidation by the shunt is due to leakage out of the vacuole. This is the reverse of the phenomenon that I have described with diffusion of H_2O_2 into the cell from the outside.

Karnovsky: I would like to say one thing, obviously prematurely, because I have no data with me. It turns out that there is enzymatic production of peroxide—I can't vouch for superoxide—*on* the membrane surface of the polymorphonuclear leukocyte. Dick Briggs and Doris Karnovsky have devised a method of detecting peroxide that yields an electron-dense stain, such that when you include external NADH in the system and let the cells phagocytize, phagocytosis turns on something in the membrane and there is immediate deposition of a metal complex around the outside of the cell, and also in the vacuole. You see it coming down the channels and it coats the interior surface of the vacuole.

Spitznagel: Just a little more information about what may be going into and what may be coming out of the polys. Dr. M. S. Leffell and I have done experiments with polys similar to the ones that Dr. Cohn described with macrophages. We gave latex particles of 1.09 nanometers diameter to polys, and, when the particles had been phagocytized, we separated the phagocytic vesicles by flotation; that is, cell homogenates were prepared from the phagocytizing cells and centrifuged at 100,000 $\times$ *g* for 1 hour. The vesicles were simply skimmed from the top of each gradient. We have used beads coated with BSA and anti-BSA antigen-antibody complexes, beads coated with BSA, and just plain latex beads. We analyzed samples of fluid in which the polymorphs performed phagocytosis so that we could measure the appearance of lactoferrin (specific granule marker) and myeloperoxidase (azurophil granule marker), beta-glucuronidase, and alkaline phosphatase outside the cells. At the same time we measured the amounts of these substances that had entered the phagocytic vesicles formed by the cells. Beads coated with antigen-antibody complexes constituted the most potent stimulus to degranulation and induced more degranulation than did antigen or antibody alone. The release of components from specific as compared with azurophil granules appeared to be independent phenomena. Relatively more specific granule proteins were translocated outside the cells while relatively more azurophil proteins appeared in the phagocytic vesicles. For example, when polys phagocytized beads coated with antigen-antibody complexes, as much as 60%

of the specific granule marker, lactoferrin, was found extracellularly after the polys had phagocytized for 60 minutes. Only 3% of the lactoferrin was found in the isolated phagolysosomes. By way of contrast 10% of the myeloperoxidase appeared extracellularly while more than 10% was incorporated in the phagocytic vesicles. When antigen- or antibody-coated beads were used, only half as much degranulation occurred, either out of the cells or into the phagosomes. This was true even though by 60 minutes bead uptake was within 10% of that observed with phagocytosis of antigen-antibody coated beads.

Alkaline phosphatase also appeared outside the phagocytizing cells, but no more than 30% was found extracellularly. The amount lost from the cells was similar regardless of the coating on the beads. In the phagosomes formed in response to antigen-antibody complexes, we found 5% of the alkaline phosphatase and we found half that much in the phagolysosomes formed in response to antigen. The results with alkaline phosphatase thus were different than those with lactoferrin. The results seem to us consistent with our findings that this enzyme is found in cell membranes and not in the specific granules of human PMN. Beta-glucuronidase, however, behaved similarly to myeloperoxidase. This was consistent with our observation that beta-glucuronidase is a part of the human azurophil granule. Loss of lactic dehydrogenase from the cells was not greater than 6%, indicating very little cell damage to account for loss of granule enzymes into the medium.

The point is that during phagocytosis there is an exit of the myeloperoxidase from the cell; the amount that leaves depends on what is on the surface of the particle that elicits the degranulation. It is important to note, however, that less than 50 percent of the translocated MPO leaves the cell, most of it stays in the phagolysosome. Lactoferrin behaves quite differently.

Holmes-Gray: We tried this flotation method, too, and we had a great deal of trouble with the nonspecific binding of enzymes to latex or at least what appears to be nonspecific binding of enzyme to the latex. What did you get with just plain latex in this top curve?

Spitznagel: Practically nothing.

Holmes-Gray: That is what we found. But when we treated latex particles with lanthinum cloride to get rid of some of the charge effects of latex, we then found up to 30 percent of enzyme in the vesicles. I wonder whether when you coat the latex with the protein (BSA) you also eliminate charge effects of latex, but it is really kind of artificial in that the enzyme has been released but is undetected because of binding to latex?

Spitznagel: No, we have complete balances on this and we are accounting for 90 to 100 percent of our substances measured. We should know if 30 percent of the substance has been lost by absorption or by some other event. It is a closed system. We are accounting for nearly 100 percent of everything we are measuring.

Holmes-Gray: Dr. Cohn, have you ever had trouble with latex in terms of binding of lysosomal enzymes.

Cohn: No, not particularly.

Hirsch: Where do you think the alkaline phosphatase is in the cell and where does it appear in the medium?

Klebanoff: Could you also discuss your results in relation to the binding of alkaline phosphatase to the plasma membrane following exocytosis as described by Peter Hensen (*J. Exp. Med.* 134:114s, 1971).

Spitznagel: I will try. I am not sure I can really answer it. The point is that in our cell fractionation studies, we found that the alkaline phosphatase travels with the microsomal or membrane fraction. It is essentially a fraction consisting of empty vesicles and it is not associated with either the specific or the azurophil granules. Our fractionation work leads us to think alkaline phosphatase in human polys is essentially a membrane enzyme. What membranes are involved remains to be determined.

Hirsch: Why should it be released by frustrated phagocytosis?

Spitznagel: We are not observing frustrated phagocytosis. These polys are really taking up the particles, and you can see there is a substantial release of the amount in the cells, up to 30 percent under these circumstances.

Karnovsky: But do you think it's going through the phagosome?

Spitznagel: The loss of alkaline phosphatase is happening from the moment the cell comes into contact with the particle or during the time the membrane is surrounding the particle and the phagosome is being formed. Since alkaline phosphatase is not part of the granule matrix, it would not necessarily leak out through a cleft. Lactoferrin and myeloperoxidase, which are granule components, probably do leak out through a cleft of the kind Dr. Karnovsky showed us.

Baehner: Do you have evidence that there is lipid released at that time?

Spitznagel: We have not studied the lipids. Dr. Becker has some additional information.

Becker: In addition, Peter Henson has also used zymosan as his phagocytic particle and even under those circumstances was not able to demonstrate alkaline phosphatase in the supernatant, even though it was, from his electron microscopic pictures, clearly being released into or bounded by the membrane.

Spitznagel: In the rabbit polymorph there is alkaline phosphatase which seems to travel with the specific granule. Recently Marco Baggiolini has found that this is associated not with the matrix of the rabbit-specific granule but the membrane that surrounds the rabbit-specific granule. At the present time we don't know enough about the different alkaline phosphatases. Perhaps the alkaline phosphatase which is seen in the rabbit cell could be different from the one we are observing in the human cell. There is a great quantitative difference in the alkaline phosphatase content of the two cells.

Cohn: Have you ever tried glycerol phosphate?

Spitznagel: We have compared the distribution of alkaline phosphatases that attack *p*-nitrophenyl phosphate and ones that attack beta-glycerolphosphate in human PMN. Both activities are localized in the microsomal fraction.

Cohn: If you use beta-glycerolphosphate do you get the same release?

Spitznagel: I have not used it in the phagocytosis experiments.

Becker: A glycerolphosphate was the same substrate used by Peter Henson.

Gallin: We have looked at the chemotactic response of three patients with chronic granulomatous disease and have not found an abnormality in any of them.

Klebanoff: That is our experience as well.

Ward: Exactly ours, too.

Snyderman: I will go along with that.

Holmes-Gray: I would have to argue about this patient who had the chemotactic defect being chronic granulomatous disease by all criteria.

Root: In my laboratory this patient had impaired killing of all catalase positive bacteria tested, including *S. aureus, E. coli, Serratia marcescens,* and *Candida albicans.* In addition, NBT reduction was markedly reduced, as were oxygen consumption, ^{14}C-1-glucose oxidation, formate oxidation, and iodination. Finally, the mother was found to be a carrier. I think he has classic chronic granulomatous disease by all criteria.

Holmes-Gray: This isn't the same patient reported by Ward and Schlegel?

Ward: This is exactly the same patient who showed a profound defect in staphylococcus killing in Bob Schlegel's tests. I think it has to be admitted this patient had an inhibitor. But we have looked at three other patients who fulfill all the conventional criteria for CGD and they clearly show normal chemotaxis. So this one case represents a very distinct exception to the rule.

Holmes-Gray: What was the bactericidal defect? It was a killing defect for *E. coli* but not *S. aureus?*

Ward: That is right.

Root: In my laboratory he did not kill *E. coli, S. aureus,* and other catalase positive organisms and his mother was an identified carrier by the NBT reduction technique.

Park: Perhaps it is about time to draw up some minimum criteria for making the diagnosis of CGD. What would be the minimum criteria for CGD?

Quie: I would say that if a patient's neutrophils do not kill catalase positive microorganisms and have evidence for decreased production of intracellular hydrogen peroxide, a diagnosis of chronic granulomatous disease can be made.

Holmes-Gray: The patient would have an abnormal NBT test.

Root: Normal G-6-PD without letting them age in the refrigerator.

Quie: The neutrophils would be morphologically normal.

Klebanoff: Dr. Good would also like to see histological evidence of granulomata formation, as the name would suggest, and has in fact suggested that patients without granulomata form a subgroup of chronic granulomatous disease. Wheter the definition is now more firmly established on metabolic and bactericidal grounds rather than on a histological grounds. . . .

Quie: I believe the diagnosis can and should be made on the basis of clinical, microbiological, and metabolic evidence.

Klebanoff: For example, patients with familial lipochrome histiocytosis have leukocytes that are comparable to CGD leukocytes metabolically and in microbicidal activity but the clinical picture differs and granulomata are not seen.

Quie: If you look at a study of monocyte function, and again it has to be qualified, because I don't think that differences in rate of ingestion versus rate of killing were appreciated, in a patient with lipochrome histiocytosis, there was normal monocyte bactericidal activity. In patients with CGD there are all kinds of questions about the resuts but the monocyte bactericidal capacity is defective. Perhaps this difference in monocyte function may account for the presence or absence of granulomas.

Baehner: I would add to the list of syndromes Job's syndrome, which is defined as a disease of recurrent abcesses occurring in young women who are fair-skinned and red-haired. Some have been studied with leukocyte function tests and have shown metabolic defects of their PMN similar to chronic granulomatous disease.

Klebanoff: That gets into another topic.

Quie: I would like to respond to that. The patient in Toronto, Canada that you referred to is a female patient with chronic granulomatous disease. She happened to have red hair and fair skin and she had problems with salmonella as well as with staphylocci.

Klebanoff: We have looked extensively at the original two patients with Job's syndrome as have Davis, Wedgwood, Ochs, and their associates, and we have never been able to find an abnormality suggestive of CGD.

Baehner: I should rephrase my original statement to say that some female patients with chronic granulomatous disease are fair-skinned and have red hair.

The Phagocytic Cell in Host Resistance, edited
by Joseph A. Bellanti and Delbert H. Dayton.
Raven Press, New York © 1975.

Abnormal Chemotaxis: Cellular and Humoral Components

John I. Gallin

Laboratory of Clinical Investigation, National Institute of Allergy and Infectious Diseases, National Institutes of Health, Bethesda, Maryland 20014

INTRODUCTION

The identification of functional abnormalities of the cellular and humoral components of leukocyte migration has contributed to our understanding of the mechanisms of impaired host defenses in a variety of clinical settings. During the past 2 years, our laboratory has studied various parameters of the chemotactic process in patients with recurrent infections. Patients with an abnormal chemotactic response but normal spontaneous motility have been described (1, 2). We have also studied patients with abnormalities of the fluid phase (serum or plasma) chemotactic mediators exemplified by deficiencies of certain components of complement (3) or the kinin and fibrinolytic systems (4). In addition, patients with deficient production of lymphocyte-derived mediators (chemotactic lymphokines) have been studied including two patients with the Sezary syndrome (5) from whom dialyzable transfer factor preparations lacked chemotactic activity; dialyzable transfer factor prepared from normal lymphocytes is chemotactic for human neutrophils and mononuclear cells (6, also Kirkpatrick and Gallin, *this volume*).

As an initial effort to understand some of these functional abnormalities, both neutrophil and mononuclear cell chemotaxis was evaluated in some of our patients to determine if, in a given patient, defects are limited to a single cell type. In addition, two parameters of human neutrophil-chemotactic factor interaction have been studied: calcium fluxes and microtubule assembly. Finally, to evaluate the relative *in vivo* roles of the different humoral chemotactic mediators, generation of chemotactic factors was studied in normal volunteers given intravenous endotoxin and compared with chemotactic factor generation *in vitro.* This chapter summarizes the current status of our findings in these normal and pathologic conditions.

METHODS

Blood

Leukocytes were obtained by either dextran sedimentation (1) or Hypaque-Ficoll separation (7) of heparinized human venous blood. The dextran sedimentation method was used to obtain cells for neutrophil chemotaxis and routinely resulted in leukocyte populations containing 80 to 85% neutrophils; residual erythrocytes were removed by hypotonic saline lysis (1). The Hypaque-Ficoll technique was utilized for mononuclear cell chemotaxis and routinely resulted in greater than 95% pure mononuclear cell populations (85% lymphocytes and 15% monocytes). For some experiments, 95% pure granulocyte populations were obtained by dextran sedimentation of the granulocyte-erythrocyte pellet resulting from Hypaque-Ficoll separation. Sera were obtained as previously described (1). For studies of the *in vivo* generation of chemotactic factors, plasma anticoagulated with EDTA (Fisher Scientific Co., Fairlawn, New Jersey, 10^{-2}M) and hexadimethrine bromide (Aldrich Chemical Co., Inc., Milwaukee, Wisconsin, 3.6 mg/10 ml whole blood) was obtained from normal volunteers at varying times after the intravenous administration of purified *Salmonella abortus equi* endotoxin (Lipexal, Dorsey Company, Lincoln, Nebraska) 5 ng/kg body weight (8). Sera or plasma were stored at −70°C until used.

Chemotactic Assay

To measure leukocyte chemotaxis, chemotactic factors were obtained from normal serum by activation of complement with endotoxin (*E. coli:* 0127:B8 lipopolysaccharide B, Difco Labs., Detroit, Michigan) as previously described (1). For assessment of chemotactic activity associated with the fibrinolytic and kinin-generating systems, whole plasma was activated with kaolin (Fisher Scientific Co.) as recently reported (4). Neutrophil chemotaxis was evaluated by means of a radioassay developed in our laboratory employing chromium-51 (^{51}Cr, Amersham/Searle, Arlington Heights, Illinois) labeled neutrophils and a modified Boyden chamber using two 5-μm micropore filters (Millipore Corp., Bedford, Massachusetts) (9). For this assay, neutrophils labeled with ^{51}Cr are placed in the upper compartment of the chemotactic chamber and the chemotactic stimulus in the lower compartment. The number of cells traversing the upper filter and migrating into the lower filter is proportional to the radioactivity incorporated into that filter. After adjusting for variable incorporation of ^{51}Cr by the leukocytes, neutrophil chemotaxis is expressed as corrected counts per minute incorporated into the lower filter (cor cpm LF) (9). This assay enables a rapid and objective quantitative assessment of leukocyte movement. Mononuclear cell chemotaxis was performed with a morphologic assay previously described by Snyderman et al. (10) employing a 5-μm Nucleopore filter (Wallabs, Inc., San Rafael, California). Chemotaxis was expressed as the mean number of cells per high power field migrating to the lower surface of the filter (1).

Spontaneous (Random or Passive) Motility

Spontaneous motility was assessed by measuring neutrophil migration through 5-μm micropore (Millipore) filters and mononuclear cell migration through

5-μm Nucleopore filters using Hank's balanced salt solution as the chemotactic stimulus and routine incubation conditions.

Calcium Fluxes

Calcium fluxes were determined by measuring neutrophil uptake of calcium-45 (New England Nuclear, Boston, Massachusetts) (calcium influx) or the release of ^{45}Ca from cells preloaded with the isotope (efflux) as recently described (11). ^{45}Ca efflux studies were carried out in modified Hank's solution (12) containing 1.0 mM calcium and 0.5 mM magnesium, and calcium influx studeis were determined in Hank's solution containing 0.5 mM magnesium and no calcium.

Electron Microscopy

Suspensions of neutrophils or micropore filters containing migrating leukocytes were prepared for electron microscopic analysis by fixing for 60 min with 1% glutaraldehyde in Tyrode's buffer, pH 7.2, followed by washing in 0.01 M phosphate buffered isotonic sucrose pH 7.2, and postfixing in 1% osmic acid solution (pH 7.2). Specimens were dehydrated through graded ethanol and propylene oxide and embedded in epoxy resin (Maraglas, Polyscience, Lydal, Pennsylvania). Thin sections were doubly stained with lead citrate and uranyl acetate and examined in a Phillips EM-300 electron microscope.

G-150 Gel Filtration, Complement Components, and Assays for Kallikrein and Plasminogen Activator

Gel filtration of 4.5 cc of whole serum or plasma was performed on a 5 × 100 cm column of Sephadex G-150 (Pharmacia Fine Chemicals, Piscataway, New Jersey) equilibrated with 0.05 M phosphate-buffered saline, pH 7.4, and run with upward flow. Goat antisera to the third or fifth components of human complement were obtained commercially (Meloy Laboratories, McLean, Virginia). Highly purified human kallikrein was obtained as previously described (13). Plasminogen activator was assayed by its ability to convert human plasminogen to plasmin (14), and kallikrein was determined with a bioassay (15).

RESULTS

Abnormal Leukocyte Responses

The possibility that chemotactic defects are restricted to a single white blood cell lineage has been suggested by isolated reports of defective mononuclear (16) or neutrophil (1, 2, 17–19) chemotaxis; however, the chemotactic responsiveness of the other cell line was not described. The following experiments demonstrate that in three patients with two diseases both neutrophil and mononuclear cell chemotactic responses to endotoxin-activated normal serum were abnormal. In addition, defective neutrophil chemotaxis was noted in two patients with hypogammaglobulinemia.

Chediak-Higashi Syndrome

The Chediak-Higashi syndrome (CHS) is a rare autosomal recessive disease characterized by partial oculocutaneous albinism, frequent pyogenic infections, neutropenia, and characteristic "giant" lysosomal granules present in all granule-containing cells (20). Neutrophil chemotactic responses in eight experiments on two patients with the CHS were markedly abnormal (40% of normal) confirming the original observation of Clark and Kimball (1). Neutrophil spontaneous motility (Boyden chamber technique) in patients with the CHS was also defective (51% of normal, Table 1). Studies of CHS mononuclear cell chemotaxis revealed

TABLE 1. *Spontaneous motility in patients with defective chemotaxis*

	Spontaneous motility			
Patient	Neutrophils (cor cpm LF)	p[a]	Mononuclear cells (cells/hpf)	p
Normal	276 ± 25(6)[b]	—	45 ± 7(5)	—
CHS[c]				
LeR.	108 ± 12(3)	<0.01	18 ± 5(3)	<0.05
LaR.	125 ± 13(5)	<0.01	22 ± 7(4)	<0.05
C.C.[d]	291 ± 14(8)	>0.05	49 ± 8(3)	>0.05
Ig-deficient				
A.R.	263 ± 8(2)	>0.05	—	—
R.S.	302 ± 29(1)	>0.05	—	—

[a] Significant level of difference from normal; Student's t-test.
[b] Number of different experiments in parentheses.
[c] Chediak-Higashi syndrome.
[d] A patient with recurrent pyogenic infections.

a mononuclear cell chemotactic defect comparable to that seen with the neutrophil (42% of normal, Fig. 1) (21). The spontaneous motility of the mononuclear cells from CHS patients had a similar defect (Table 1). As shown in Fig. 2, the rate of CHS neutrophil migration through the micropore filter was markedly diminished compared to normal throughout the 3 hr of incubation. The kinetic curve of mononuclear cell chemotaxis of CHS patients exhibited a similar defect. Studies of mononuclear cell chemotaxis in a strain of Hereford cattle and a strain of mink, both of which have the CHS (22), revealed similar mononuclear cell chemotactic abnormalities (21). CHS sera activated with endotoxin revealed normal chemotactic activity for homologous neutrophils (1) and mononuclear cells (21), indicating that the defect in this disorder is one of cellular responsiveness.

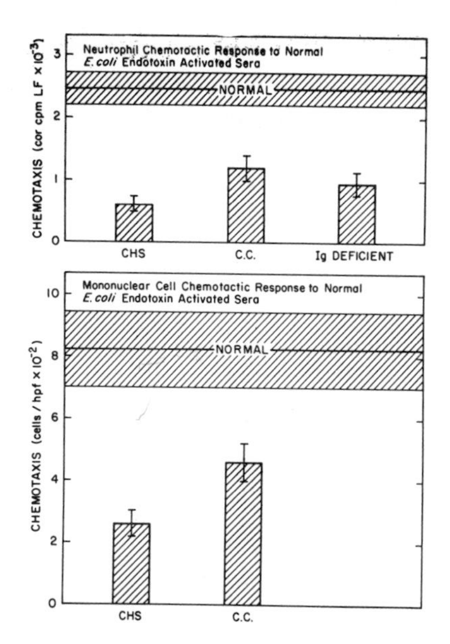

FIG. 1. Chemotactic response of neutrophils using a ^{51}Cr radioassay (upper panel) and mononuclear cells using a morphologic assay (lower panel) to normal *E. coli* endotoxin-activated human sera. The normal response is the mean ± SE of eight experiments. The bars denote the mean ± SE chemotactic response for Chediak-Higashi syndrome (CHS) cells, a patient with recurrent pyogenic infections (C.C.) and two patients with hypogammaglobulinemia (Ig-deficient) (see text).

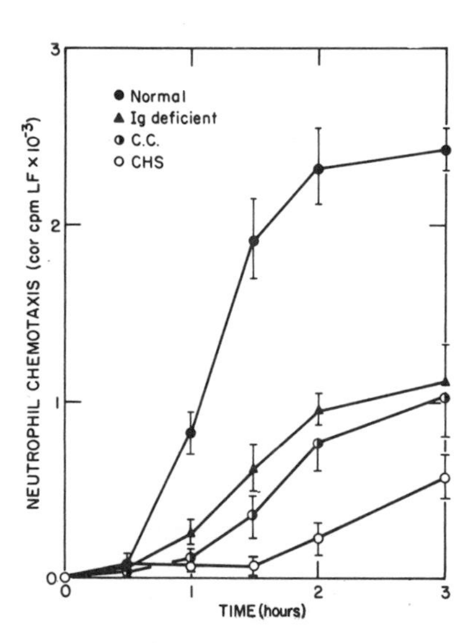

FIG. 2. Kinetics of neutrophil migration into the lower filter of radioassay chamber of a normal subject, a patient deficient in gamma globulin (A.R.), a patient with recurrent pyogenic infections (C.C.), and a patient with Chediak-Higashi syndrome (CHS). The bars denote the mean ± SE at each time for quadruplicate chambers.

It is interesting that our observation of abnormal random motility of CHS cells using the Boyden chamber technique is in sharp contrast with the normal findings reported using the capillary tube method (1). This provides supportive evidence for Dr. Michael Miller's claim that these two assays measure different parameters. (see Miller, *this volume*).

Abnormal Leukocyte Chemotaxis in a Child with Recurrent Pyogenic Infections, Mucocutaneous Candidiasis, and Defective Delayed Hypersensitivity

Abnormal neutrophil chemotaxis in this patient (C. C.) has been recently documented by Clark et al. (2), utilizing the morphologic Boyden chamber technique. As shown in Fig. 1, these results have been confirmed using the ^{51}Cr radioassay of neutrophil chemotaxis. In contrast to the patients with the CHS, this patient's neutrophils had normal spontaneous motility as measured by the capillary tube migration test (2) and by migration of her neutrophils through a micropore filter (Table 1). Studies of the *in vitro* chemotactic activity of her mononuclear cells revealed an abnormality (51% of normal) similar to that noted with her neutrophils (Fig. 1). As shown in Fig. 2, the rate of this patient's neutrophil chemotactic response was abnormal throughout the time period examined and the kinetics of her mononuclear cell chemotactic response exhibited a similar abnormal pattern. No complement-related mediator defect was noted in this patient's sera. However, associated with her mucocutaneous candidiasis was absent delayed hypersensitivity to Candida antigen characterized by negative skin tests and failure of her lymphocytes to release MIF or chemotactic lymphokine when stimulated with Candida antigen (23). It is of interest that treatment of this patient with multiple doses of dialyzable transfer factor failed to correct her chemotactic defect (23), which distinguishes her from the patient described by Snyderman et al., in whom a mononuclear cell chemotactic defect was corrected with transfer factor therapy (16).

Defective Neutrophil Chemotaxis in Hypogammaglobulinemia

Abnormal neutrophil chemotaxis has been reported in a patient with a sex-linked form of congenital agammaglobulinemia (19). We, therefore, studied neutrophil chemotactic function in two patients with deficiencies of gamma globulin (Fig. 1). One of these patients (R. S., Table 1) was a 29-year-old man with panhypogammaglobulinemia with a serum IgG of 110 mg% (normal 700 to 1,800), no detectable IgA or IgM, and nodular lymphoid hyperplasia of the small intestine. The other patient (A. R.) was a 9-year-old boy with recurrent, severe upper respiratory tract infections, otitis media, and a serum IgG of 100 mg%, IgA of 2.5 mg% (normal 60 to 250), and IgM of 9.0 mg% (normal 50 to 150). Neutrophils from both of these patients were found to have defective chemotaxis ($p < 0.01$, Student's *t*-test) with mean neutrophil chemotactic responses of 43% of normal. In four studies of each patient the kinetics of neutrophil migration revealed an abnormal pattern similar to that noted in CHS and in patient C. C. (Fig. 2). Their neutrophil spontaneous motility was normal (Table 1).

Abnormalities of Chemotactic Factor Generation from Fluid Phase Components

Complement Defects

We have recently shown that analysis of the kinetics of generation of chemotactic activity by complement activation of human serum enables distinction of classical and alternate complement pathway function (3, 24). Similar findings were noted using guinea pig serum (25). Activation of the classical pathway results in rapid generation of chemotactic activity with significant activity noted within 5 to 10 min. In contrast, alternate complement pathway activation was characterized by a 15- to 30-min delay before generation of chemotactic activity. Using such kinetic analysis, it was demonstrated that activation of both complement pathways in human sera deficient in the second component of complement yielded an abnormal pattern with a 30-min delay prior to chemotactic factor generation (3, 24). The chemotactic activity of these sera 1 hr after activation was normal, reflecting normal alternate pathway function. The addition of C2 to the C2-deficient sera restored a normal kinetic pattern. Recently, we have obtained similar results in a patient deficient in the r fragment of the first complement component (C1r deficiency, 26). In contrast to normal serum the kinetic pattern of activation of C1r-deficient serum with *E. coli* endotoxin, which activates the classical and alternate complement pathways in normal humans, was characterized by a 15- to 20-min delay before the generation of chemotactic activity (Fig. 3). As in the patient with C2 deficiency, the chemotactic activity

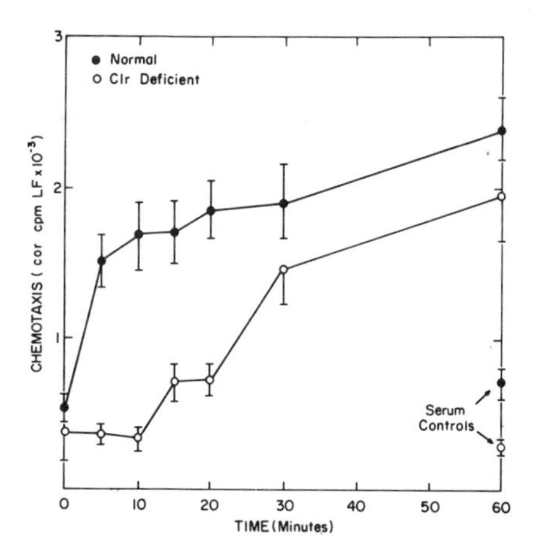

FIG. 3. Generation of chemotactic factors in normal and C1r-deficient human serum activated with *E. coli* endotoxin. Control serum contained no endotoxin. The test cells were normal human neutrophils. The differences between normal and C1r-deficient activated serum were significant at 5 to 20 min ($p < 0.01$) but were not significant at 30 and 60 min ($p > 0.05$).

after 1 hr of activation was normal. Thus, kinetic analysis of chemotactic factor generation may be essential for distinguishing a nonfunctioning classical but normal alternate complement pathway.

Abnormal Kinin-Generating System

Highly purified preparations of human kallikrein and plasminogen activator have been shown to be chemotactic for human neutrophils (13, 27) and more recently for mononuclear cells (28). In addition to the chemotactic activity of such highly purified serum components, kaolin activation of whole serum yielded chemotactic activity that could be distinguished from the complement-derived chemotactic factors (4). Moreover, as shown in Fig. 4, human plasma deficient in prekallikrein (Fletcher factor), which has a diminished rate of Hageman factor activation, revealed diminished chemotactic activity after kaolin activation unless the absent substrate is added back to the plasma (4).

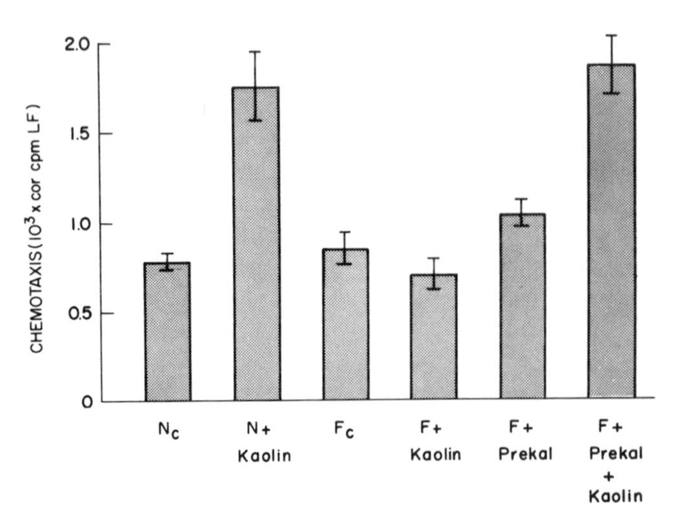

FIG. 4. Comparison of kaolin-activated chemotactic activity in normal serum and Fletcher factor-deficient serum. The bars indicate the mean ± SE (three determinations) of the chemotactic activity of normal control serum (Nc), normal serum activated with kaolin (N + kaolin), Fletcher factor-deficient control serum (Fc), Fletcher factor-deficient serum activated with kaolin (F + kaolin), Fletcher factor-deficient serum reconstituted with prekallikrein (F + prekal), and Fletcher factor-deficient serum activated with kaolin after reconstitution with prekallikrein (F + prekal + kaolin). From Weiss et al. (4), reproduced by permission of the publisher.

Normal Chemotaxis

In Vivo Generation of Chemotactic Factors

Previous *in vitro* studies of chemotactic factor generation from serum have suggested that the most important chemotactic factor resulting from complement activation is the cleavage product of the fifth component of complement, C5a (29). *In vitro* activation of the fibrinolytic and kinin-generating systems in whole plasma has suggested that plasminogen activator and kallikrein may have physiologic roles in amplifying the inflammatory response (4). To assess the *in vivo* relevance of these *in vitro* studies, we have given intravenous endotoxin or saline to normal volunteers and assessed their plasma for *in vitro* neutrophil chemotactic activity 30 min, 1, 2, 4, 12, and 24 hr after injection. At present, we have studied nine volunteers. None of the volunteers receiving saline had any increase of chemotactic activity over the base line chemotactic response. Four volunteers who received endotoxin increased their chemotactic activity twofold between 30 and 90 min after the intravenous injection (about 1 hr preceding the febrile response). To evaluate the source of the increased chemotactic activity, zero time and 30-min plasma were chromatographed on G-150 Sephadex; the results from one subject are shown in Fig. 5. The protein elution profile

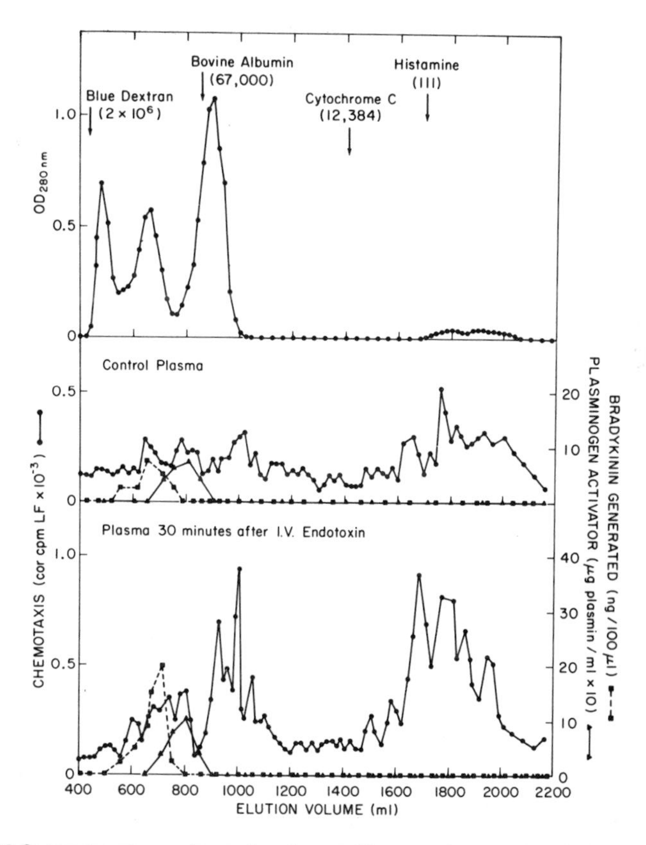

FIG. 5. G-150 Sephadex chromatography of normal human plasma taken before (middle panel) and 30 min after (lower panel) intravenous endotoxin. The protein elution profile (absorbance at 280 nm) is shown in the upper panel. In the lower two panels, chemotactic activity is represented by circles, kallikrein (bradykinin-generated) by squares, and plasminogen activator by triangles.

(absorbance at 280 nm) was identical at zero and 30 min. The major chemotactic activity of control (zero time) plasma eluted in four regions corresponding to the elution positions of kallikrein, plasminogen activator, just after the molecular weight marker bovine albumin, and as a broad peak in the region of the molecular weight marker histamine. Thirty minutes after the administration of intravenous endotoxin, increases in chemotactic activity were noted at each of the same elution volumes (Fig. 5). In no studies did the chemotactic activity of any of the fractions from the control plasma exceed the 30-min, post-endotoxin samples. In one volunteer an additional peak of chemotactic activity was noted in the 30-min sample that eluted just prior to the cytochrome C marker. This material was stable at 56°C, was inactivated by goat antisera to the fifth but not the third component of human complement, and presumably was C5a. The most prominent peak of chemotactic activity in every study eluted at the end of the column in the region of the histamine marker. This material was heat labile at 56°C for 30 min but was not inactivated by goat antisera to human C3 or C5 and did not cause contraction of guinea pig ileum. At the present time, this material has not been identified; however, it does not appear to correspond to any of the previously described chemotactic factors of serum. In a related series of experiments, G-150 Sephadex chromatography of *in vitro* endotoxin-activated *(E. coli)* serum resulted in a large peak of chemotactic activity with an estimated molecular weight of 15,500 (presumably C5a), as well as small increases in the chemotactic peaks eluting with kallikrein or plasminogen activator. Chromatography of kaolin-activated (Hageman factor activation) whole plasma resulted in increased chemotactic activity in the elution position of kallikrein, plasminogen activator, and at the histamine marker. Chromatography of prekallikrein-deficient human plasma activated with kaolin yielded no peaks of chemotactic activity. Since this plasma is incapable of generating kallikrein (4, 30) and also possesses a diminished rate of Hageman factor activation (4), the major noncomplement-dependent peaks observed appear to be dependent on Hageman factor activation.

Normal Neutrophil-Chemotactic Factor Interaction

In addition to studies of the generation of chemotactic factors in normal subjects, we have studied three parameters of normal neutrophil-chemotactic interaction that may be relevant to certain pathologic events. These include divalent cation requirements, calcium fluxes, and microtubule assembly. It was reported by Becker and Showell (31) that calcium and magnesium were required for optimal rabbit neutrophil chemotaxis. We have confirmed these observations with human neutrophils and found that 2 mM of calcium and 0.5 mM of magnesium were required for optimal human granulocyte chemotaxis (11). As little as a threefold change in either divalent cation concentration significantly diminished the optimal chemotactic response. The relationship of this to impaired host defenses in certain endocrine disorders, such as hypoparathyroidism (32), is currently under investigation.

Studies have also been performed evaluating calcium fluxes (using calcium-45) into and out of neutrophils during exposure to the chemotactic factors C5a, dialyzable transfer factor, and kallikrein. We could not demonstrate an influx of ^{45}Ca into cells exposed to chemotactic stimuli. However, as shown in Table 2, a significant ^{45}Ca efflux was demonstrated from neutrophils to the surrounding media for each of three different chemotactic stimuli. It is noted that the kallikrein preparation, which possessed one-half of the chemotactic activity of C5a, had twice as much ^{45}Ca efflux as C5a. Since kallikrein is a proteolytic enzyme, this quantitative difference in efflux and chemotactic activity between C5a and kallikrein may be related to different mechanisms of initiating the chemotactic response. Kinetic analysis of the chemotactic factor-induced Ca^{2+} efflux showed that it occurred early (within 1 min) after exposure of cells to the stimulus (11). Nonspecific proteins, such as ovalbumin, horseradish peroxidase, and human

TABLE 2. *Chemotactic factor-induced ^{45}Ca efflux from human neutrophils*

	Chemotactic activity (cor cpm LF)[a]	Ca^{++} efflux	
		Net % change[b]	p[c]
Buffer control	212 ± 15	0	—
C5a	2211 ± 125	+16 ± 2	<0.01
Kallikrein	1136 ± 94	+36 ± 11	<0.02
Transfer factor	1866 ± 178	+21 ± 1	<0.01

[a] Mean ± SE; four determinations.
[b] Net % change from buffer controls; mean ± SE, four determinations.
[c] Significance level of differences of ^{45}Ca efflux between stimulated and control cells; Student's *t*-test.

albumin, which do not have chemotactic activity, did not cause ^{45}Ca efflux. In related studies in which the intracellular distribution of ^{45}Ca was assessed by counting ^{45}Ca in various fractions of neutrophil lysates (differential centrifugation), a small (10%), yet significant ($p < 0.05$), decrease in ^{45}Ca was noted in a 27,000 *g* supernatant or "cytoplasmic" fraction of cells exposed to C5a compared to buffer. These calcium flux data were interpreted as suggesting that ^{45}Ca efflux from neutrophils may be important for a normal chemotactic response.

Calcium flux studies done on neutrophils from patients with the CHS, which have abnormal chemotaxis and spontaneous motility, were normal. Neutrophils from patient C. C., whose neutrophils have normal spontaneous movement but abnormal chemotaxis (Fig. 1 and Table 1), also showed a normal net increment of calcium efflux when exposed to chemotactic factors; however, her cells "leaked" calcium-45 after ^{45}Ca loading with a threefold more rapid efflux of calcium from her resting (buffer exposed) cells than normal. The relevance of this observation to C. C.'s abnormal chemotactic response has not been established.

With the recent demonstrations that *in vitro* assembly of brain microtubules is favored by a low calcium environment (33), that chemotaxis is inhibited by microtubule lysing agents (34, 35), and that C5a-induced microtubule assembly in cytochalasin B-treated neutrophils (36), we looked for the assembly of microtubules in human neutrophils either exposed to C5a in suspension or migrating through millipore filters in response to a gradient of C5a. Significantly increased numbers of microtubules were readily demonstrated in cells exposed to C5a in suspension compared with cells exposed to buffer (Table 3). Similar results were noted in cells actively migrating through a millipore filter. An example of C5a-treated cells with prominent microtubules is shown in Fig. 6.

TABLE 3. *C5a-induced assembly of microtubules in human neutrophils*

Experiment	Chemotactic factor	Total number of fields examined	% containing microtubules	Chi-squared[a]	*p*
1	None	70	9	27.4	<0.001
	C5a	79	49		
2	None	38	11	22.4	<0.001
	C5a	25	72		
3	None	67	22	17.4	<0.001
	C5a	11	91		

[a] One degree of freedom.

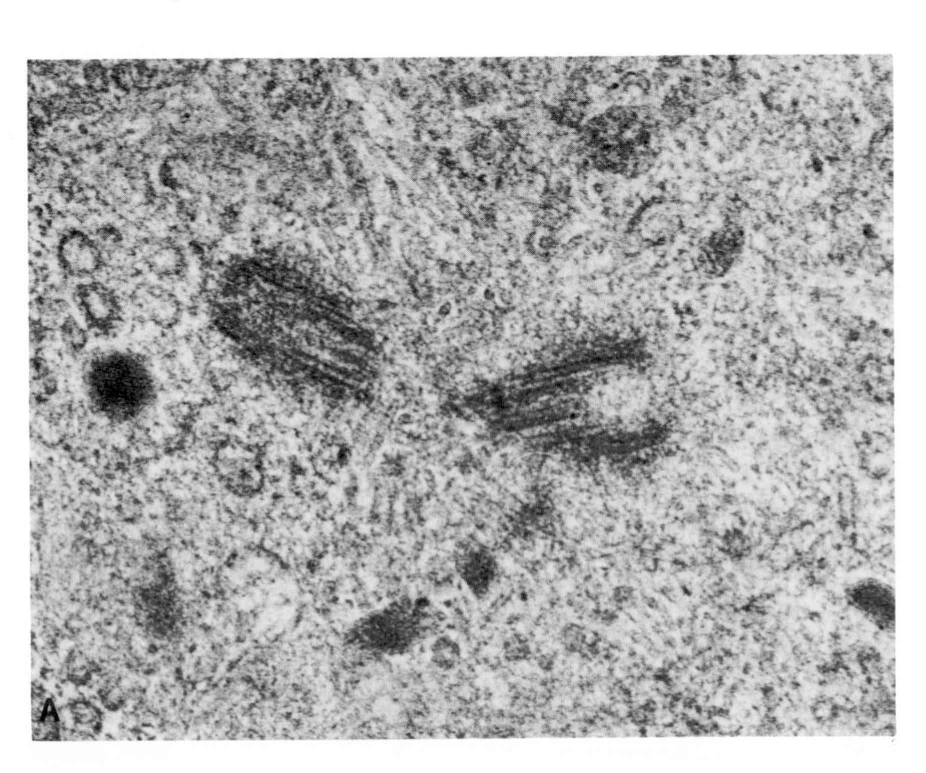

DISCUSSION

The increasing reports of defective leukocyte movement in patients with recurrent infections as assessed by a Boyden-type chamber have demonstrated that this *in vitro* assay has a major role in characterizing certain defects of host defenses. Obviously, if any *in vivo* therapeutic manipulations of the chemotactic process are to be developed, then the biochemical events associated with leukocyte locomotion must first be elucidated. The demonstration of different chemotactic-related "activatable" serine esterases in rabbit neutrophils and mononuclear cells (37) suggested at least some different enzyme requirements for the neutrophil and mononuclear cell chemotactic responses. This notion was supported by isolated reports of abnormal leukocyte locomotion, which suggested defective chemotaxis of only one cell line (mononuclear cells or neutrophils). We have studied mononuclear and neutrophil locomotion in two clinical settings and in each found abnormal chemotaxis for both cell lines, although the spontaneous motility (Boyden chamber assay) of neutrophils and mononuclear cells of one

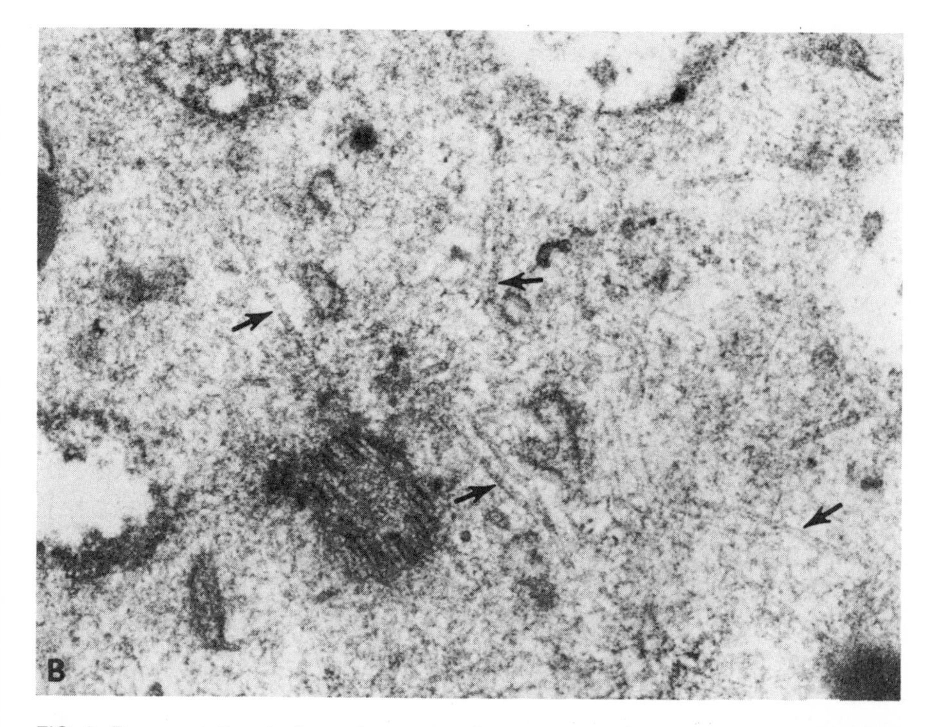

FIG. 6. Representative electron micrographs of the centriole regions of neutrophils migrating through a micropore filter under the influences of a concentration gradient of C5a. A nonmigrating cell from the upper surface of the filter, i.e., a region of low C5a concentration, exhibits few microtubules (A), whereas a migrating cell deep within the filter nearest the source of C5a possesses easily demonstrable centriole-associated microtubules (arrows, B) (magnification X 65,450).

group was abnormal (CHS) and the other normal (C. C.). These data suggest that within each of these patients the biochemical-biophysical defects may reflect a general abnormality of all migrating cells. Although there is good evidence that an association exists between defective *in vitro* leukocyte movement and pathological conditions, the importance of deficiencies of some humoral (serum-plasma) mediators has been more difficult to establish. For example, patients deficient in prekallikrein or the second component of complement do not have major problems with infections. This may reflect the presence of alternative pathways that are sufficient to maintain adequate host defenses. These patients may have to be evaluated under settings of stress before any clinical relevance will be demonstrated. Our preliminary studies on *in vivo* chemotactic factor generation in normal volunteers given endotoxin provides additional support for a physiologic role of the *in vitro* chemotactic activity associated with products of the complement, fibrinolytic, and kinin-generating systems.

The mechanism by which leukocytes respond to chemotactic stimuli remains unknown. Recently, there has been considerable discussion about the differences between chemotaxis and random (spontaneous) migration (18, 31, 38). It seems reasonable to assume that the chemotactic process and the random-spontaneous process share many of the same mechanisms and perhaps chemotaxis represents a perturbation of random locomotion. In support of this have been the descriptions of patients with abnormal spontaneous motility and defective chemotaxis (17), normal spontaneous motility and abnormal chemotaxis (2, 18), and to our knowledge no descriptions of patients with abnormal spontaneous motility (using the Boyden chamber technique) and normal chemotaxis. However, the recent description of patients with abnormal spontaneous motility using the capillary tube assay and normal chemotaxis (38) suggests that the differences between these two processes may be more complicated and additional clinical studies are necessary.

It has recently been proposed by Allison et al. (39) that the mechanism responsible for establishing the net vector of directed macrophage locomotion is dependent on microtubule assembly. Our demonstration of microtubule assembly in neutrophils actively migrating through a micropore filter supports such a concept. However, the additional observation of microtubule assembly in neutrophils exposed to chemotactic stimuli in suspension (no chemotactic gradient) suggests that microtubule assembly is also necessary for the increased random motility induced by chemotactic factors (11). We have speculated that polarized assembly of microtubules (perhaps in part secondary to local decreases in cytoplasmic calcium) is necessary for establishing the net vector of locomotion (11). Other parameters, such as the levels of cyclic AMP, GTP, or cyclic GMP, which apparently influence both microtubule assembly (40–42) and chemotaxis (43), are also probably critical. Thus a reasonable hypothesis is that a major difference between random-spontaneous motility and chemotaxis could be the disorganized and organized assembly of tubulin proteins, respectively. Patients with normal spontaneous motility but abnormal chemotaxis may have abnormalities in the regulation of such polarized microtubule assembly.

Although many questions remain unanswered, it seems apparent that the chemotactic process is essential for normal host defenses. Continued characterization of clinical abnormalities of chemotaxis and study of the biochemical and biophysical events that lead to a chemotactic response will hopefully make possible the therapeutic intervention of chemotactic disorders.

SUMMARY

Defective neutrophil and mononuclear cell chemotaxis has been noted in patients with the Chediak-Higashi syndrome and a patient with chronic mucocutaneous candidiasis and recurrent pyogenic infections. The former had abnormal, and the latter normal, random motility studies. Two patients with hypogammaglobulinemia had abnormal neutrophil chemotaxis and normal spontaneous motility. Abnormalities of humoral mediators of chemotaxis were noted in patients deficient in complement components (C1r and C2) and components of the kinin-generating system. In related studies, *in vivo* chemotactic factor generation was demonstrated in plasma from normal volunteers given endotoxin; these *in vivo*-generated chemotactic factors included molecules tentatively identified as products of the complement, fibrinolytic, and kinin-generating systems and two unidentified molecules, one with an estimated molecular weight slightly less than 65,000 and one less than 5,000. Additional studies of chemotactic factor-neutrophil interaction demonstrated that calcium efflux ($^{45}Ca^{2+}$) and assembly of microtubules are associated with the chemotactic process; the possibility of a correlation between these observations and the clinical distinction of abnormal chemotaxis and spontaneous (random) motility is discussed.

ACKNOWLEDGMENTS

I wish to thank my colleagues, Allen Kaplan, who performed the assays of kallikrein and plasminogen activator and critically reviewed the manuscript; Alan Rosenthal, who performed the electron microscopy; and Charles Kirkpatrick and Michael Frank, who provided the dialyzable transfer factor and the C1r-deficient sera, respectively.

REFERENCES

1. Clark, R. A., and Kimball, H. R.: Defective granulocyte chemotaxis in the Chediak-Higashi syndrome. *J. Clin. Invest.* 50:2645, 1971.
2. Clark, R. A., Root, R. K., Kimball, H. R., and Kirkpatrick, C. H.: Defective neutrophil chemotaxis and cellular immunity in a child with recurrent infections. *Ann. Int. Med.* 78:515, 1973.
3. Gallin, J. I.: Radioassay of granulocyte chemotaxis: Studies of human granulocytes and chemotactic factors. In Sorkin, E. (ed.): *Chemotaxis, Its Biology and Biochemistry, Antibiotics and Chemotherapy,* Karger, Basel. 19:146, 1974.
4. Weiss, A. P., Gallin, J. I., and Kaplan, A. P.: Fletcher factor deficiency. A diminished rate of Hageman factor activation caused by absence of prekallikrein with abnormalities of coagulation, fibrinolysis, chemotactic activity, and kinin generation. *J. Clin. Invest.* 53:622, 1974.

5. Zucker-Franklin, D., Melton, J. W., and Quagliata, F.: Variants of chronic lymphocytic leukemia with cells having surface properties of T lymphocytes. *J. Clin. Invest.* 52:92a, 1973.
6. Gallin, J. I., and Kirkpatrick, C. H.: Chemotactic activity in dialyzable transfer factor. Proc. Natl. Acad. Sci. 71:498, 1974.
7. Boyum, A.: Isolation of mononuclear cells and granulocytes from human blood. *Scand. J. Clin. Lab. Invest.* (Suppl. 97) 21:77, 1968.
8. Wolff, S. M.: Biological effects of bacteral endotoxins in man. *J. Infect. Dis.* 128:S259, 1973.
9. Gallin, J. I., Clark, R. A., and Kimball, H. R.: Granulocyte chemotaxis. An improved *in vitro* assay employing ^{51}Cr labeled granulocytes. *J. Immunol.* 110:233, 1973.
10. Snyderman, R., Altman, L.C., Hausman, M. S., and Mergenhagen, S. E.: Human mononuclear leukocyte chemotaxis: A quantitative assay for humoral and cellular chemotactic factors. *J. Immunol.* 108:857, 1972.
11. Gallin, J. I., and Rosenthal, A. S.: Regulatory role of divalent cations in human granulocyte chemotaxis: Evidence for an association between calcium exchanges and microtubule assembly. *J. Cell Biol.* 62:594, 1974.
12. Mickenberg, I. D., Root, R. K., and Wolff, S. M.: Leukocyte function in hypogammaglobulinemia. *J. Clin. Invest.* 49:1528, 1970.
13. Kaplan, A. P., Kay, A. B., and Austen, K. F.: A prealbumin activator of prekallikrein. III. Appearance of chemotactic activity for human neutrophils by the conversion of human prekallikrein to kallikrein. *J. Exp. Med.* 135:81, 1972.
14. Kaplan, A. P., and Austen, K. F.: The fibrinolytic pathway of human plasma. Isolation and characterization of the plasminogen proactivator. *J. Exp. Med.* 136:1378, 1972.
15. Kaplan, A. P., and Austen, K. F.: A prealbumin activator of prekallikrein. *J. Immunol.* 105:802, 1970.
16. Snyderman, R., Altman, L. C., Frankel, A., and Blaese, R. M.: Defective mononuclear leukocyte chemotaxis: A previously unrecognized immune dysfunction. *Ann. Int. Med.* 78:509, 1973.
17. Miller, M. E., Oski, F. A., and Harris, M. B.: Lazy leukocyte syndrome. A new disorder of neutrophil function. *Lancet* 1:665, 1971.
18. Miller, M. E., Norman, M. E., Koblenzer, P. J., and Schonauer, T. J.: A new familial defect of neutrophil movement. *J. Lab. Clin. Med.* 82:1, 1973.
19. Steerman, R. L., Snyderman, R., Leikin, S. L., and Colten, H. R.: Intrinsic defect of the polymorphonuclear leukocyte resulting in impaired chemotaxis and phagocytosis. *Clin. Exp. Immunol.* 9:939, 1971.
20. Blume, R. S., and Wolff, S. M.: The Chediak-Higashi syndrome: Studies in four patients and a review of the literature. *Medicine* 51:247, 1972.
21. Gallin, J. I., Klimerman, J. A., Padgett, G. A., and Wolff, S. M.: Defective mononuclear cell chemotaxis in the Chediak-Higashi syndrome of humans, mink and cattle. *Clin. Res.* 22:441 A (Abs.), 1974.
22. Padgett, G. A., Leader, R. W., Gorham, J. R., and O'Mary, C. C.: The familial occurrence of the Chediak-Higashi syndrome in mink and cattle. *Genetics* 49:505, 1964.
23. Kirkpatrick, C. H., and Gallin, J. I.: Suppression of cellular immune responses following transfer factor. Submitted for publication.
24. Gallin, J. I., Clark, R. A., and Frank, M. M.: Kinetic analysis of chemotactic factor generation in human serum via activation of the classical and alternate complement pathway. *Immunopath. Clin. Immunol. (in press)*
25. Clark, R. A., Kimball, H. R., and Frank, M. M.: Generation of chemotactic factors in normal and C4 deficient guinea pig serum by activation with endotoxin and immune complexes. *Immunopath. Clin. Immunol.* 1:415, 1973.
26. Day, N. K., Geiger, R. S., De Braco, M., Mancado, B., Windhorst, D., and Good, R. A.: C1r deficiency: An inborn error associated with cutaneous and renal disease. *J. Clin. Invest.* 51:-1102, 1972.
27. Kaplan, A. P., Goetzl, E. J., and Austen, K. F.: The fibrinolytic pathway of human plasma. II. The generation of chemotactic activity by activation of plasminogen proactivator. *J. Clin. Invest.* 52:2591, 1973.
28. Gallin, J. I., and Kaplan, A. P.: Mononuclear cell chemotactic activity of kallikrein and plasminogen activator and its inhibition by $C\bar{1}$ inhibitor and α_2 macroglobulin. *J. Immunol. (in press)*
29. Snyderman, R., and Mergenhagen, S. E.: Characterization of polymorphonuclear leukocyte chemotactic activity in serum activated by various inflammatory agents. In Ingram, D. G. (ed.): *Proc. Fifth Int'l. Symp. Canad. Soc. Immunol.* Karger, Basel, p. 117. 1972.

30. Wuepper, K. D.: Prekallikrein deficiency in man. *J. Exp. Med.* 138:1345, 1973.
31. Becker, E. L., and Showell, H. J.: The effect of Ca^{2+} and Mg^{2+} on the chemotactic responsiveness and spontaneous motility of rabbit polymorphonuclear leukocytes. *Z. Immunitaetsforsch.* 143:-466, 1972.
32. Blizzard, R. M., and Gibbs, J. H.: Candidiasis: Studies pertaining to its association with endocrinopathies and pernicious anemia. *Pediatrics* 42:231, 1968.
33. Weisenberg, R. C.: Microtubule formation *in vitro* in solutions containing low calcium concentrations. *Science* 177:1104, 1972.
34. Caner, J. E. Z.: Colchicine inhibition of chemotactic migration of human polymorphonuclear leukocytes. *Arthritis Rheum.* 7:297, 1964.
35. Ward, P. A.: Leukotactic factors in health and disease. *Am. J. Pathol.* 64:521, 1971.
36. Goldstein, I., Hoffstein, S., Gallin, J., and Weissman, G.: Mechanisms of lysosomal enzyme release from human leukocytes: Microtubule assembly and membrane fusion induced by a component of complement. *Proc. Natl. Acad. Sci.* 70:2916, 1973.
37. Ward, P. A.: Chemotaxis of mononuclear cells. *J. Exp. Med.* 128:1201, 1968.
38. Miller, M. E.: Leukocyte movement—*In vitro* and *in vivo* correlates. *J. Pediat.* 83:1104, 1973.
39. Allison, A. C., Davies, P., and De Petris, S.: Role of contractile microfilaments in macrophage movement and endocytosis. *Nature* [*New Biol.*] 232:153, 1971.
40. Berry, R. W., and Shelanski, M. L.: Interactions of tubulin with vinblastine and guanosine triphosphate. *J. Mol. Biol.* 71:71, 1972.
41. Shelanski, M. L., Gaskin, F., and Cantor, C. R.: Microtubule assembly in the absence of added nucleotides. *Proc. Natl. Acad. Sci.* 70:765, 1973.
42. Shelanski, M. L.: Chemistry of the filaments and tubules of brain. *J. Histochem. Cytochem.* 21:529, 1973.
43. Estensen, R. D., Hill, H. R., Quie, P. G., Hogan, J., and Goldberg, N. D.: Cyclic GMP and cell movement. *Nature* 245:458, 1973.

DISCUSSION

Ward: In your studies of the kinetic differences in the generation of activity of immune complexes versus lipopolysaccharide, is this lag period a function of the amount of activating substance added to the serum?

Gallin: No, it doesn't appear to be. Our studies were done in the presence of excess endotoxin. We have seen some variability among sera in the duration of the latency associated with activation using *S. typhosa* endotoxin. We have also been able to show that addition of magnesium to the system shortens the latency. Moreover, addition of magnesium-EGTA to immune complex-activated serum converted the kinetics of activation from a rapid to a delayed pattern providing additional evidence that the different kinetics are related to activation of the classical and alternate complement pathways (Gallin, J. I., Clark, R. A., and Frank, M. M.: Human chemotactic factors generated by activation of the classical and alternate complement pathways. *Clin. Res.* 21:579 abs; 1973).

Miller: I have several questions. The first pertains to concentration of neutrophils in the Chediak patient. As you pointed out, minimum concentrations of neutrophils seem necessary. Were these concentrations present in the Chediak patient? Do you have any data pertaining to whether this also holds in terms of the random chamber motility assay? In other words, is that concentration still necessary?

Gallin: For the first question, are you referring to the capillary tube assay of spontaneous motility?

Miller: Right.

Gallin: For the random motility studies of granulocytes from patients with the Chediak-Higashi syndrome, the concentration of granulocytes used was adjusted to 3.0×10^6 per milliliter and a normal response was noted; similar results were obtained with mononuclear cells. For random leukocyte motility using the Boyden chamber, we routinely use a neutrophil or mononuclear cell density of 2.6 $\times 10^6$ cells per cc. We have not determined if this density is critical. In contrast to the normal random motility of Chediak-Higashi leukocytes in studies employing the capillary tube assay, abnormal spontaneous locomotion was noted using the Boyden chamber assay. Thus, these two assays of random locomotion are clearly measuring different parameters.

Miller: Did you obtain white blood cell counts in your *in vivo* studies? The classic time one sees maximum leukocytosis after *in vivo* endotoxin is about 4 hours.

Gallin: That is true.

Miller: You don't have the counts on these particular subjects?

Gallin: No.

Becker: I have several comments and one question. The first is in regard to patients that have a normal random mobility as measured in the Boyden chamber and decreased chemotaxis. One possible explanation based on the theory I presented would be that the neutrophils of these patients have a defect in their deactivation process, although the proesterase content of their cells is normal. The prediction would then be that their neutrophils would deactivate poorly. Their proesterase activation, on the other hand, should be normal or reasonably normal. One would hope that within a relatively short time one could actually test to find whether this prediction is in fact correct.

The second comment that I'd like to make is in regard to your speculation on cyclic AMP. Isreal Rivkin, when in my laboratory, did extensive work trying to relate cyclic AMP to chemotactic processes and to random motility. In general, he found that the agents which increase the intracellular cyclic AMP of the neutrophil will also inhibit random motility and chemotactic responsiveness. But he could not find that either the bacterial chemotactic factor or C5a had any effect on levels of cyclic AMP in the cell. This was studied over an extensive range of concentrations of chemotactic factor and over a wide time course. From this we believe that cyclic AMP can affect random motility and therefore affect chemotaxis. However, it affects it by modulating one of the steps in the sequence but is not in the direct sequence itself.

In regard to microtubules, one wonders whether the increase in microtubules induced by C5a that you found is related to the chemotactic response that one can obtain from this chemotactic factor or to the lysosomal enzyme release that one also obtains from this and other chemotactic factors.

In regard to your findings with calcium exchange, you have found a distinct efflux that is stimulated by C5a. Could a small calcium influx also be present under these circumstances which would not be detectable or be swamped by the efflux of calcium? This is, I think, of some importance in just how we view the role of calcium. It could be that the situation is similar, as your results imply, to what Bygdeman and Starjne found with the platelet release reaction in which there is an absolute requirement for calcium but yet they could find absolutely no evidence for calcium influx. If this is so, it would suggest very strongly that the role for external calcium is on a membrane reaction, rather than being similar, for example, to the requirement for external calcium in cardiac contractility.

Gallin: To answer your question I will refer to an experiment we have performed in which neutrophils were exposed to calcium-45 for a period of time and, during the process of uptake of calcium-45, C5a or buffer was added (Gallin, J. I., and Rosenthal, A. S.: Regulatory role of divalent cations in human granulocyte chemotaxis: Evidence for an association between calcium exchanges and microtubule assembly. *J. Cell. Biol.*, 62:594, 1974). There was no detectable increase in ^{45}Ca influx in C5a-exposed cells; rather there was an immediate and persistent decrease in ^{45}Ca content in the C5a-treated cells. I agree with your suggestion that the role of external calcium may be one of a membrane-associated phenomenon. However, I still do not believe we have ruled out the possibility that intracellular calcium movements play a critical role in establishing the net vector of directed locomotion, perhaps by modulating microtubule assembly. Membrane surface calcium may be required for macrofilament function and random locomotion or for chemotactic factor-cell interaction.

Klebanoff: The patient of Steerman, Snyderman et al. (*Clin. Exp. Immunol.* 9:939, 1971) with agammaglobulinemia also had a minor serum defect. Did yours have a serum defect?

Gallin: The serum properties of our patients with agammaglobulinemia are rather confusing. When we activated their serum with *E. coli* endotoxin, we got abnormal results. However, when activated with *S. typhosa* endotoxin, the results were normal. This may reflect different mechanisms of chemotactic factor generation by these endotoxins.

Klebanoff: I'd like to explore the difference in the *in vitro* and *in vivo* effects of endotoxin on the chemotactic activity of serum. Your results on the *in vitro* effect of endotoxin indicated that the predominant chemotactic agent was C5a. Is that because the serum was heated, thus inactivating the heat-labile low molecular weight agent?

Gallin: Our *in vitro* studies with serum have confirmed Dr. Snyderman's results. Sephadex chromatography of activated serum that Dr. Snyderman has published I believe is of serum heated at 56 degrees after activation.

Snyderman: We have done it both ways.

Gallin: Careful examination of published figures of the Sephadex chromatography reveals some chemotactic activity eluting with the protein at the bed volume of the column. However, this was not commented on in the text (Snyderman, R., and Mergenhagen, S. E.: Characterization of polymorphonuclear leukocyte chemotactic activity in serums activated by various inflammatory agents. In Ingram, D. G. (ed.): *Proc. Fifth Int'l Symp. Canad. Soc. Immunol.* Karger, Basel, p. 117, 1972). The predominant chemotactic activity was the C5a. The material we are seeing with *in vivo* generation is heat labile at 56 degrees Centigrade. Similarly, if serum is activated with *E. coli* endotoxin, a small amount of the low molecular chemotactic material is generated, but much less than with kaolin activation.

Klebanoff: Is the absence of C5a on *in vivo* activation due to its diffusibility?

Gallin: No. I think that in the *in vivo* studies the C5a inactivator may be destroying it; we did detect C5a in one of the volunteers.

Snyderman: I think you have to be very cautious interpreting what you see circulating free in serum. Obviously the C5a could be formed in the circulation itself, but we know endotoxin is cleared very rapidly and a predominant amount of the chemotactic activity could be formed in the spleen, liver, or lung, wherever the endotoxin is going. Therefore, the amount you find in serum is only a very small portion of what chemotactic activity is being formed at a local site. The other thing is we really don't know anything about how long C5a would circulate if it were formed *in vivo,* or whether it would be inactivated by the anaphylatoxin activator. I think you should not conclude from what you see in serum what the important factors are that are produced in local sites. As we showed in the peritoneal cavity, they form and hold a lot of C5a there.

Frank: I think there are two other points that ought to be made. The studies Dr. Gallin talked about were done in human beings where you can't give large doses of endotoxin. These were tiny doses, I am sure. I didn't study these patients but in similar studies we looked for a depression in C5, and with the doses of endotoxin that were being used you could not detect a drop in circulating complement components. But again these were very, very tiny doses. Another point that should be considered is that most of these studies done *in vitro* are done in serum. Endotoxin in serum may behave very differently from endotoxin in the blood stream.

Ward: The half-life of the C5 fragment or the chemotactic fragment when injected IV is less than 20 minutes. It is probably more on the order of 8 or 10 minutes. Whether or not it is being inactivated, simply disappearing from the circulation in an unaltered state, or what, we don't know, but it sticks around only for very brief periods.

Baehner: Is that in humans?

Ward: No, this is in animals.

Snyderman: In terms of the interpretation of calcium flux, the amount of C5a you used was approximately 50 to 100 micrograms for your maximal activity. If one deals with highly purified C5a, the maximum activity in the Boyden chamber can occur at about 1/100th that amount of C5a. I assume that what you did was take the crude material from isolated serum and do a protein determination on that. I would venture to say that is about 1 percent C5a.

Gallin: We used C5a that was partially purified from whole serum by G-75 Sephadex chromatography. I agree it contains other contaminants.

Snyderman: You have to be cautious in terms of interpreting the data because the 99 percent of something else certainly could be having an effect.

Gallin: I think I can satisfactorily respond to that. On disc gel electrophoresis of our C5a preparation the major contaminating protein was albumin. We have run specificity control studies using the purified nonchemotactic proteins human albumin, horse radish peroxidase, and ovalbumin (Gallin, J. I., and Rosenthal, A. S.: The regultory role of divalent cations in human granulocyte chemotaxis: Evidence for an association betwen calcium exchanges and microtubule assembly. *J. Cell Biol.,* 62:594, 1974). These proteins did not induce changes of calcium fluxes. Two other chemotactically active materials kallikrein (Kaplan, A. P., Kay, A. B., and Austen, K. F.: A prealbumin activator of prekallikrein. III. Appearance of chemotactic activity for human neutrophils by the conversion of human prekallikrein to kallikrein. *J. Exp. Med.* 135:81, 1972) and dialyzable transfer factor (Gallin, J. I., and Kirkpatrick, C. H.: Chemotactic activity in dialyzable transfer factor. *Proc. Natl. Acad. Sci.* 71:498, 1974) resulted in enhanced calcium release. It is of interest that the most impressive calcium efflux occurred with kallikrein which had only one-half the chemotactic activity of C5a. Kallikrein is an enzyme whereas C5a is not and these differences may reflect different mechanisms of initiating the chemotactic response.

Snyderman: Another thing has been confusing me, and I think maybe we could straighten it out. When I went to Duke a couple of years ago, it was very much a gout center and I thought it would be good to see if colchicine inhibited chemotaxis, and I was sure it would. I found, although I tried it many, many times with about every dose range I could get into, that I could not get inhibition of chemotaxis to C5a with colchicine. There is some question as to whether it decreases spontaneous motility, but I could not get a decrease in directed chemotaxis. What have other people's experiences been with that?

Baum: We went through a number of concentrations of colchicine and got no effect. We used 25 micrograms to 0.2 micrograms per milliliter and found no difference.

Snyderman: We did it from 10^{-3} to 10^{-10} molar.

Baum: That would be about the same.

Snyderman: This included people without gout.

Becker: What we found in our studies of microtubular disaggregating agents was that depending upon the concentration of colchicine or vinblastine and depending upon the strength of the chemotactic stimulus, one could find either inhibitors, no effect, or decided and distinct enhancement of either chemotaxis or lysosomal enzyme release. In general, although not invariably, if the concentrations of chemotactic factor employed were distinctly less than that which would give a maximum response, the colchicine had a greater tendency to give enhancement than it did if our chemotactic activity was used at a level that gave a maximum response. In order to inhibit, we had to go to quite high concentrations depending on the cell from 10^{-3} to 10^{-4} molar colchicine or 10^{-4} to 10^{-5} molar vinblastine. The enhancement was obtained with anywhere from two to three logs less than these concentrations. The enhancement depended in part on the fact that we used crystalline bovine serum albumin as the protein in our upper chamber.

Gallin: Did you preincubate your cells?

Becker: These cells were preincubated for 45 minutes at 37 degrees with either colchicine or vinblastine.

Gallin: We found inhibition of chemotaxis with 10^{-3} or 10^{-4} molar colchicine using partially purified C5a (10 milligrams protein per milliliter) obtained from G-75 Sephadex chromatography.

Cohn: I think one has to be careful interpreting data. One ought to use a lumicolchicine control to see whether that is effective or not, since it is becoming apparent that colchicine is doing more to cells than disrupting microtubules.

Becker: That was one of the points of the paper that we are publishing.

The Phagocytic Cell in Host Resistance, edited
by Joseph A. Bellanti and Delbert H. Dayton.
Raven Press, New York © 1975.

Defective Neutrophil Chemotaxis Associated with Hyperimmunoglobulinemia E

Harry R. Hill and Paul G. Quie

Department of Pediatrics and Clinical Laboratory Medicine and Pathology, University of Minnesota Medical School, Minneapolis, Minnesota 55455

The initial response to invasion of the body by pathogenic microorganisms is critical as a determinant of the outcome of infection. Animal studies have demonstrated that an intact inflammatory response must be present at the onset if invasion is to be contained and infection suppressed (1). We have documented that, early in active bacterial infection and before suppression of infection by antibiotic therapy, circulating neutrophils are hyperactive *in vitro* in response to chemotactic stimulation. In patients with superficial streptococcal and staphylococcal skin infections, neutrophil chemotactic responses are markedly increased when compared with controls (2). A hyperactive chemotactic response by circulating neutrophils was also observed in patients with pulmonary (3) and systemic bacterial infection (4). In contrast with these findings, however, we have recently discovered several patients who have a profound defect in neutrophil chemotactic responsiveness both during active infection and later after infection has been eradicated. Each of the patients had severe or recurrent infections with bacterial or fungal pathogens including *Staphylococcal aureus,* beta-hemolytic streptococci, and *Candida albicans,* and, in addition, each had clinical manifestations of allergic disease such as eczema or urticaria. Subsequently, each of the patients was found to have hyperimmunoglobulinemia E. In this chapter we review the clinical and laboratory data on these patients and examine the possible pathogenetic mechanisms involved in the production of abnormal neutrophil function in allergic diseases.

METHODS AND MATERIALS

A brief description of our method of measuring neutrophil chemotaxis and random migration is presented since there is wide diversity in the procedures currently being utilized. Our procedure (3, 5) is actually a modification of the methods described by Ward and co-workers (6) and Baum et al. (7). Leukocyte-rich plasma is obtained by allowing the erythrocytes in 10 ml of heparinized blood to settle over a 1-hr period without the addition of dextran or other settling agents. The concentrations of PMN's per milliliter of leukocyte-rich plasma is then determined by quantitative and differential cell counts. A one to four dilution of the leukocyte-rich plasma is then made with tissue culture medium 199

(Microbiol. Assoc., Bethesda, Maryland) and the PMN's in this suspension are then deposited on one side of a 5-μ pore size Millipore filter (Millipore Corp., Bedford, Massachusetts) utilizing a cytocentrifuge (Shandon Scientific Co., Sewickley, Pennsylvania). The filters are immediately placed in modified Boyden chambers (Neuroprobe Corp., Bethesda, Maryland) and a chemotactic stimulus is added to the attractant side.

After incubation for 3 hr at 37°C, the filters are removed and stained, and the number of cells that have migrated completely through the filter within 10 random fields is determined by visual counting (using a 10 $\times$ ocular, 45 $\times$ objective and 5 mm $\times$ 5 mm photographic reticule). A chemotactic index is then calculated by dividing the number of PMN's that have migrated completely through the filter within the reticule in 10 random fields by the total number of PMN's ($\times 10^6$) delivered to the starting side of the filter.

$$\text{Chemotactic index} = \frac{\text{Number of PMN's in 10 random fields}}{\text{Number of PMN's } (\times 10^6) \text{ delivered to the Millipore filter}}$$

This method of calculating the chemotactic index takes into account only the number of PMN's delivered to the filter and the number moving completely through the filter and thus appears to measure intrinsic chemotactic activity. The percentage or total number of mononuclear cells in the suspension does not affect the chemotactic index and there is no association between the number of PMN's in the leukocyte-rich plasma or the number delivered to the filter and chemotactic activity (4).

Chemotactic assays are routinely performed in triplicate; occasionally small amounts of blood allowed only duplicate samplings. Using this method, the standard deviation of triplicate samples is approximately 10% of the mean, whereas the standard error of the mean when the same person is tested on three separate occasions is 6%. In testing the leukocytes of more than 200 individuals, this method has proved to be sensitive and reproducible. In contrast to other systems for measuring chemotaxis, addition of settling agents such as dextran is not required, extensive handling of the cells is not necessary, and the presence of serum or albumin on the cell side of the chamber is not required to obtain optimal chemotaxis (5). As shown in Table 1, neutrophils washed one or two times, resuspended in medium 199 and deposited on the filter are as responsive in the chemotactic assay as those deposited on the filter from a suspension containing approximately 25% homologous plasma. In addition, the presence of homologous or heterologous plasma in the initial cell solution from which the cells are deposited on the Millipore filter has no apparent effect on the chemotactic index (Table 1). Gently washing the cells once or twice prior to leukocyte testing does not significantly alter chemotactic activity. Excessive washing does, however, markedly decrease chemotactic responsiveness, and the addition of serum or plasma to these "damaged" cells does not restore chemotactic function.

TABLE 1. *Effect of plasma on the chemotactic response of control neutrophils to bacterial chemotactic factor*

Leukocyte donor	PMN's deposited on filter suspended in[a]	Chemotactic index
B.H.	25% homologous plasma	130
	Medium 199	125
N.H.	25% homologous plasma	58
	Medium 199	48
H.G.	25% homologous plasma	76
	Medium 199	72
L.C.	25% homologous plasma	85
	25% heterologous plasma	79
L.H.	25% homologous plasma	92
	25% heterologous plasma	88

[a] Tissue culture medium 199 alone is added to the top or cell side of the chemotactic chamber after the filter is inserted.

This suggests that the decrease in chemotactic responsiveness of the excessively washed neutrophils is not due to removal of humoral factors but rather is the result of trauma to the cells. For this reason, we attempt to avoid excessive handling of the cells and, unless otherwise stated, have a small amount of the patient's plasma present in the cell suspension deposited on the Millipore filter. In contrast to other systems, no serum, plasma, or albumin is present, however, in the solution on the upper or cell side of the chamber during the assay.

Chemotactic Factors

A bacterial chemotactic factor is prepared from a culture filtrate of *E. coli* grown in medium 199 for 24 hr at 37°C (8). After passage through a 0.22-μ pore size Millipore filter, this bacterial chemotactic factor is frozen at −70°C in 1-ml ampoules. Each day an ampoule is thawed and diluted in medium 199 so that each milliliter of the solution contains 50 μl of the factor. Serums from controls and patients are assayed for spontaneous complement-associated chemotactic activity and for activity following incubation with zymosan or antigen-antibody complexes using methods described by Ward and co-workers (6).

Random Mobility

Random mobility of leukocytes is determined by a modification of the method of McCall et al. (9). Glass capillary tubes are filled with a solution containing 1×10^7 PMN's per milliliter. After centrifugation, the tubes are cut at the cell-fluid interface and placed in Sykes-Moore chambers. Following incubation for 4 hr, the leading edge of migrating granulocytes is mapped by projection microscopy and compared with a standard projected square centimeter to determine the absolute area of migration. Random mobility of PMN's is also evaluated by determining the leukotactic index when no chemotactic stimulus is added to the attractant side of the modified Boyden chamber.

RESULTS

Association of Eczema, Recurrent Bacterial Infections, Defective Neutrophil Chemotaxis, and Increased IgE

Patients with severe eczema often have an increased incidence of superficial bacterial infections due, in part, to the breakdown of the anatomic barriers of normal skin. Some patients with eczema, however, have severe and recurrent superficial and deep bacterial infections suggesting an underlying defect in the host defense mechanisms. Leukocyte function was assessed in three such individuals in order to determine if abnormal function might be contributing to the development of infections (10).

The clinical data from these three patients are shown in Table 2. Each had early onset of eczema that was followed by the development of multiple superficial

TABLE 2. *Clinical data from three patients with eczema, recurrent abscesses, and increased IgE*

Patient	Age	Sex	Onset eczema	Onset abscesses	Comments
M.D.	2 yr	F	5 wk	10 wk	Each patient had recurrent superficial and deep abscesses of the scalp,
M.M.	2 yr	M	10 da	4 wk	buttocks, thighs, and trunk, suppurative lymphadenitis,
R.M.	18 mo	M	8 wk	10 wk	cellulitis, and marked pruritis.

abscesses, areas of cellulitis, suppurative lymphadenitis, and deep tissue abscesses of the scalp, buttocks, and thigh areas. The abscesses were accompanied by a marked surrounding inflammatory reaction and often necessitated hospitalization for incision and drainage. Cultures of the abscess material grew *S. aureus* or *S. aureus* and beta-hemolytic streptococcus on each occasion.

Each of the children had severe eczema, and pruritis was so severe in each case that the child often had to be restrained with protective coverings to prevent excessive excoriation. Following even minor skin trauma, a marked wheal and then flare reaction occurred which along with the severe pruritis suggested increased histamine release.

These three patients with eczema and recurrent abscesses had their leukocytes tested initially upon admission to the hospital for incision and drainage of *S. aureus* and beta-hemolytic streptococcal abscesses. At the time of active infection, the chemotactic responses of the patients' cells were significantly lower than that of 20 uninfected controls (Fig. 1). Furthermore, when compared with the hyperactive chemotactic responses observed in 20 otherwise normal children with *S. aureus* and beta-hemolytic streptococcal pyoderma, the decreased chemotactic responses of the patients' neutrophils became even more apparent. Random migration, phagocytosis, bactericidal capacity, and nitroblue tetrazolium dye reduction by the neutrophils of the three patients did not differ from that of controls.

The patients were tested again after infection had been eradicated by appropri-

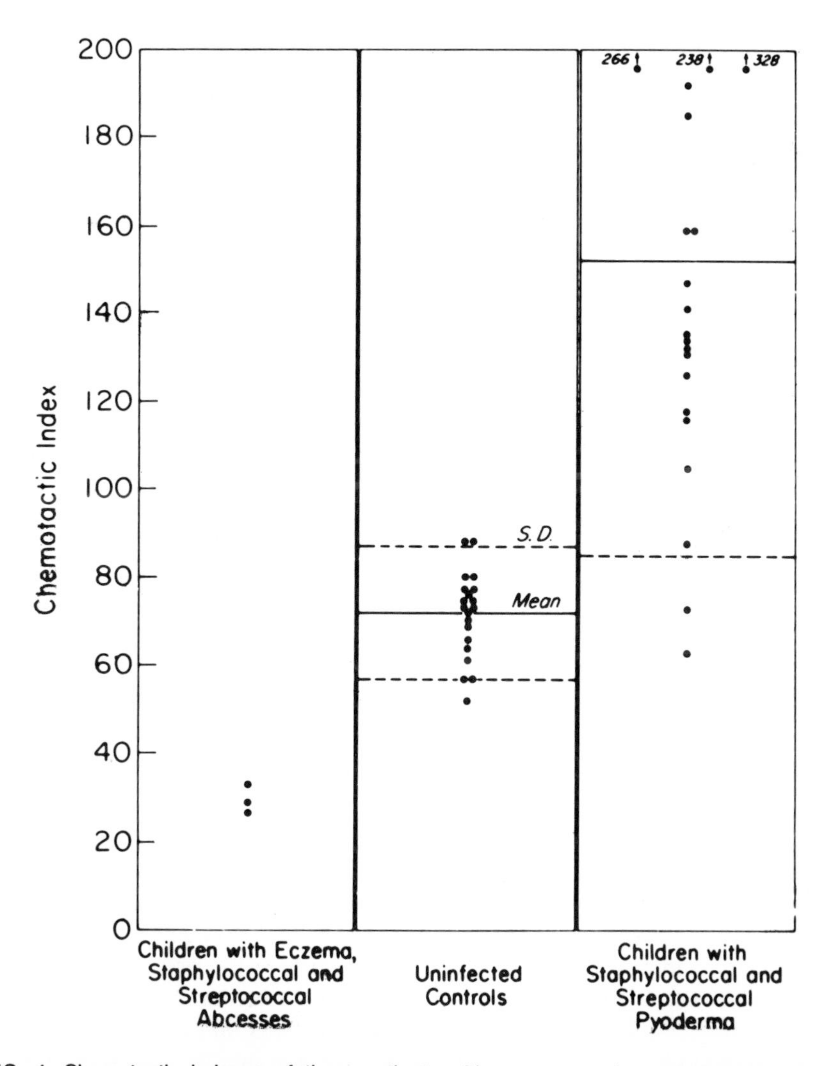

FIG. 1. Chemotactic indexes of three patients with eczema and recurrent infections, 20 uninfected controls, and 20 children with staphylococcal and streptococcal pyoderma.

ate antibiotic therapy and incision and drainage of the abscesses. Once again, their chemotactic indexes were significantly depressed when compared with controls. Serum IgE concentrations were markedly increased in each case, however (Table 3).

TABLE 3. *Serum IgE levels, chemotactic indexes, and NBT dye reduction by neutrophils of patients with eczema and recurrent infection*

Case number	NBT positive PMN's (%)	Serum IgE IU per ml	Chemotactic index
1. M.D.	3	10,000	12
2. M.M.	10	2,500	25
3. R.M.	5	5,780	12
Age-matched controls (10)	3 ± 4	30–440	68 ± 15

Job's Syndrome, Hyperimmunoglobulinemia E, and Defective Chemotaxis

Davis, Schaller, and Wedgwood in 1966 (11) described two females who had suffered recurrent "cold" staphylococcal abscesses since birth. In addition to the abscesses, these patients had several other remarkable features including red hair, hyperextensible joints, atrophic fingernails, and severe atopic dermatitis. Each has subsequently been found to have extreme hyperimmunoglobulinemia E. Recently, we have studied a patient with features typical of Job's syndrome. This patient, who has red hair, hyperextensible joints, and atrophic fingernails, had early onset of eczema followed by repeated "cold" nontender abscesses which have grown *S. aureus* on culture. This patient also has marked pruritis and flare reactions following trauma, suggesting increased release of histamine. The patient's chemotactic index was 19 whereas that of 10 age-matched controls was 71 ± 16. In addition, the patient's serum IgE concentration was 6,020 IU per ml.

Mucocutaneous Candidiasis, Eczema, and Increased IgE

Patients who suffer recurrent superficial candida infections are believed to have an underlying defect in cell-mediated immunity to candida antigens (12). Tritiated thymidine uptake by lymphocytes in the presence of candida antigen is depressed in a proportion of these patients and the lymphocytes of others fail to produce macrophage migration inhibition factor in the presence of candida antigen (13). Clark and co-workers (14) have described an 11-year-old female patient with a history of recurrent bacterial infections and chronic mucocutaneous candidiasis. This patient had deficient *in vivo* and *in vitro* responses to candida antigen, extreme hyperimmunoglobulinemia E, and defective neutrophil chemotaxis. Recently we have studied two patients with a life-long history of recurrent candida infection and recurrent superficial and deep bacterial infections. The first patient was a 23-year-old male who was first noted to have eczema and oral moniliasis at 7 months of age (15). He later developed candida infection about the nails and had areas of eczema with abscess formation on the scalp and face. Purulent blepharitis due to *S. aureus* and *C. albicans* occurred on several occasions and lid abscess which grew these same organisms twice required incision and drainage. The patient also had marked pruritis and had positive intradermal tests for molds and dust along with persistent allergic rhinitis. This patient's IgE was markedly elevated at 2,615 IU per ml, and his chemotactic index was 28 compared to a mean index of 71 ± 10 for 10 age-matched controls.

In association with Drs. Robert Van Scoy and Roy Ritts of the Mayo Clinic (16), we have recently had the opportunity to examine leukocyte function in a 20-year-old female who has had eczema, chronic mucocutaneous candidiasis, and recurrent bacterial infections since infancy. This patient also had abnormal *in vitro* and *in vivo* lymphocyte responses to candida antigen. In addition, the chemotactic activity of her neutrophils was markedly depressed when compared to controls, and her serum IgE level was extremely elevated (Table 4).

TABLE 4. *Chemotactic indexes and serum IgE concentrations of family members of the patient with chronic mucocutaneous candidiasis and recurrent bacterial infection*

Patient	Age	Serum IgE IU per ml	Chemotactic index
S.K.	20	16,333	16
Daughter	1	20,004	27
Brother	16	1,500	30
Father	47	750	44
Grandfather	87	463	42
Controls (20)	1–50	30–440	79 ± 16

The patient's 1-year-old daughter had onset of eczema and cutaneous and oral moniliasis at 2 months of age and at 10 months of age, superficial and deep abscesses of the scalp occurred. At the time of initial testing, the daughter had a positive skin test and normal *in vitro* lymphocyte responses to candida antigen, but markedly depressed chemotactic responsiveness and extreme hyperimmunoglobulinemia E (Table 4). The presence of a chemotactic defect in this patient with chronic mucocutaneous candidiasis and normal lymphocyte function suggests that functional neutrophil abnormalities may contribute to the development of superficial fungal infection and may precede the development of altered cell-mediated immunity. It is with great interest that we continue to follow this patient's *in vivo* and *in vitro* lymphocyte responses.

The familial nature of the syndrome of hyperimmunoglobulinemia E and defective neutrophil chemotaxis was further documented by the finding of moderate increases in serum IgE concentrations with less severe reductions of neutrophil chemotactic responsiveness in the patient's brother, father, and paternal grandfather (Table 4). Although no relative had suffered recurrent bacterial infection, the grandfather had chronic candida infection of the nails and deficient lymphocyte response to candida antigen. These data suggest a familial syndrome of hyperimmunoglobulinemia E and defective neutrophil granulocyte chemotaxis.

DEFECTIVE NEUTROPHIL CHEMOTAXIS, SEVERE STAPHYLOCOCCAL INFECTION, AND HYPERIMMUNOGLOBULINEMIA E

Three additional patients with severe staphylococcal infection, hyperimmunoglobulinemia E, and manifestations of allergic disease have been found to have a profound defect in neutrophil chemotactic responsiveness (17). One patient, a 21-month-old male, had onset of urticarial rashes approximately 6 weeks prior to his admission to the hospital. These appeared intermittently and could not be related chronologically to any specific allergens. Two weeks prior to admission to the hospital, the patient began having temperature spikes to 102°F daily and 1 day prior to admission developed a tender, warm, erythematous mass in the right axillae. Past medical history revealed that the patient had recurrent episodes of acute otitis media and bronchitis and had been noted to wheeze on occasion. On admission to the hospital, the patient had a generalized erythematous, urticarial rash. A tender node (6 cm diameter) was palpated in the right axillae. Blood cultures were positive for *S. aureus* and incision and drainage of the right axillary node grew *S. aureus* on culture.

The patient's neutrophils were tested shortly after admission and showed markedly depressed chemotactic activity (Table 5). Moreover, moderate hyperimmunoglobulinemia E was also noted. While on methicillin therapy, the patient developed a marked neutropenia. Despite discontinuation of the antibiotic, the neutropenia persisted. A bone-marrow examination showed an increase in neu-

TABLE 5. *Chemotactic indexes and serum IgE concentrations of patients with severe staphylococcal infection and allergic manifestations*

Patient	Age	Serum IgE IU per ml	Chemotactic index
1. K.H.	21 mo	550	17
2. L.H.	8 yr	1,860	23
3. S.G.	9 yr	7,250	10
Controls (20)	—	30–440	72 ± 16

trophils and neutrophil precursors, but epinephrine and solucortef challenge failed to effect an increase in circulating neutrophil counts. All other immunologic tests including random migration, phagocytosis, and bactericidal activity were normal. The marked neutropenia and urticarial skin rashes have persisted as well as the marked defect in neutrophil chemotaxis.

The second patient was an 8-year-old female who had "eczema" and "bronchial asthma" and a history of allergy to penicillin. Approximately 1 week prior to admission to the hospital, she was treated with penicillin for an upper respiratory tract infection. Shortly thereafter, she broke out in a total body erythematous, urticarial rash. She was switched to erythromycin, but the rash persisted and 2 days later she developed spiking fevers. Upon admission to the hospital, she was noted to have a profuse urticarial rash, moist, cracking rales in the left lung fields, and a left upper lobe pneumonia on X-ray with several radiolucent areas suggesting early pneumatocoele formation. Blood cultures grew *S. aureus* and the patient was treated with high intravenous doses of clindamycin to which she gradually responded. As shown in Table 5, the patient's chemotactic index was markedly depressed when compared with controls and she had extreme hyperimmunoglobulinemia E.

The third patient was a 9-year-old male with a history of persistent allergic rhinitis and intermittent erythematous skin rashes. At 5 years of age, he developed a suppurative staphylococcal lymphadenitis of the right submandibular area and later had staphylococcal deep tissue abscesses of the knees and buttocks. At 7 years of age, the patient developed staphylococcal pneumonia with massive effusion and pneumatococcal formation. A severe spontaneous pneumothorax necessitated a right pneumonectomy.

One day prior to the patient's most recent hospital admission, he developed a generalized urticarial rash and began spiking fevers up to 104°F. Physical examination revealed an urticarial erythematous rash over the back, legs, and trunk and rales in the left lower lobe. X-ray revealed a left lower and upper lobe pulmonary infiltrate and upper respiratory cultures grew coagulase-positive staphylococci. The patient was not treated with antibiotics initially and continued to spike fevers to 103°F. Because of clinical deterioration, intravenous clindamycin therapy was initiated and continued for 3 weeks during which time the temperature gradually came down to normal range, the sputum cleared, and the chest roentgenograms showed clearing of the infiltrate. The chemotactic activity of this patient's neutrophils was also markedly depressed throughout his entire clinical course and remained low 1 month after hospital admission (Table 5). The patient also had extreme hyperimmunoglobulinemia E.

Mechanism of Defective Chemotaxis in Patients with Hyperimmunoglobulinemia E

Humoral inhibitors of chemotaxis both cell directed (18–20) and those directed at chemotactic factors have been described (21). For this reason, an intensive search was made for such inhibitors in the serum or plasma of the patients with hyperimmunoglobulinemia E and defective chemotaxis. Washing the leukocytes of the patients followed by incubation in normal plasma did not restore chemotactic responsiveness. Furthermore, incubation of washed control neutrophils in the plasma of the patients had no inhibitory effect on their chemotactic responsiveness. Thus the decreased chemotactic responsiveness by the neutrophils of the patients here could not be related to a direct effect of the increased concentrations of IgE present in their plasma. We cannot rule out the possibility, however, that the IgE is tightly bound to the patients' cells and resists removal by extensive washing. In a similar manner, control neutrophils may have surface-binding sites taken up by other immunoglobulin and are thus resistant to the inhibitory effects of the IgE in the patients' serum. Incubation of the serum of these patients with the bacterial chemotactic factor failed to reveal an inhibitor that directly affected these factors. Moreover, the spontaneous chemotactic activity of the patients' serum did not exceed that of controls and, following activation with zymosan, each produced a normal amount of chemotactic activity.

Phagocytosis of antigen or antigen-antibody complexes might be another mechanism responsible for the defective chemotaxis. Patients with atopic eczema may well have circulating tissue or bacterial antigens secondary to breakdown of the normal skin. Mowat and Baum (22) have shown that phagocytosis of rheumatoid complexes or iron-dextran particles leads to deficient chemotactic responsiveness. Furthermore, we have demonstrated that patients with coagulase-negative staphylococcal shunt nephritis with evidence of circulating antigen-antibody complexes also have defective neutrophil chemotaxis (23). For this reason control PMN's were rotated in the plasma of the patients with eczema and defective chemotaxis. No inhibitory effect on chemotaxis was produced, however.

Since each of the patients had either atopic eczema, severe pruritis, or urticarial rashes suggesting increased histamine release, the effect of histamine on human neutrophil chemotactic responsiveness was determined. As shown in Table 6, histamine markedly depressed chemotactic responses of control neutrophils. If

TABLE 6. *Effect of histamine on the chemotactic responses of human neutrophil granulocytes*

Concentration of histamine (M)	% Inhibition of chemotaxis[a]
10^{-3}	70 ± 5
10^{-4}	56 ± 9
10^{-5}	40 ± 13
10^{-6}	20 ± 27
10^{-7}	18 ± 26

[a] Results of triplicate sampling on three separate occasions.

histamine was responsible for the defect in neutrophil chemotaxis, one would expect the patients' plasma to have an inhibitory effect on control neutrophils. This was not observed. For this reason the following experiment was performed. Histamine was added to the leukocyte-rich plasma resulting in a final concentration of 10^{-4} molar. The leukocyte-rich plasma was incubated at room temperature for 30 min; the cells were then removed by centrifugation, washed and resuspended in normal plasma. These cells had markedly decreased chemotactic activity. The original supernatant plasma was then added to an untreated aliquot of leukocytes. This suspension was incubated 30 min and tested for chemotactic activity. These cells had normal chemotactic activity suggesting that the initial cells had absorbed the histamine from the plasma. Neutrophils are known to rapidly take up histamine (24) and, thus, may remove a sufficient quantity of the mediator from plasma so that subsequent incubation of control cells in the plasma does not inhibit chemotactic responsiveness.

COMMENT

We have reviewed the clinical and laboratory data from four groups of patients who have in common (a) recurrent or severe bacterial or fungal infections, (b) clinical manifestations of allergic disease, (c) hyperimmunoglobulinemia E, and (d) defective neutrophil chemotaxis. We have not been able to demonstrate that the abnormal chemotaxis is a direct effect of the IgE in the serum, nor have we found abnormal chemotactic responsiveness in all patients with increased IgE. Notable among these patients with increased IgE and normal chemotaxis are ones with a past history of eczema but no present manifestations of atopic disease or recurrent infection. Others have shown, however, that persons with "healed" atopic disease often have increased IgE without clinical evidence of atopy or histamine release (25). In fact, hypersensitivity reactions appear to depend more upon the number and affinity of IgE molecules for receptor sites on basophils and mast cells than the circulating level of IgE (26). An increase in the number of molecules of IgE bound to basophils increases the sensitivity of histamine release in response to antigen or anti-IgE serum. The histamine, in turn, has a number of effects on different tissues. The receptor for histamine on leukocytes produces an increase in the intracellular concentration of cyclic 3′5′-adenosine monophosphate. Recently, we have shown that substances that increase the intracellular concentration of cyclic AMP including epinephrine, norepinephrine isoproterenol, aminophylline, cholera enterotoxin, and prostaglandin E_1 and E_2 inhibit the chemotactic response (27, 28). Histamine has been shown to inhibit chemotaxis of rabbit neutrophils (29), and we have shown that it is also capable of inhibiting chemotaxis of human neutrophils (10). Diphenylhydramine has no effect on the leukocyte receptor for histamine and does not block the effect of histamine on chemotaxis *in vitro.* Preliminary experiments with burimamide, which does block the leukocyte receptor for histamine, indicates that this compound is effective in blocking the effect of histamine on control neutrophils *in vitro* (30). Further studies are needed to delineate the role of histamine and altered concentrations of intracellular cyclic AMP and cyclic GMP in the pathogenesis of abnormal leukocyte chemotaxis. Such studies will hopefully lead to pharmacologic modification of neutrophil function.

ACKNOWLEDGMENTS

The authors gratefully acknowledge the technical assistance of Nancy Hogan and Hattie Gray and the secretarial aid of Patti Lorenz.

The work reported in this chapter was supported by U.S. Public Health Service grants AI 08821 and AI 06931 and the Department of Pediatrics training grant HD 00053–13. Part of these studies were conducted under the sponsorship of the Commission on Streptococcal and Staphylococcal Disease of the Armed Forces Epidemiological Board with support by the Medical Research and Development Command, U.S. Army, under contract DADA–17–70–C–0082.

REFERENCES

1. Miles, A. A., Miles, E. M., and Burke, J.: The value and duration of defense reactions of the skin to primary lodgement of bacteria. *Br. J. Exp. Pathol.* 38:79, 1957.
2. Hill, H. R., Kaplan, E. L., Dajani, A. S., Wannamaker, L. W., and Quie, P. G.: Leukotactic activity and nitroblue tetrazolium dye reduction by neutrophil granulocytes from patients with streptococcal skin infection. *J. Infect. Dis. (in press).*
3. Hill, H. R., Warwick, W. J., Dettloff, J., and Quie, P. G.: Neutrophil granulocyte function in patients with pulmonary infection. *J. Pediatr.* 84:55, 1974.
4. Hill, H. R., Gerrard, J. M., Hogan, N. A., and Quie, P. G.: Hyperactivity of neutrophil leukotactic responses during active bacterical infection. *J. Clin. Invest.* 53:996, 1974.
5. Hill, H. R., Mitchell, T. G., Hogan, N. A., and Quie, P. G.: An improved assay method for the laboratory assessment of neutrophil granulocyte chemotaxis *(submitted for publication).*
6. Ward, P. A., Cochrane, C. G., and Müller-Eberhard, H. J.: The role of serum complement in chemotaxis of leukocytes *in vitro. J. Exp. Med.* 122:327, 1965.
7. Baum, J., Mowat, A. G., and Kirk, J. A.: A simplified method for the measurement of chemotaxis of polymorphonuclear leukocytes from human blood. *J. Lab. Clin. Med.* 77:501, 1971.
8. Ward, P. A., Lepow, I. H., and Neuman, L. J.: Bacterial factors chemotactic for polymorphonuclear leukocytes. *Am. J. Pathol.* 52:725, 1968.
9. McCall, C. E., Caves, J., Cooper, R., and DeChatelet, L.: Functional characteristics of human toxic neutrophils. *J. Infect. Dis.* 124:68, 1971.
10. Hill, H. R., and Quie, P. G.: Raised serum IgE levels and defective neutrophil chemotaxis in three children with eczema and recurrent bacterial infections. *Lancet* 1:183, 1974.
11. Davis, S. D., Schaller, J., and Wedgwood, R. J.: Job's syndrome. *Lancet* 1:1013, 1966.
12. Quie, P. G., and Chilgren, R. A.: Acute disseminated and chronic mucocutaneous candidiasis. *Semin. Hematol.* 8:227, 1971.
13. Valdimarsson, H., Riches, H. R., Holt, L., and Hobbs, J. R.: Lymphocyte abnormality in chronic mucocutaneous candidiasis. *Lancet* 1:1259, 1970.
14. Clark, R. A., Root, R. K., Kimball, H. R., and Kirkpatrick, C. H.: Defective neutrophil chemotaxis and cellular immunity in a child with recurrent infections. *Ann. Int. Med.* 78:515, 1973.
15. Hill, H. R., and Quie, P. G.: Impaired neutrophil granulocyte chemotaxis, recurrent bacterial and fungal infections and hyperimmunoglobulinemia E. *Clin. Res.* 22:229A, 1974 (Abst.).
16. Van Scoy, R. E., Ritts, R. E., Jr., Hill, H. R., and Quie, P. G.: A familial syndrome of defective neutrophil chemotaxis associated with hyperimmunoglobulinemia E *(submitted for publication).*

17. Hill, H. R., and Quie, P. G.: Defective neutrophil chemotaxis, severe staphylococcal infection and hyperimmunoglobulinemia E. *Ped. Res.* 8:152, 1974.
18. Ward, P. A., and Schlegel, R. J.: Impaired leukotactic responsiveness in a child with recurrent infections. *Lancet* 2:344, 1969.
19. Smith, C. W., Hollers, J. C., Dupree, E., Goldman, A. S., and Lord, R. A.: A serum inhibitor of leukotaxis in a child with recurrent infections. *J. Lab. Clin. Med.* 79:878, 1972.
20. Soriano, R. B., South, M. A., Goldman, A. S., and Smith, C. W.: Defect of neutrophil motility in a child with recurrent bacterial infection and disseminated cytomegalovirus infection. *J. Pediatr.* 83:951, 1973.
21. Ward, P. A., and Berenberg, J. L.: Defective regulation of inflammatory mediators in Hodgkin's disease. *N. Engl. J. Med.* 290: 76, 1974.
22. Mowat, A. G., and Baum, J.: Chemotaxis of polymorphonuclear leukocytes from patients with rheumatoid arthritis. *J. Clin. Invest.* 50:2541, 1971.
23. Hill, H. R., and Quie, P. G.: *Unpublished observations.*
24. Kelley, M. T., and White, A.: Histamine release induced by human leukocyte lysates. *J. Clin. Invest.* 52:1834, 1973.
25. Berg, T., and Johansson, S. G. O.: IgE concentrations in children with atopic diseases. *Int. Arch. Allergy* 36:319, 1969.
26. Ishizaka, T., Soto, C. S., and Ishizaka, K.: Mechanisms of passive sensitization III. Number of IgE molecular and their receptor sites on human basophils granulocytes. *J. Immunol.* 111:500, 1973.
27. Estensen, R. D., Hill, H. R., Quie, P. G., Hogan, N., and Goldberg, N. D.: Cyclic GMP and cell movement. *Nature* 245:458, 1973.
28. Hill, H. R., Estensen, R. D., Goldberg, N. D., Hogan, N. A., and Quie, P. G.: Cyclic nucleotide modulation of human neutrophil responses to chemotactic stimulation. *Submitted for publication.*
29. Rivkin, I., and Becker, E. L.: Possible implication of cyclic 3′5′ adenosine monophosphate in the chemotaxis of rabbit peritoneal polymorphonuclear leukocytes. *Fed. Proc.* 31:657, 1972 (abst.).
30. Hill, H. R., Estensen, R. D., Goldberg, N. D., Hogan, N. A., and Quie, P. G. *Unpublished observations.*

DISCUSSION

Bellanti: What is burimamide?

Hill: It is a drug we and Dr. Richard Estensen have become very interested in at the University of Minnesota. As I understand it, it is from a plant. It is an acetate and a cocarcinogen which will promote the development of tumors in the presence of a carcinogenic agent. It has been found to increase the cellular concentration of cyclic GMP.

Ward: It also stimulates and enhances phagocytic bactericidal killing, doesn't it?

Hill: Yes, some people have reported this. We have never gotten consistent results in phagocytic assays with the compound, however.

Holmes-Gray: What did you say burimamide blocks?

Hill: It blocks the H_2 receptor for histamine on the leukocyte. This receptor is responsible for increasing cyclic AMP.

Becker: What sort of stimulation do you get in normal cells, or the cells from normal individuals with normal chemotactic agents?

Hill: With phorbol it differs among individuals. I'd say probably 200 percent. We have gotten up to 900 percent on occasions with from 1 to 10 nanograms of the agent. The most effective concentration of cyclic GMP is 10^{-8} molar but effects are seen in a range of 10^{-6} to 10^{-9} molar. The most effective concentration of Levamisole is 50 to 100 nanograms per milliliter and with these concentrations we can enhance chemotactic responses of control neutrophils.

Becker: And your burimamide?

Hill: This doesn't seem to affect normal cells but again these are very preliminary studies.

Bellanti: Is it an antihistamine?

Hill: Yes.

Holmes-Gray: How do you interpret the results you get with the patients which contrast with the results you get with controls? You do get some differences, right?

Hill: I think the main point is that we never get enhancement of chemotaxis of normal neutrophils with the antihistamine.

Holmes-Gray: What do you think it's doing then?

Hill: The working hypothesis is that it is blocking the effect of histamine on the neutrophil.

Ward: This is correcting the chemotactic defect perhaps by blocking the histamine receptor. Is that the interpretation?

Hill: Perhaps that is what is happening. We have taken histamine and added it to cells along with burimamide and have seen no depressive effect on chemotaxis.

Alper: Did you incubate the patient's cells for 12 hours before testing their chemotaxis again?

Hill: On this one?

Alper: You have shown that neutrophils exposed to histamine and incubated for 12 hours return to normal responsiveness. Did you try preincubating your patients' cells to see if they could be normalized by this procedure?

Hill: No, we have not done that with patients.

Mandell: Are the abscesses these patients have full of good-looking polys, and, if so, how do you explain this?

Hill: The studies of Miles and co-workers have indicated that there is a critical period in the first 2 to 4 hours during which an intact response must be present if bacterial invasion is to be suppressed. It is my understanding that the initial response characterized by a massive influx of PMN's will suppress infection. If this response is impeded, abscess formation occurs and the various enzymes of the white cell and components of the complement system will perpetuate the abscess and allow it to progress. I think this concept applies for all patients with defective chemotaxis. If you look at the patients with impetigo with increased chemotactic activity, they have a nice localized infection and almost never turn up with abscesses or systemic infection.

Becker: I have two questions. The first is: You mentioned that you did random motility studies. How were these performed?

Hill: The random motility studies were performed by a method described by McCall in the *Journal of Infectious Diseases* which is essentially like the MIF assay. You fill the capillary tube with leukocytes and place it in a Sykes-Moore chamber. After 4 hours the PMN's migrate out and the area of their migration is measured. These patients had normal random migration by this technique.

Becker: You also mentioned you do them in the Boyden chamber. Were those results normal also?

Hill: Yes.

Becker: The second question is: Have you tested atopic patients with high IgE or individuals with worm infections with high IgE?

Hill: We have not studied a great number of these patients. We have studied some older patients who had eczema as children who now have normal chemotaxis. Healed atopic patients have high IgE levels but the IgE does not appear to be releasing chemical mediators. We postulate this is the reason that they have normal chemotaxis with extremely high IgE levels.

Becker: But what about the atopic eczema individuals without infection who, from the pruritis, presumably have high histamine levels?

Hill: I can only think of one or two patients with eczema without infection that we have studied because most of our patients come to us for recurrent infections. One patient I remember had eczema without infection, and that patient had normal chemotactic activity, but I don't know what the IgE level was.

Miller: I might answer, too. Of course, the interest is with C5—we have studied a great many patients with eczema, somewhere between 50 and 100, and all have had normal chemotaxis. I don't believe we have studied any patients similar to the ones Dr. Hill described.

Becker: Did all of these have high IgE?

Miller: Perhaps five or six. Most of them did not.

Kirkpatrick: Atopic, with high serum IgE?

Miller: High, but not within the levels Dr. Hill is talking about.

Snyderman: Rebecca Buckley and I have studied a fair number of patients with atopic eczema, high IgE, as well as a number of children with high IgE and depressed cellular immunity. We find that many of the atopic children have had abnormal chemotaxis.

But I agree with what Dr. Miller just said.

Bellanti: With regard to the familial tendency to IgE, I think one has to be careful in interpreting data of this type until one has examined a larger population of atopics, because you may find similar deficiencies in this group. In our own laboratory, Dr. Santilli has studied a group of atopics who don't have this syndrome and has found that 24 of these patients have defective uptake of radioactively labeled ragweed pollen. These are ragweed-sensitive individuals who have defective uptake. The reason we became interested in these studies is the association of defective antigenic processing in other entities with high IgE such as the Wiskott-Aldrich syndrome. Have you studied uptake of antigens in any of these patients?

Hill: We have just done the routine phagocytosis assays for *S. aureus* and *E. coli* and they appear to be normal. There is a report in *Acta Dermatologica* (1973) in which yeast phagocytosis in a stationary system appears to be defective in patients with high IgE's.

Bellanti: Are these patients with this disease different from those with the syndrome of hyperimmunoglobulin E and staph infections that Buckley described? Do you think they are the same?

Hill: Certainly the patients with urticaria are not. The patients with eczema, recurrent abscesses and high IgE probably are very similar in nature to those described by Buckley. We found normal *in vitro* cell-mediated functions in our patients at least to PHA. We didn't study Candida lymphocyte responses, however. Did Buckley's patients have abnormal *in vitro* responses?

Bellanti: I believe they were depressed.

Hill: This is with skin-test reactions. These patients, the small ones, had normal stimulation with PHA. They also had positive Candida skin tests in the range of three to five millimeters. [The data of Buckley as well as that of Tada indicate there is a control of IgE production by a subpopulation of the cells in negative feedback fashion. These patients may be suffering from deficiencies of subpopulations of the cells that are the same as those elaborating the chemotactic factors.]

Baehner: I'd like to know how you control for the contamination of eosinophils which I presume would be a problem in these patients with allergies. We know eosinophilia is usually a prevalent part of their hematologic picture. Can we assume that the eosinophil response is the same as the neutrophil? It seems to me there could be some inhibition effect by physical blockade of certain cells in the Millipore. For example, if the eosinophils are present in high enough concentration, they might block the movement of the neutrophil as it travels through the Millipore in response to chemotactic factor.

Hill: We have looked at this, particularly with mononuclear cells, because we don't use purified neutrophil preparation. We have found that any time you start manipulating the neutrophils you decrease their activity rather significantly, so we don't purify the neutrophils. There is a paper coming out in the *Journal of Clinical Investigation* in which we list the concentration of mononuclear cells and polys, and there is no evidence that mononuclear cells block the Millipore filter. One of the patients of the first three had a high eosinophil count but his chemotactic index was corrected for the number of PMN's present. The other patients have had relatively low eosinophil counts between 0 and 5 to 10 percent.

Ward: With regard to Dr. Bellanti's speculation about the modulating effects of lymphocytes on polymorphochemotaxis, I think the evidence indicates that lymphoid cells are certainly important in modulating and controling monocyte chemotaxis and I think the studies of Dr. Snyderman and many others confirm this. But I think the evidence that lymphocytes or lymphocyte products can really have direct effect on the polymorph in terms of chemotaxis is very minimal.

Gallin: Have you looked to see if the random process in your patients with abnormal chemotaxis is normal or abnormal if you put a chemotactic factor on both sides of your chamber and have no gradient?

Hill: No.

Gallin: In studies on neutrophils from our patient C. C., with abnormal neutrophil and mononuclear cell chemotaxis, defective delayed hypersensitivity and hyper-IgE (Clark, R. A., Root, R. K., Kimball, H. R., and Kirkpatrick, C. H.: Defective neutrophil chemotaxis and cellular immunity in a child with recurrent infections. *Ann. Int. Med.* 78:515, 1973), I have noted that when C5a is placed in both compartments of the Boyden chamber we did not get the increased spontaneous locomotion noted with normal neutrophils *(unpublished observation).*

Snyderman: I'd like to get back to a different area for a moment. I imagine most of these patients with the eczema, even though having infections, were on antihistamines. What do the antihistamines do to the patient's cells *in vitro* and *in vivo?*

Hill: Number one, most of the patients have been studied off medication. When they were on the usual antihistamines, we have not witnessed any effect on chemotactic activity.

Snyderman: In vitro or *in vivo?*

Hill: When they are taking the medicine *in vivo,* as assayed *in vitro.* And I have not been able to produce any effect on their cells with benadryl and similar compounds *in vitro,* which would go along with the fact that benadryl blocks the H-1 histamine receptor.

Bellanti: I'd like to return to Dr. Ward's comment about chemotaxis with polys. I appreciate that the question of chemotactic factors is unclear with regard to polys, but, unless I misheard, I thought this issue was raised a couple of times here. Dr. David commented on the observation of an inhibitory factor for polys that has recently been described, and I also understand from Dr. Kirkpatrick's remarks that there are factors released from lymphocytes that have chemotactic effects on polys.

Ward: But, if you take the overview, and take a look at these patients who have had these reported defects, their defects have been in cell-mediated immune expression. They haven't been obviously defective in the marshalling of polymorphs. And I think in some you have to look at it with this general perspective, notwithstanding the fact that Dr. Kirkpatrick can show that a polymorph chemotactic factor is extractable from lymphocytes. In general, defects in polymorph activity in patients bearing lymphocyte defects seem not to be a significant problem.

Bellanti: Yes, I understand. I was simply suggesting that the lymphocyte be looked at as a possible source of the defective chemotaxis.

Baum: You have to have something to stimulate the lymphocyte, and the way the chambers are set up you are not putting in a stimulus for the lymphocyte.

David: The material that Ross Rocklin has found which inhibits PMN cell migration should not be considered as a chemotactic factor yet. Chemotactic studies are about to be carried out with it.

Park: I was wondering if there is any correlation or link between abnormal immune response, namely, high IgE, and the inheritance of HLA antigen.

Hill: I'm sorry; we haven't looked at that.

Frank: These patients have had frequent infections and your chemotactic factor is a bacterial product. Have you tried other chemotactic factors?

Hill: We have on a couple of patients and they seem to have depressed responses to other chemotactic factors also. We get much more reliable results with the bacterial factor, however, and I believe Drs. Becker and Ward feel all of the factors work in similar fashion on the serine esterases of the neutrophil.

The Phagocytic Cell in Host Resistance, edited
by Joseph A. Bellanti and Delbert H. Dayton.
Raven Press, New York © 1975.

Defective Immune Effector Function in Patients with Neoplastic and Immune Deficiency Diseases

Ralph Snyderman and Chris Stahl

Departments of Medicine and Immunology, Duke University Medical Center, Durham, North Carolina 27710

Phagocytosis and degradation of antigen by macrophages at sites of cellular immune inflammation are final links in a chain of events which serves to protect the host against microbial invasion and development of neoplasms. The events that lead to immunologically mediated destruction of antigen may be characterized as occurring in three stages: recognition of antigen, production or activation of effector molecules, and accumulation of phagocytic and cytotoxic cells at the antigenic site. The recognition stage is highly specific and, in cellular immunity, is mediated by thymic-derived lymphocytes. Production and release of effector molecules (lymphokines) by lymphocytes stimulated by antigen amplify the initial reaction. Lymphokines are capable of mediating lymphocyte blastogenesis, cytotoxicity, leukotaxis, and macrophage activation (1). In response to the local release of lymphokines, macrophages accumulate at the antigenic site (2) and, once there, phagocytize and degrade the antigen.

Disruption of this chain of events could conceivably occur at any point. A host may be unable to recognize as foreign microbial agents or neoplastic cells. Effector molecules may not be released, or those that are released may not be biologically active. Defective effector cells may be unable to respond to the chemotactic or activating factors released by stimulated lymphocytes, or they may be unable to phagocytize and degrade the antigen. Any defect that disrupts cellular immunity represents a threat to the health of the host. Knowing the point at which a defect occurs may prove essential to rationally managing the disease that ensues.

Methods have recently been developed to quantitate delayed hypersensitivity *in vitro* in terms of both recognition and effector function. When lymphocytes in culture are exposed to mitogen or a specific antigen to which they are sensitive, ^{3}H-thymidine in the supernatant of the culture will be incorporated by the transforming cells as they increase their rate of nucleic acid synthesis (3). The amount of radiolabel recovered in the acid-precipitable fraction of the cultured cells can serve as a measure of lymphoproliferation. Prior to and concomitant with transformation lymphocytes synthesize new proteins which are released into the surrounding medium. Among the proteins released is a lymphokine which is chemotactic for human peripheral blood monocytes (4–6). We have recently developed a method to quantitate the chemotaxis of human mononuclear leukocytes (MNL's) *in vitro,* and this method can be used as a measure of chemotactic lymphokine production as well as of effector cell chemotactic function (4–6). Briefly, the chemotaxis assay entails isolation of MNL's from human peripheral blood by Ficoll-Hypaque density gradients (7). The cell suspension is standardized to contain 1.5×10^6 monocytes per ml and placed in the upper compartment of a modified Boyden chamber (8) with the material to be tested for chemotactic activity placed in the lower compartment and a 5.0-micron polycarbonate [Nuclepore®, Wallabs, Inc., San Rafael, California] filter used to separate the two compartments. Lymphokine production is quantitated by determining the chemotactic activity in supernatants of stimulated leukocyte cultures, using normal MNL's as the responder cells (4–6). *In vitro* assays of lymphocyte transformation, lymphokine production, and monocyte chemotaxis have enabled us to detect defects of immune effector function in several groups of patients including individuals with chronic infections or neoplastic diseases.

DEFICIENT MNL CHEMOTACTIC RESPONSIVENESS IN A PATIENT WITH CHRONIC MUCOCUTANEOUS CANDIDIASIS

Chronic mucocutaneous candidiasis (CMC) is a nonlethal, disfiguring infection of cutaneous and mucosal surfaces by *Candida albicans.* Previous investigations have shown that patients with CMC often have defects of cell-mediated immunity (9). Among the defined defects have been subnormal lymphoproliferative responses and deficiencies in lymphokine production (9). In addition to lymphoproliferation and lymphokine production, a normal cellular immune response requires the local accumulation of effector cells such as MNL's. Therefore, in addition to the previously defined immune dysfunctions, it is possible that a defective cell-mediated immune response might be due to abnormal effector cell function. To evaluate this possibility, MNL's from a patient with CMC and delayed cutaneous anergy were tested for their chemotactic responsiveness (10) to two defined chemotactic stimuli: a chemotactic lymphokine which we have termed lymphocyte-derived chemotactic factor (LDCF) and C5a, a cleavage product of the fifth component of complement (4). Since this patient was later treated with transfer factor, we were able to test the effect of this therapy on her MNL chemotactic responsiveness. Before transfer factor therapy was started, the patient's MNL's migrated poorly in response to both C5a and LDCF (Table 1). The chemotactic defect could not be reversed by incubating the patient's cells in normal plasma, and the patient's plasma did not diminish the chemotactic responsiveness of normal MNL's. After transfer factor treatment, the responsiveness of the patient's MNL's to both chemotactic agents gradually improved to approximately 80% of normal. In addition, after transfer factor treatment and concomitant with the improvement of her MNL chemotactic responsiveness, her delayed skin reaction to candidin became positive, and clinical improvement of her disease ensued.

The mechanism by which transfer factor restored the ability of the patient's MNL's to respond chemotactically is as yet unknown. One might speculate that

TABLE 1. *Effect of transfer factor therapy on the chemotactic responsiveness of monocytes from a patient with chronic mucocutaneous candidiasis*[a]

Date	Chemotactic index (%)[b]	
	C5a	LDCF
06/26/71	11.1	N.D.[d]
07/02/71	8.1	21.7
07/19/71[c]	2.0	19.4
08/09/71	33.0	26.6
10/27/71	64.4	38.7
01/26/72	48.6	N.D.
04/19/72	76.4	79.6

[a] Adapted from (8).
[b] Mean chemotactic response of patient's MNL's/mean chemotactic response of normal MNL's X 100. Mean chemotactic response is defined as the mean of triplicate samples expressed as cells per oil immersion field.
[c] Transfer factor therapy begun.
[d] Not done.

transfer factor directly affected her monocytes, somehow "arming" them for an appropriate migratory response to chemotactic factors. Such a mechanism might also explain the positive skin-test responses after transfer factor therapy in severely lymphocytopenic patients with combined immunodeficiency (11). In this regard, Evans and Alexander (12) have shown that supernatants of immune lymphocytes will "arm" macrophages from nonimmune animals for specific cytotoxic lysis of target tumor cells. Alternatively, some lymphocyte-derived factor usually produced *in vivo* might be necessary for the normal chemotactic function of MNLs. Our patient, one might suggest, failed to produce this lymphocyte-derived factor until after she received transfer factor. Although one cannot conclude that the patient's chronic candidiasis was entirely due to defective MNL chemotaxis, these results do document a previously unrecognized immune dysfunction in this disease. Therefore, it can be speculated that certain deficiency states may be due to MNL chemotactic dysfunction rather than abnormalities of lymphocyte recognition or lymphokine production.

DEFECTIVE CONTROL OF LYMPHOKINE SYNTHESIS IN PATIENTS WITH WISKOTT-ALDRICH SYNDROME

Wiskott-Aldrich syndrome is a sex-linked recessive disorder associated with a markedly enhanced susceptibility to infections and neoplasms. Defective humoral and cellular immunity has repeatedly been noted in patients with this syndrome (13). In order to define more precisely the mechanism of defective cellular immunity in this disorder, Altman, Blaese, and Snyderman (14) quantitated lymphoproliferation, lymphokine production, and monocyte chemotactic responsiveness in six patients with Wiskott-Aldrich syndrome.

We found that peripheral blood lymphocytes from these patients produced normal amounts of LDCF when the lymphocytes were stimulated with nonspecific mitogen or ubiquitous antigens, although the proliferative response of these patients' lymphocytes to the same stimulants was frequently depressed. When no exogenous antigens or mitogens were used as stimulants, lymphocytes from patients with Wiskott-Aldrich syndrome nevertheless produced significantly more LDCF than unstimulated lymphocytes from normal individuals (Table 2). The chemotactic responsiveness of monocytes from patients with this

TABLE 2. *Enhanced production of LDCF by unstimulated lymphocytes from patients with Wiskott-Aldrich syndrome (WAS)*[a]

Patient	No. of trials	LDCF production[b] (% of normal[c])
B.M.	5	210 ± 54
M.M.	9	430 ± 102
A.D.	6	172 ± 47
C.B.	5	159 ± 27

[a] Adapted from (12).
[b] LDCF production was quantitated by determining the chemotactic activity in supernatants of unstimulated lymphocyte cultures using normal MNL's as responder cells.
[c] Mean chemotactic activity produced by unstimulated WAS lymphocytes ± 1 SEM/mean chemotactic activity produced by unstimulated normal lymphocytes ± 1 SEM X 100.

syndrome was significantly impaired, and our studies showed that plasma from Wiskott-Aldrich patients inhibited the chemotactic responsiveness of normal human monocytes (Table 3). During the course of these studies, we showed that preincubation of normal MNL's with LDCF could likewise inhibit the chemotactic responsiveness of these cells to LDCF.

These data indicate that synthesis of LDCF by unstimulated peripheral blood lymphocytes from patients with Wiskott-Aldrich syndrome is elevated, a finding which may be analogous to the hypersynthesis and catabolism of immunoglobulins in patients with this disease (15). Furthermore, the data suggest that elevated plasma levels of LDCF may "deactivate" the circulating monocytes of patients

TABLE 3. *Effect of normal or Wiskott-Aldrich syndrome (WAS) plasma on the chemotactic responsiveness of normal monocytes*[a,b]

Source of plasma	Chemotactic factor	
	C5a	LDCF
Wiskott-Aldrich syndrome	57.8 ± 7.7	67.8 ± 11.1
Normal	93.0 ± 12.3[c]	106.4 ± 13.8[d]

[a] Adapted from (12).
[b] Triplicate samples containing 4×10^6 normal MNL were incubated in either normal or WAS plasma for 30 min at 37°C, then washed twice in Gey's salt solution (pH 7.0) and the chemotactic responsiveness of these cells to C5a or LDCF tested. These data represent the mean of five experiments in which plasma samples from four patients and five normals were studied. Results are expressed as cells per oil immersion field (mean ± 1 SEM).
[c] Normal versus WAS $p < 0.025$.
[d] Normal versus WAS $p < 0.050$.

with Wiskott-Aldrich syndrome and thus contribute to the anergy characteristic of this disease.

DEFECTIVE MNL CHEMOTACTIC RESPONSIVENESS IN PATIENTS WITH CANCER

During the past 20 years much data have accumulated that suggest a central role for the immune system in protecting the host against the development and spread of neoplasm (16). A review of this evidence is beyond the scope of our discussion, but certain facts should be stated. (A) Patients with naturally occurring immune deficiency diseases have a high incidence of developing spontaneous neoplasms. (B) Patients treated with immunosuppressants to prevent transplantation rejection develop tumors at a far higher rate than nonimmunosuppressed individuals. (C) In experimental animals a cellular-immune inflammatory response is capable of destroying tumor (17).

Since cellular immunity can destroy tumor and since the accumulation of macrophages at cellular-immune sites is associated with tumor killing, it is essential to answer the following question: Is the ability of macrophages to respond to chemotactic stimuli and thus accumulate at sites of delayed hypersensitivity deficient in individuals with tumors?

In order to answer this question, it was necessary to establish the range of monocyte chemotactic responsiveness to LDCF in normals, as well as to determine the limits of individual variability. We assayed the chemotactic responsiveness of peripheral blood monocytes from 34 normal volunteers repeatedly over a 4-month time course, with most individuals tested on at least four occasions. The mean chemotactic responsiveness (MCR) of our normal population was 73.2

± 1.7 (SEM) migrating monocytes per oil immersion field (Fig. 1). Typical examples of the variability of MNL chemotactic responsiveness in individuals tested repeatedly are seen in Table 4. Monocyte chemotactic responsiveness was also determined for 11 hospitalized patients with non-neoplastic diseases. The mean chemotactic response of this control group was 73.6 ± 4.9 (SEM) and did not significantly differ from normal.

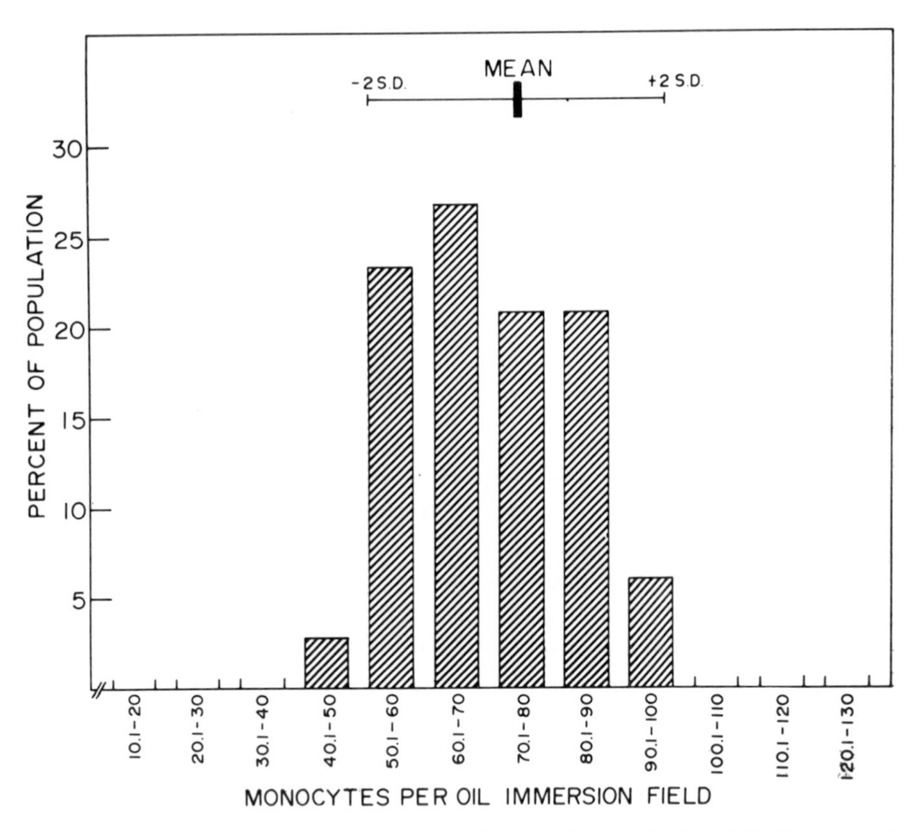

FIG. 1. Monocyte chemotactic responsiveness of a normal population to LDCF. The mean of triplicate samples was determined for each of 34 normal individuals repeatedly (2 to 5 times). The responses thus obtained were grouped as indicated in the figure.

Monocyte chemotactic responsiveness was quantitated in 20 patients with recurrent malignant melanoma or adenocarcinoma of the kidney prior to treatment. Of these patients, 55% had depressed chemotactic responsiveness, with values at least 2SD below normal. The range of the patients' monocyte chemotactic responsiveness compared to the mean of normal controls is seen in Fig. 2.

The patients with malignant melanoma tested in this study were individuals who were to be placed on a Bacille-Calmette-Guérin (BCG) immunotherapy protocol as part of a cooperative study led by H. Seigler. A description of this

TABLE 4. *Chemotactic responsiveness of normal individuals tested on multiple occasions*

Normal control		Date tested	Mean chemotactic response[a]
No.	Age		
1	20	11/05/73	83.8 ± 6.9
		11/12/73	73.9 ± 5.0
		11/19/73	80.2 ± 3.0
		11/26/73	72.9 ± 3.6
		12/10/73	83.8 ± 3.6
2	57	11/06/73	97.0 ± 4.6
		11/13/73	83.8 ± 6.3
		11/20/73	91.4 ± 9.6
		11/27/73	81.8 ± 4.6
		12/06/73	91.1 ± 6.6
3	40	11/06/73	64.4 ± 4.0
		11/13/73	84.2 ± 5.6
		11/20/73	68.3 ± 5.3
		12/04/73	69.3 ± 5.6
4	52	11/14/73	76.9 ± 5.9
		11/21/73	59.4 ± 2.6
		12/14/73	61.0 ± 2.3

[a] Mean chemotactic response (± 1 SEM) to LDCF. Each value represents the mean of triplicate samples and is expressed as cells per oil immersion field.

protocol has been published elsewhere (18), but, briefly, patients in stage I have not yet received immunotherapy, patients in stage II have been sensitized to BCG by intradermal injection (4 weeks earlier), and patients in stage III have received intracutaneous injection of BCG into tumor nodules (4 weeks earlier). Of patients with malignant melanoma tested prior to receiving BCG therapy, 46% had depressed monocyte chemotaxis. The chemotactic responsiveness of these individuals was compared to the responsiveness of patients with malignant melanoma who had been treated with BCG (Fig. 3). It should be noted that BCG immunization and subsequent intralesional injection of BCG significantly diminished the percentage of patients with deficient chemotactic responsiveness ($p < 0.01$) and increased the number of individuals with MCR greater than 2 SD above the normal mean. The prognostic significance of monocyte chemotactic responsiveness has not yet been determined but will become apparent in our future studies.

Markedly depressed chemotaxis was also found in patients with renal adenocarcinoma (Table 5). It is interesting to note that by 3 weeks after removal of the tumors by surgery, monocyte chemotactic responsiveness returned to normal in all patients retested. In addition to these patients, we have also begun testing the MNL chemotactic responsiveness of individuals with other types of neoplasms including breast cancer, lung cancer, and liposarcoma. Of six patients

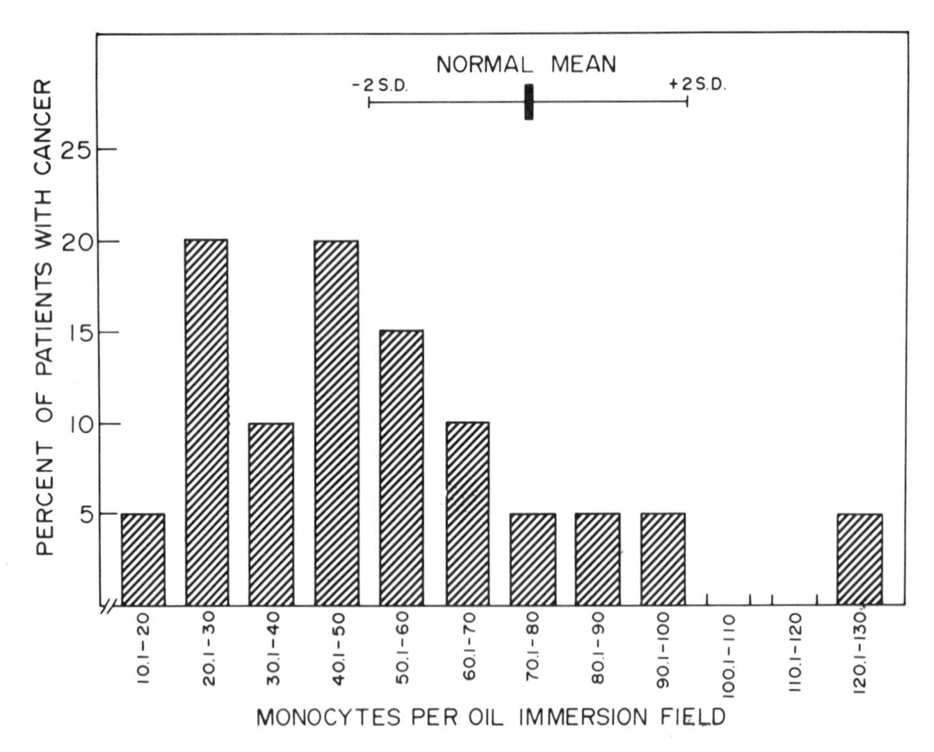

FIG. 2. Monocyte chemotactic responsiveness to LDCF of 20 patients with malignant melanoma or adenocarcinoma of the kidney. The mean of triplicate samples was determined for each individual and the mean chemotactic responses grouped as indicated. Fifty-five percent of these patients had chemotactic responses at least 2 SD below the normal mean.

tested thus far, five are below the normal mean and two are more than 2 SD below the normal mean.

Data obtained thus far clearly demonstrate that a large percentage of patients with cancer have deficient MNL chemotactic responsiveness and that in some of these individuals, the chemotactic responsiveness of their MNL's is enhanced by therapeutic intervention (19). Certain critical questions remain unanswered.

Is depressed MNL chemotactic responsiveness a contributing cause or an effect of tumor development?

What is the mechanism(s) by which MNL chemotactic responsiveness is depressed in patients with cancer?

Is MNL chemotactic responsiveness of any prognostic significance in patients with cancer?

Should enhancing MNL chemotactic responsiveness to normal or supernormal levels be a goal of immunotherapy in patients with cancer?

Do apparently healthy individuals with depressed MNL chemotactic responsiveness run a greater risk of developing cancer?

Answers to these questions should improve our understanding of the role

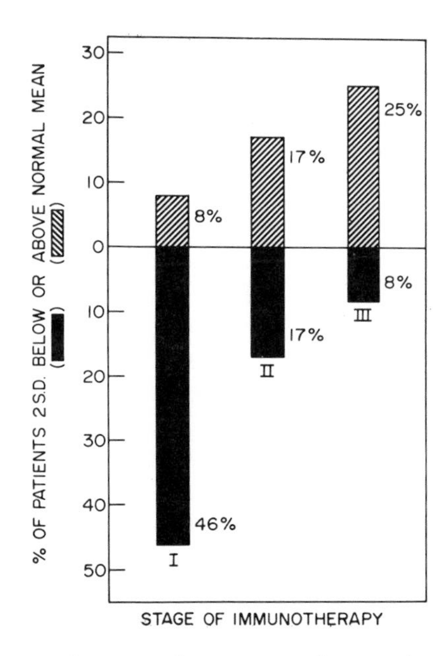

FIG. 3. Effect of BCG immunotherapy on the monocyte chemotactic responsiveness of patients with malignant melanoma. The black bar indicates the percent of individuals within each group whose mean chemotactic response was at least 2 SD below the normal mean. The hash-marked bar indicates the percent of individuals within each group whose mean chemotactic response was at least 2 SD above the normal mean. Stage I = 13 patients before BCG. Stage II = 17 patients 4 weeks after sensitization with BCG. Stage III = 13 patients 4 weeks after inoculation of tumor nodules with BCG.

TABLE 5. *Monocyte chemotactic responsiveness*[a] *in patients with renal adenocarcinoma*

Patient	Preoperative	Postoperative[b]
A	21.3 ± 4.3	83.2 ± 8.6
B	20.9 ± 8.3	86.9 ± 7.6
C	25.9 ± 2.6	N.D.[c]
D	58.3 ± 2.9	N.D.
E	67.9 ± 3.6	82.3 ± 11.6
F[d]	26.6 ± 1.3	N.D.
G[d]	31.3 ± 4.6	N.D.
Patient mean	36.0 ± 3.9	84.1 ± 9.3
Normal mean	73.2 ± 1.3	—

These studies are in collaboration with G. Hemstreet.
[a] Mean chemotactic response (± 1 SEM) to LDCF.
[b] Retested 2 to 4 weeks after surgery.
[c] Not done.
[d] Inoperable neoplasms.

played by the immune system in tumor suppression as well as provide new clinical insight regarding the diagnosis and treatment of neoplastic diseases.

SUMMARY

Using a sensitive, reproducible assay for human monocyte chemotaxis and chemotactic lymphokine production, we studied these parameters of immune function in patients with neoplastic disease, Wiskott-Aldrich syndrome, and chronic mucocutaneous candidiasis. The majority of patients with untreated neoplastic disease had depressed monocyte chemotactic responsiveness. Immunotherapy with BCG or removal of the tumor by surgery enhanced chemotactic responsiveness in many patients. The data suggest that depressed monocyte chemotactic responsiveness could, at least in part, account for the depressed delayed hypersensitivity found in patients with cancer.

Patients with Wiskott-Aldrich syndrome also had depressed monocyte chemotaxis in addition to supernormal chemotactic factor production by lymphocytes unstimulated by antigen or mitogen *in vitro.* Moreover, plasma from these patients inhibited the chemotactic responsiveness of MNL's from normal controls. Collectively these findings prompted the speculation that in patients with Wiskott-Aldrich syndrome supernormal production of a chemotactic lymphokine by unstimulated circulating lymphocytes might desensitize circulating MNL's so as to diminish their chemotactic responsiveness, and thus contribute to the anergy characteristic of this disease.

A patient with CMC and delayed cutaneous anergy was also found to have defective monocyte chemotactic responsiveness that was corrected by treatment with transfer factor. As the patient's MNL chemotactic responsiveness returned to normal, she developed cutaneous reactivity to candidin and improved clinically.

Thus, defects of MNL chemotactic responsiveness and LDCF production have been found in association with chronic infections and neoplastic disease. Further studies of these parameters of immune function in patients with defective immunity should improve our understanding of diseases in which immune deficiency plays a role and may provide a more rational basis for treatment of such patients.

ACKNOWLEDGMENTS

The work reported in this chapter was supported in part by U.S. Public Health Service grant 1 RO1 DE 03738–01 and N.C.I. NO1 CP 33313. Snyderman is a Howard Hughes Medical Investigator.

REFERENCES

1. Snyderman, R., and Altman, L. C.: Mediators of delayed hypersensitivity. In Frazier, C. A. (ed.): *Annual Review of Allergy.* Medical Examination Publ. Co., Flushing, New York, pp. 377–387, 1973.

2. Postlethwaite, A., and Snyderman, R.: Mononuclear leukocyte chemotactic activity *in vivo* in delayed hypersensitivity. *Fed. Proc.* 32:989, 1973.
3. Oppenheim, J. J.: Relationship of *in vitro* lymphocyte transformation to delayed hypersensitivity in guinea pigs and man. *Fed. Proc.* 27:21, 1968.
4. Snyderman, R., Altman, L. C., Hausman, M. S., and Mergenhagen, S. E.: Human mononuclear leukocyte chemotaxis: A quantitative assay for humoral and cellular chemotactic factors. *J. Immunol.* 108:857–860, 1972.
5. Altman, L. C., Snyderman, R., Oppenheim, J. J., and Mergenhagen, S. E.: A human mononuclear leukocyte chemotactic factor: Characterization, specificity, and kinetics of production by homologous leukocytes. *J. Immunol.* 110:801–810, 1973.
6. Snyderman, R., Altman, L. C., and Mergenhagen, S. E.: Human mononuclear leukocyte chemotaxis: Definition of two chemotactic factors and a previously unrecognized immune dysfunction. In *Proceedings of a Conference on "Non-Specific" Factors Influencing Host Resistance,* Karger, Basel, pp. 180–189, 1973.
7. Böyum, A.: Isolation of leukocytes from human blood, further observations. *Scand. J. Clin. Lab. Invest.* 21, Suppl. 97:31–50, 1968.
8. Snyderman, R., Shin, H. S., Phillips, J. K., Gewurz, H., and Mergenhagen, S. E.: A neutrophil chemotactic factor derived from C'5 upon interaction of guinea pig serum with endotoxin. *J. Immunol.* 103:413–421, 1969.
9. Kirkpatrick, C. H., Rich, R. R., and Bennett, J. E.: Chronic mucocutaneous candidiasis: Model-building in cellular immunity. *Ann. Int. Med.* 74:955–978, 1971.
10. Snyderman, R., Altman, L. C., Frankel, A., and Blaese, R. M.: Defective mononuclear leukocyte chemotaxis: A previously unrecognized immune dysfunction. Studies in a patient with chronic mucocutaneous candidiasis. *Ann. Int. Med.* 78:509–513, 1973.
11. Meuweissen, H. J., Pickering, R., Litwin, S. et al.: Maternal intrauterine graft of B lymphocytes in combined immunological deficiency disease. *Pediatr. Res.* 6:379, 1972.
12. Evans, R., and Alexander, P.: Rendering macrophages specifically cytotoxic by a factor released from immune lymphoid cells. *Transplantation* 12:227–229, 1971.
13. Blaese, R. M., Strober, W., and Waldmann, T. A.: Immunodeficiency in the Wiskott-Aldrich syndrome. In *Proceedings of the Second International Workshop on Immunodeficiency Diseases.* National Foundation, 1973 *(in press).*
14. Altman, L. C., Snyderman, R., and Blaese, R. M.: Abnormalities of chemotactic lymphokine synthesis and mononuclear leukocyte chemotaxis in Wiskott-Aldrich syndrome. *J. Clin. Invest.* 54:486, 1974.
15. Blaese, R. M., Strober, W., Levy, A. L., and Waldmann, T. A.: Hypercatabolism of IgG, IgA, IgM and albumin in the Wiskott-Aldrich syndrome. A unique disorder of serum protein metabolism. *J. Clin. Invest.* 50:2331–2338, 1971.
16. Waldmann, T. A., Strober, W., and Blaese, R. M.: Immunodeficiency disease and malignancy: Various immunologic deficiencies of man and the role of immune processes in the control of malignant disease. *Ann. Int. Med.* 77:606–628, 1972.
17. Zbar, B., Wepsic, H. T., Rapp, H. J., Stewart, L. C., and Borsos, T.: Two-step mechanism of tumor graft rejection in syngeneic guinea pigs. II. Initiation of reaction by a cell fraction containing lymphocytes and neutrophils. *J. Natl. Cancer Inst.* 44:710–713, 1970.
18. Seigler, H. F., Shingleton, W. S., Metzgar, R. S., Buckley, C. E., and Bergoc, P. M.: Immunotherapy in patients with melanoma. *Ann. Surg.* 178:352–359, 1973.
19. Snyderman, R., Dickson, J., Meadows, L., and Pike, M.: Deficient monocyte chemotactic responsiveness in humans with cancer. *Clin. Res.* 22:430, 1974

DISCUSSION

Ward: I think these are very exciting studies. The data associated with the Wiskott-Aldrich syndrome seem to be part of a spectrum of T and B cell abnormalities in which lymphokines are present and floating around in the circulation. Most of the materials that have been so far described are demigration and inhibition activities which seem to be, by physicochemical criteria, slightly different from what one gets from the standard culture situations *in vitro.* But this is one additional aspect of the whole system which one finds in many of the syndromes associated with deficient lymphokine production *in vitro;* these patients have the paradox of lymphokines floating around in the circulation. I think this is going to be a whole new area of study in immune deficiency.

Snyderman: I agree with you fully. I think there seems to be some abnormal modulation of B cell—T cell interaction in a large number of these patients. The patients with Wiskott-Aldrich do seem to turn over immunoglobulin at a rapid rate. We are far from understanding this but I fully agree with what you just said.

Alper: Is the inhibitory factor for monocyte migration an acute phase reactant? Have you examined serum from other infected patients?

Snyderman: Yes. When you look at a whole battery of infected patients, if anything their monocytes are always supernormal and the serum enhances rather than suppresses their chemotaxis. This is a real finding. It is unusual. We looked at so many people with infections and these stand out as a group as being very abnormal. But in general you do not find this. If you take children, let's say, with cystic fibrosis who are infected all the time, their plasma has no inhibitory activity whatever and, if anything, enhances the response.

Frank: I assume that these patients were not on therapy at the time they were studied.

Snyderman: Right.

Frank: Were they sufficiently sick and debilitated so that they were not eating and losing weight and in negative nitrogen balance, etc.?

Snyderman: I didn't mention that we had a large patient control of people who were quite ill and their mean and standard deviation did not vary significantly from normal. The only patient control that was abnormal was somebody who was uremic and had a very high BUN. In terms of the malignant melanoma patients—these are people who had had recurrent disease. Everyone had had the initial nodule removed and had a recurrence. That is why they were in the protocol. As to whether or not they were very sick, some looked perfectly healthy. None with malignant melanoma was hospitalized. This was a matter of coming into the clinic.

Frank: Do you think that these tumors could have produced a circulating factor that might have been stimulating it or turned off the chemotactic response?

Snyderman: We have been looking at serum factors to see if they block normal cells. We haven't tested that many, but, maybe out of four of the lowest, two of them have completely obliterated the normal response. But what they seem to have done is to clump up the cells on top of the filter, almost as if they had some kind of anti-monocyte or agglutinating factor. We are going to try to investigate this to see exactly what it is.

Gallin: In view of your report of the successful correction of a mononuclear cell chemotactic defect with dialyzable transfer factor (Snyderman, R., Altman, L. C., Frankel, A., and Blaese, R. M.: Defective mononuclear leukocyte chemotaxis: A previously unrecognized immune dysfunction. *(Ann. Int. Med.* 78:509, 1973), have you tried transfer factor in any of the patients you discussed?

Snyderman: No, we haven't tried transfer factor. I think it would be very nice to see if this were reproducible. The reported patient was the only opportunity we had with transfer factor. We have given transfer factor to other patients but they haven't been people with monocyte defects so I don't have any further experience.

David: Did you fractionate the serum that was anti-chemotactic?

Snyderman: No, but we will do this and have the serum available.

David: One comment concerning the statement that B cells make chemotactic factor. Chess, McDermott, and Schlossman have been able to separate immunoglobulin-bearing cells from nonimmunoglobulin cells with immunoabsorbent columns so that each population is about 98% pure. With Dr. Ross Rocklin and in collaboration with Dr. Schlossman's group, we have found that both T and B cell populations make MIF, but only the T cells make mitogenic factor. So, there is a difference there. Further, Chess et al. have shown that both T and B cells will show enhanced thymidine incorporation by PHA, Con A, and pokeweed mitogen whereas only the T cells were stimulated to incorporate thymidine by antigen.

Karnovsky: With respect to the prostaglandin studies, I wouldn't immediately share your doubts that stem from the temporal sequence that you saw, because you have an increase and you have got the diesterase operative, too. Did you have any studies with prostaglandin and/or theophylline?

Snyderman: Yes. We found theophylline did not enhance the effect of prostaglandin, which was very puzzling to us. We also looked at human monocyte chemotaxis in the presence of aspirin and in the presence of Indocin. We found that levels incubated *in vitro* up to the maximum we ever give in humans, let's say with rheumatoid arthritis, had no effect on monocyte chemotactic responsiveness. This again is puzzling. Steroids did. They minimally inhibit it. But aspirin and Indocin, at fairly high doses, at least in our hands, haven't been very significant in inhibiting chemotaxis.

Kirkpatrick: Did you say the patients with the hyper-IgE syndrome had high background levels of chemotactic activity even if the cells aren't separated by Hypaque-Ficoll?

Snyderman: Yes. That was something else. We didn't use those. That was a sad experience we had to learn.

Kirkpatrick: But these patients with the hyper-IgE syndrome have high levels of chemotactic activity in their cultures, and in the serum they have an inhibitor. It would be interesting to know if this is a characteristic of patients with skin disease. There is another disorder in which mediators have been described, and that is the Sezary syndrome. This is a variant of lymphocytic leukemia with erythroderma in which the skin is infiltrated with lymphocytes that are like T cells. That raises the possibility that when you sample the blood you are missing the right pool; the pool is sequestered elsewhere.

Snyderman: Certainly everyone that we have looked at has had skin disease.

Kirkpatrick: That is what I was thinking about because all three of our patients with hyper-IgE have something wrong with their skin.

Blaese: The Sezary patients have not had high background synthesis of LDCF by peripheral blood lymphocytes. However, this does not rule out elevated synthesis by the leukemic cells in the skin infiltrates.

Kirkpatrick: They have a plasma inhibitor.

Becker: To return to the prostaglandins, I can't really say anything about prostaglandins and monocyte chemotaxis, but we could not confirm Caley and Wiener that prostaglandins are chemotactic. However, we could show that PGE1, PGE2, and PGA1 inhibited chemotaxis and also increased the cyclic AMP of the neutrophil. PGF2α did not inhibit chemotaxis or increase the cyclic AMP of the polymorphonuclear leukocyte. I agree with Manfred in terms of the temporal relationship change you found. Certainly the increases in cyclic AMP following prostaglandin are quite rapid and are over with relatively shortly. But you can't really say anything about whatever secondary changes may or may not have occurred.

Snyderman: I agree with your findings completely on the neutrophils, and we thought it quite interesting that the same factor that enhanced the monocytes decreased the neutrophil.

Hill: We have done some studies on prostaglandins and with PGE1 and 2 we get marked inhibition of chemotaxis. With PGF2α at high concentrations, we get inhibition but at lower concentrations we get a marked stimulation of chemotaxis.

Becker: We were working with PGF2α in the same range as the PGE1 and PGE2. The latter two were inhibitory and the PGF2α was not.

Hill: F2α certainly inhibits chemotaxis at higher concentrations, like PGE1 and 2.

Becker: With varying concentrations of PGF2α we could find no effect on cyclic AMP.

Frank: Are all these prostaglandin preparations equally pure?

Snyderman: They all come from Upjohn. You have to use them fresh because they tend to convert while on the shelf.

Bellanti: Did you incubate the cancer patient's serum with normal monocytes to see if there was an inhibitory effect?

Snyderman: We really haven't had an opportunity to do enough of these yet to know if there are any consistent findings. We have tested four: two have inhibited and the other two haven't. What this means I really don't know.

Park: In your mononuclear cells isolated by your Ficoll-Hypaque technique, what proportion of those are in fact phagocytizing?

Snyderman: It usually runs somewhere around 30 percent.

Park: Might this technique of isolating the mononuclear cell also stimulate the cell to produce LDCF.

Snyderman: Yes.

Park: I assume that in your incubating chamber you are, in fact, producing LDCF in enormous amounts. How can you interpret your data on that?

Snyderman: The way we interpret this is, number one, the cells we use are washed a number of times. The production of LDCF in the Ficoll-Hypaque cells takes somewhere around 2 days—at least 24 hours until you start seeing the LDCF production. The entire chamber experiment takes 90 minutes. So whatever effect the one has with the B cells on top of the filter producing LDCF, apparently it doesn't do enough to completely foul up the system. The point you make is one we have to be concerned about. We are dealing with cells that have been in contact with Ficoll-Hypaque, but if we look at the supernatants from the top of the chamber we don't find chemotactic activity there in the 90-minute period. We have done some very careful studies because we were concerned about this, too, and found no activity with the 90-minute incubation.

David: Again with the Wiscott-Aldrich patients, would you put theirs underneath and show a chemotactic activity?

Snyderman: Yes, you can do this and show they have elevated chemotactic activity.

David: In the serum?

Snyderman: Yes. It isn't a very consistent finding in having a one-for-one relationship.

David: Would it inhibit a chemotactic activity if you put it in? Would it feed back?

Snyderman: I see what you mean. I don't believe we have ever done that experiment. Dr. Blaese, are you aware of that?

Blaese: No.

The Phagocytic Cell in Host Resistance, edited
by Joseph A. Bellanti and Delbert H. Dayton.
Raven Press, New York © 1975.

Chemotaxis in Human Disease

John Baum

Arthritis and Clinical Immunology Unit, University of Rochester School of Medicine and Dentistry, Rochester, New York 14620

One of the functions of the polymorphonuclear leukocyte is its directed migration toward a specific location in the body. A number of factors have been found to be responsible for this directed migration. These, and principally the serum factors, have been extensively studied by Ward (1). In our laboratory at the Monroe Community Hospital (University of Rochester School of Medicine and Dentistry) over the past few years we have concentrated on the study of chemotaxis of the polymorphonuclear leukocyte directed by chemotactic factors produced by complement activation under a number of conditions and in a number of disease states.

Our method, a modification of Boyden's original technique, and similar to that used by several other investigators, uses small amounts of peripheral blood. This has enabled us to study the cell function in a number of human disease states as well as the ability of the sera in several of these conditions to produce chemotactic factors. We have also studied the effect of several drugs on chemotaxis both *in vitro* and *in vivo.* The technique was developed with the collaboration of Kirk, now of Christchurch, New Zealand, and Mowat, now of Oxford, England (2). A basic feature of the method was the use of a cytocentrifuge (Shandon Scientific Co. Inc., Sewickley, Pennsylvania) that enabled us to deposit a concentrated amount of polymorphonuclear leukocytes from 5 to 10 ml of heparinized blood directly onto a circumscribed area of a membrane filter (7 mm diameter). We tested various size filters to finally arrive at the use of a 3-micron Millipore cellulose acetate membrane filter. Subsequently, because of changes in the manufacturing process, our results with this filter became irregular. We are grateful for the advice of Ward and Becker who suggested the Schleicher & Schuell (Keene, New Hampshire) 3-micron membrane filter, which we are now using for all of our studies. The initial chamber we used was an adapted Sykes-Moore Tissue Culture Chamber. This chamber has been modified for us by the Bellco Glass Company (Vineland, New Jersey) and has been changed in two major respects. The individual compartments on either side of the filter (which is held in place by O rings) are slightly larger so that the total volume in each chamber is 0.75 ml. In addition, the ports for the introduction of material on both sides of the filter have been offset so that material can be placed in the chamber without fear of damaging the filter.

In our initial studies each filter was read by hand. Preparations were read in triplicate and occasionally duplicate with 10 readings for each preparation. Because the "attractant side" had fewer cells, a total of 10 fields were scanned. Fifty boxes of a 5 X 5 ocular grid were read on this side while 10 boxes were read on the "starting side." Although this method produced good reproducibility (2), it was exceedingly tedious and in the past year we have used an automated method. We have used the πMC particle counter (Millipore Corporation, Bedford, Massachusetts) and the Bausch and Lomb Omnicon (Fig. 1). These machines have proven to be quite effective for the counting of large numbers of cells on the filters. At the present with a normal preparation we count about 1,500 to 3,000 cells

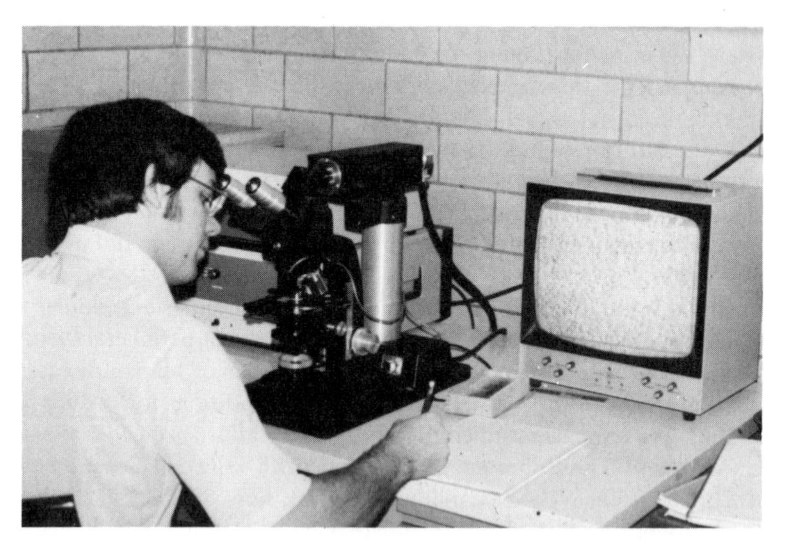

FIG. 1. Use of the ΠMC particle counter (Millipore Corporation) in counting cells on the membrane filter.

on the starting side and, with normal chemotaxis, about 300 to 600 cells on the attractant side. To keep our results with this instrument consistent with our previous methods, we use a different constant from that reported in our earlier studies.

Another major problem one faces with this technique, and especially with the method we use, is the endotoxin. We have found variations among different batches of the *E. coli* endotoxin (Difco Corporation, Detroit, Michigan) used for activation of the chemotactic factors from complement. As much as a 10-fold difference in concentration can be required for approximately the same degree of chemotaxis.

Aggregated and unaggregated IgG have also been used with this technique for stimulating complement (3). The considerations discussed in this section indicate the problems that are faced with each part of the procedure used in the *in vitro* study of chemotaxis.

Our initial interest was in the connective tissue diseases and in Table 1 are seen the results of our studies in some of the rheumatologic disorders. This was based on a series of studies that were performed by Zivkovic of Belgrade, Yugoslavia (4). The results in the patients with rheumatoid arthritis, although limited in this particular group of experiments, were similar to the findings in the original study which was done in patients with this condition in cooperation with Mowat (5). It is apparent that a deficiency of cellular function was found in patients with rheumatoid arthritis and its variant, Felty's syndrome. Although systemic lupus erythematosus is known to be an inflammatory disease triggered by immune complexes quite often to a greater degree than that seen in patients with rheumatoid arthritis, cell function was found to be normal in this disease.

TABLE 1. *Results of studies in rheumatologic disorders*

Group	Number	Chemotactic index	p
Rheumatoid arthritis	6	370 (182–740)	<0.05
Felty's syndrome	7	211 (19–428)	<0.01
Systemic lupus erythematosus	14	437 (154–1,035)	NS
Ankylosing spondylitis	5	613 (550–735)	NS
Normals	21	500 (300–810)	NS

A series of studies with normal cells incubated in the presence of rheumatoid factor complexes indicated that the phagocytosis of these complexes was probably responsible for the decreased chemotactic properties of the polymorphonuclear leukocytes in this condition (5).

Since gold compounds are used extensively in the treatment of rheumatoid arthritis, Orozco of Guadalajara, Mexico, and I (6) have looked at the effect of gold sodium thiomalate (Myochrysin) on chemotaxis. We were unable to detect any effect of the gold compound on the directed migration of the polymorphonuclear leukocyte or on the chemotactic activity of endotoxin-activated complement fractions.

Zivkovic and I (7) have also looked at the effect of colchicine on complement chemotactic factors and on the polymorphonuclear leukocytes. Our results are shown in Table 2. We found no effect of colchicine on chemotaxis inducted by

TABLE 2. *Effect of colchicine on endotoxin-activated complement chemotaxis*

		Chemotactic index	
Colchicine (μg/ml)	No. of experiments	Endotoxin + C	Endotoxin + C + colchicine
25	14	310	264
2.5	32	324	306
0.25	17	310	254

the activation of complement. In these experiments the colchicine was placed in both compartments of the chemotaxis chamber, i.e., on the cell starting side and on the activated complement side so no effect was found on the cell.

Byers, Ward, and their colleagues (8) have stated that it is probably complement activation with the production of chemotactic factors C5a and C$\overline{567}$ that mediate the acute inflammation in acute gout. However, Phelps and Spilberg and his colleagues (9, 10) showed that chemotaxis induced by a chemotactic factor released from PMN's after phagocytosis of urate crystals was inhibited by colchicine. Caner (11) showed inhibition of chemotaxis induced by staphylococci.

Our studies do not confirm Caner's findings but are consistent with the work of Phelps and Spilberg and what is known in the usual clinical situation. We were unable to find any inhibition of complement chemotactic factors in our system. This could explain the failure of colchicine to successfully terminate any other acute arthritis besides gouty arthritis. Colchicine would have its specificity in gout by a specific reaction with the chemotactic factors of the lysosomal fraction of the cell and be unable to inhibit complement-derived chemotactic factors.

In further support of this concept it is well known that complement levels are normal, if not high, in the synovial fluid of patients with acute gouty arthritis (12, 13).

In studies of the polymorphonuclear leukocytes obtained from patients with diabetes mellitus we found deficient chemotaxis which could be returned to normal levels by the addition of glucose and insulin to the cells *in vitro* (14). The deficiency noted in the diabetic cells could not be reproduced in normal cells by concentrations of glucose up to 900 mg/100 ml. Since both glucose and insulin were required for the return of cell function to normal, we felt this may be due to a necessity for potassium movement into the cells. This was based on the work of Ward and Becker (15) who induced deficient chemotaxis by poisoning the potassium pump of the cell with ouabain.

We wondered whether this mechanism might have any role in the deficiency seen with the polymorphonuclear leukocytes of the patients with rheumatoid arthritis. Cells from normals and patients with systemic lupus erythematosus were also included although the latter group in this case, since their chemotaxis was normal, could be considered part of the normal group. The results are seen in Table 3 (16). They were not significant. The changes produced by phagocytosis cannot be restored by subsequent treatment with insulin and glucose *in vitro*.

We found that similar reductions in chemotaxis were seen in patients with

TABLE 3. *Effect on chemotaxis of added insulin and glucose*

Group	No.	% Change
Rheumatoid arthritis	7	+18
Systemic lupus erythematosus	14	−10
Normals	10	+5

acute infections (17). On the basis of our previous studies we have attributed this deficiency to phagocytosis of bacteria in the presence of opsonins with chronic infection chemotaxis returned to normal.

In collaboration with Cestero and Freeman of the renal dialysis unit of the University of Rochester School of Medicine we are presently looking at chemotaxis in uremic patients and patients on chronic hemodialysis. These studies are still in progress.

We found deficient chemotaxis in cells obtained from six of eight uremic patients. Most patients on chronic hemodialysis, at some time during the dialysis, show a chemotactic index in the normal range. We have noted in 16 patients who have been followed serially for 6 months that falls in the average chemotactic index to less than normal levels were seen when the ambient temperature rose during a summer heat wave and again during the winter when temperatures fell below 41°F (Fig. 2). We believe this may represent a sensitivity of cellular

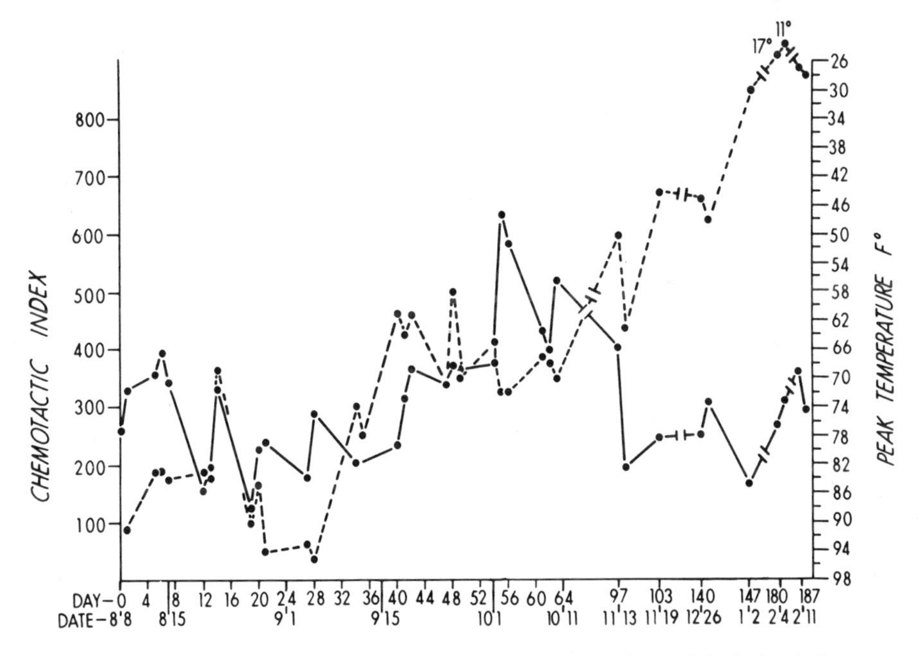

FIG. 2. Chemotaxis of peripheral PMN's from patients on chronic hemodialysis. Each dot represents mean of four to six patients (connected by solid bar). Dotted bar connects highest ambient temperature on day before hemodialysis.

function to the environment in patients on chronic hemodialysis. Preliminary studies of the serum obtained from these patients show mostly normal levels of hemolytic complement with a correspondingly normal production of chemotactic factors after the addition of endotoxin. However, we have found one patient who shows significantly greater production of chemotactic factors as well as a few whose production is less than normal. Endotoxin has been used in these studies (18).

Since we have used chemotaxis to investigate diseases in which infection can be a significant problem, Zivkovic also studied patients with acute and chronic asthma. Normal levels of chemotaxis were found in this group of patients (19).

An interesting group that was looked at with Zivkovic was a large number of patients with carcinoma (20). A group of patients were followed in the oncology clinic at Strong Memorial Hospital for a number of months. We found that patients with deficient chemotaxis had a poor prognosis whereas patients who maintained their chemotactic index in the normal range had a prolonged survival. The predictability of this measurement extended to patients whose chemotactic index fell and who subsequently expired. In most cases this predictability could not be determined by any clinical parameters.

Specific complement-deficient states have been studied in collaboration with John Leddy. We have looked at the development of chemotactic factors in an individual with absence of the sixth component of complement (21). She was an 18-year-old female in good general health. The serum of this patient was tested with the addition of both endotoxin and aggregated F-II to stimulate chemotactic factor. She demonstrated a normal capacity to generate chemotactic activity. This appears to be due to adequate production of C5a. This supports the concept of Snyderman and his colleagues who have described C5a as being the major chemotactic factor (22).

Serum from an individual with C2 deficiency was also tested for chemotactic activity, using both endotoxin and aggregated IgG. This was from a 59-year-old male with dermatomyositis (23). Induced chemotactic activity was found to be normal. This would indicate that this individual produced chemotactic factor by activation of the alternate complement pathway. The data from these patients does not give any information on the relative importance of the chemotactic factors which can be C3a, C5a, or $C\overline{567}$.

A 15-year-old girl with serious problems with recurrent infection, who has been found to have deficient C5, is at present being studied. Our preliminary results show a definite deficiency in the production of chemotactic factors from the serum of this individual. This data, if found consistent with further studies, would indicate that in the absence of the potential production of C5a and $C\overline{567}$ the most likely explanation for the chemotactic activity present in this patient is the availability of C3a. However, the total amounts of chemotactic factor produced are grossly deficient (24).

A summary of our studies in chemotaxis are listed in the next two tables. In Table 4, part 1 shows those diseases in which we have found normal and abnormal chemotaxis with the polymorphonuclear leukocyte obtained from individuals with these conditions. In part 2 are shown the results when sera from the patients with these specific complement adherences were incubated with endotoxin and then tested against normal polymorphonuclear leukocytes. In part 3 are shown the results of studies performed by the addition of three pharmaceutical agents

TABLE 4. *Chemotaxis in human disease*

Normal	Abnormal
1. Polymorphonuclear leukocyte function	
Systemic lupus erythematosus	Rheumatoid arthritis
Ankylosing spondylitis	Felty's syndrome
	Diabetes mellitus
(Chronic hemodialysis)	Uremia
Chronic bacterial infection	Acute bacterial infection
Acute asthma	Carcinoma (poor prognosis)
Chronic asthma	
2. Complement function (chemotactic factors)	
C2 deficiency	C5 deficiency
C6 deficiency	
3. Drugs effects (on PMN's and complement)	
Colchicine	
Corticosteroids	
Gold sodium thiomalate	

to chambers containing normal cells and normal chemotactic factor. Table 5 shows the results we have obtained by manipulation of normal cells in some cases and the abnormal cells in diabetes mellitus and the result of a "normalizing" process in patients with uremia.

We feel that the results presented in this chapter show that the study of the chemotaxis of the polymorphonuclear leukocyte can be an exciting method with which we can look at disease processes and perhaps even use as a valuable clinical tool.

TABLE 5. *Chemotaxis in human disease*

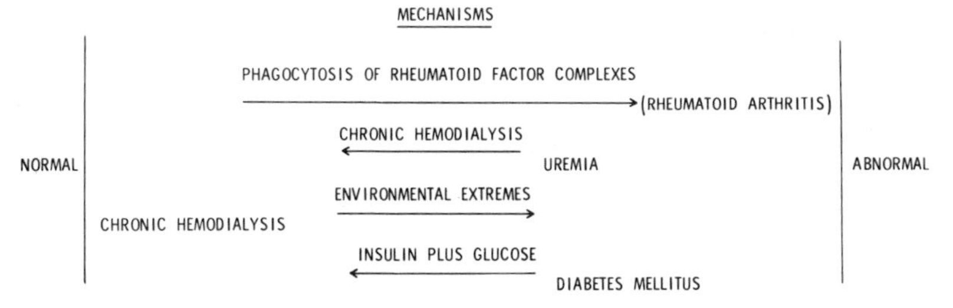

ACKNOWLEDGMENTS

Most of the studies reported here were supported by grants from the Monroe County Chapter of the Arthritis Foundation. Part of the studies was supported by contract no. NO1-AM-3-2221 from the National Institute of Arthritis, Metabolism, and Digestive Diseases.

REFERENCES

1. Ward, P. A.: Neutrophil chemotactic factors and related clinical disorders. *Arthritis Rheum.* 13:181, 1970.
2. Baum, J., Mowat, A. G., and Kirk, J. A.: A simplified method for the measurement of chemotaxis of polymorphonuclear leukocytes from human blood. *J. Lab. Clin. Med.* 77:501, 1971.
3. Wagner, T., Abraham, G., and Baum, J.: Induction of polymorphonuclear leukocyte chemotaxis by gammaglobulin, rheumatoid factor and their complexes. *Arthritis Rheum.* 15:458, 1972.
4. Zivkovic, M., and Baum, J.: Chemotaxis of polymorphonuclear leukocytes from patients with systemic lupus erythematosus and Felty's syndrome. *Immuno. Comm.* 1:39, 1972.
5. Mowat, A. G., and Baum, J.: Chemotaxis of polymorphonuclear leukocytes from patients with rheumatoid arthritis. *J. Clin. Invest.* 50:2541, 1971.
6. Orozco, J. and Baum, J.: *Unpublished observations.*
7. Zivkovic, M., and Baum, J.: *Unpublished observations.*
8. Byers, P. H., Ward, P. A., Kellermeyer, R. W., and Naff, G. B.: Complement as a mediator of inflammation in acute gouty arthritis. II. Biological activities generated from complement by the interaction of serum complement and sodium urate crystals. *J. Lab. Clin. Med.* 81:761, 1973.
9. Phelps, P.: Polymorphonuclear leukocyte motility *in vitro.* II. Stimulatory effect of monosodium urate crystals land urate in solution; Partial inhibition by colchicine and indomethacin. *Arthritis Rheum.* 12:189, 1969.
10. Spilberg, I., Mandell, B., and Wochner, R. D.: Studies on crystal-induced chemotactic factor. I. Requirement for protein synthesis and neutral protease activity. *J. Lab. Clin. Med.* 83:56, 1974.
11. Caner, J. E. Z.: Colchicine inhibition of chemotaxis. *Arthritis Rheum.* 8:757, 1965.
12. Pekin, T. J., Jr., and Zvaifler, N. J.: Hemolytic complement in synovial fluid. *J. Clin. Invest.* 43:1372, 1964.
13. Townes, A. S., and Sowa, J. M.: Complement in synovial fluid. *Johns Hopkins Med. J.* 127:23, 1970.
14. Mowat, A. G., and Baum, J.: Chemotaxis of polymorphonuclear leukocytes from patients with diabetes mellitus. *N. Engl. J. Med.* 284:621, 1971.
15. Ward, P. A., and Becker, E. L.: Potassium reversible inhibition of leukotaxis by ouabain. *Life Sci.* 9:355, 1970.
16. Mowat, A. G., and Baum, J.: *Unpublished observations.*
17. Mowat, A. G., and Baum, J.: Polymorphonuclear leukocyte chemotaxis in patients with bacterial infections. *Br. Med. J.* 3:617, 1971.
18. Baum, J., Cestero, R. V. M., and Freeman, R. B.: *Unpublished observations.*
19. Zivkovic, M., and Baum, J.: *Unpublished observations.*
20. Zivkovic, M., and Baum, J.: Chemotaxis in malignant diseases. *Submitted for publication.*
21. Leddy, J. P., Frank, M. M., Gaither, T., Baum, J., and Klemperer, M. R.: Hereditary deficiency of the sixth component of complement in man. I. Immunochemical, biologic and family studies. *J. Clin. Invest.* 53:218, 1974.
22. Snyderman, R., Phillips, J., and Mergenhagen, S. E.: Polymorphonuclear leukocyte chemotactic activity in rabbit serum and guinea pig serum treated with immune complexes: Evidence for C5a as the major chemotactic factor. *Infect. Immun.* 1:521, 1970.
23. Leddy, J. P., Griggs, R. C., Klemperer, M. R., and Frank, M. M.: Hereditary complement (C3) deficiency with dermatomyositis. *Submitted for publication.*
24. Rosenfeld, S., Leddy, J., and Baum, J.: *Unpublished observations.*

DISCUSSION

David: Which is the temperature in Fig. 2?

Baum: The dotted line is temperature. It was of interest that most of the infections occurred in these patients while chemotaxis was low. Chemotaxis improved in the autumn, but in the winter, as the temperature started to fall, it started to drop. In the last few, the chemotaxis is coming up to the earlier range even though the temperature has continued to drop in that period.

Miller: Do you have a comparable group of normals in the same period?

Baum: No, I don't. We have looked at the patients as their own controls during this study.

Becker: There are ways of comparing time series of this kind. Have you compared these two time series to see whether there is any statistical correlation?

Baum: We ran a correlation coefficient on the data through the summer and autumn and the p value was 0.02.

Snyderman: Did you have inhouse patients that weren't exposed to ambient temperature?

Baum: No, we didn't. This was an ambulatory chronic dialysis program and all the patients came in for dialysis. Each of the points represents from three to four patients. The whole group is composed of 16 patients whom we have been able to follow all the way through. We have also, with John Leddy, looked at some patients with complement deficiencies, and we found normal chemotaxis in the C2- and C6-deficient patients. The C5 patient is abnormal and it is interesting that the abnormality was more apparent when we incubated her serum with aggregated gammaglobulin G than with endotoxin.

Frank: Wasn't it stated that the patient has a zero C5 level?

Baum: Yes. Her sister has about a 1 percent C5 level, and her chemotaxis is closer to normal.

Frank: I have actually seen some of the C5 data of John Leddy's although I have never run any titrations. He has performed these titrations in several ways. The patient has no antigenic C5. The patient's whole complement titer (CH_{50}) is zero, and the way they picked up the deficiency originally was the patient had no C5 with an antibody to C5.

Gallin: How long did you activate the C2-deficient serum to get the abnormal results? When we did kinetic studies of the activation of C2-deficient serum outside the Boyden chamber, we noted an abnormality in the kinetics of formation of chemotactic activity. However, after 1 hour of activation, chemotaxis was normal, presumably due to normal C5a formation with the intact alternate complement pathway (Gallin, J. I.: Radioassay of granulocyte chemotaxis: Studies of human granulocytes and chemotactic factors. In Sorkin, E. (ed.): *Chemotaxis, Its Biology and Biochemistry.* Karger, Basel, *in press*). How did you generate chemotactic activity in your studies?

Baum: We ran it for the full 3 hours in our system. In your method it was slower with the endotoxin, also.

Frank: You activate in the chamber, don't you?

Baum: Yes.

Frank: This represents a major difference between your technique and that of Dr. Gallin's.

Baum: We have looked at the chemotactic factors from the sera of these chronic hemodialysis patients and they seem to be normal. There are some who are low but in this group of experiments we are using the same control. This control has low chemotaxis. All of these samples—we will get three samples on each patient at different times—are run with one individual and his blood is used each time.

Klebanoff: Did these patients have azotemia?

Baum: Yes, to some degree.

Klebanoff: In the animal model that Bob Clark studied, decreased chemotactic factor generation in serum could be correlated with the degree of azotemia (Clark et al., *J. Infect. Dis.* 126:460, 1972).

Baum: No, I can't correlate it, not in these people. Table 4 is pretty much a summary of some of the information that we found over the years. Abnormal chemotaxis was found in the rheumatoid arthritics, Felty's syndrome, diabetes, acute bacterial infection (in chronic infection they seemed to return to a normal state), and in patients with carcinomas with a poor prognosis. We did not find any deficiency with colchicine or corticosteroids, although we recently found something interesting on the corticosteroids working with Dr. Jacob Nussbacher. He is giving a large dose of corticosteroids to normal individuals. To increase peripheral polymorphonuclear leukocytes, we have looked at chemotaxis in some of these people after they have gotten a single large dose of steroids. They have completely normal chemotaxis. However, the random migration of their cells goes up for a few days after they get the steroids. Perhaps the new population of younger cells being pushed out of the bone marrow are more active. We will do some more before I am really sure of that result. Table 5 shows you what we think may be some of the mechanisms involved. If you take normal cells and feed them rheumatoid factor complexes you go into the abnormal state. In the diabetics, their cells start out abnormally, but then added insulin plus glucose returns this group to normal. There are a number of different mechanisms which we have found in clinical disease related to abnormalities in chemotaxis and also improvement in chemotaxis.

Bellanti: Were the leukocytes obtained from patients with diabetes in a state of metabolic balance?

Baum: Yes.

Bellanti: Were they taking sulfonylurea drugs?

Baum: Some were taking sulfonylurea and some insulin and we could find no difference. We also checked their blood insulin and glucose levels, which were normal.

Bellanti: Were the arthritis patients receiving steroids?

Baum: Some of the arthritis patients were on steroids. Some were on aspirin. And again we tried to see if there was any relationship and we could find none. As far as steroids go, we found that if you put steroids in the chamber you didn't get any change in chemotaxis. We had a very ill patient with SLE and a very ill patient with rheumatoid arthritis who were immediately put on large doses of steroids, and their chemotaxis, after a week, came back up to normal.

Bellanti: Did you examine any patients with juvenile rheumatoid arthritis?

Baum: Yes, and they acted the way the adults did. They tend more toward normal than the adults.

Snyderman: In your normal control your value is 540 plus or minus 297. What is that 297? Is that a standard error?

Baum: No, one standard deviation.

Klebanoff: Can I ask you a philosophical question? In the paper on SLE and Felty's syndrome (*Immun. Commun.* 1:39, 1972) you reported that the leukocytes of 13 patients with lupus had a mean chemotactic activity which was not significantly different from normal, yet four of these patients had values which were outside of the normal range. Is it better to treat the patients as a group and say that leukocytes in lupus have normal chemotactic activity, or is it better to say that some patients with lupus have defective chemotactic activity?

Baum: When we got those patients at other times, we'd get them more toward the normal range. I gave the extreme for the values we had. But on a repeat of some of those people they were normal.

Hill: I'd like to point out that we also have studied 30 patients with diabetes mellitus and found approximately one-third of them did have depressed chemotaxis and it could be corrected with insulin. I'd like also to make a comment about your patients with bacterial infections. We first studied cystic fibrosis patients like Dr. Snyderman did and found there was remarkably increased chemotaxis when they had active infection. We then went on to the patients I showed you with streptococcal skin lesions and found again chemotaxis was enhanced. I have a group of patients with systemic bacterial infection, including 25 patients who have the other infections. The chemotactic indexes of these patients, tested before suppression of infection by antibiotics, were markedly elevated. And as therapy progressed and the patients began to respond clinically, the chemotactic activity of the PMN of the vast majority of them came back down within normal ranges. I question whether some of your patients might have been less acute, and whether some might have been treated with antibiotics prior to testing.

Baum: I don't know what the discrepancy would be because we did follow some patients, and they did return to normal. We had patients with acute pneumonia. The patients with acute disease we got out of the emergency room, so we got them before they were started on any kind of therapy.

Hill: One-half of our patients were tested before they had any antibiotics. One-half had been treated, but none for more than 48 hours. I would like to point out that our patients were younger than yours.

Baum: Yes, most of our patients were old and some were definitely elderly.

The Phagocytic Cell in Host Resistance, edited
by Joseph A. Bellanti and Delbert H. Dayton.
Raven Press, New York © 1975.

Developmental Maturation of Human Neutrophil Motility and Its Relationship to Membrane Deformability

Michael E. Miller

Department of Pediatrics, Charles R. Drew Postgraduate Medical School, Los Angeles, California 90059

Consideration of developmental aspects of leukocyte function is a particularly appropriate concluding section for this volume. First, major recent advances have occurred in our understanding of the inflammatory response of neonates. These include recognition of the deficiencies in *both* the humoral and cellular components of polymorphonuclear leukocyte (PMN) ingestion and movement. Second, the neonatal PMN provides an accessible and appropriate model for in depth study of the newly recognized abnormalities of leukocyte mobility. In the truest sense, understanding of the functional maturation of the neonatal PMN may be expected to yield significant insight into PMN activity in the normal inflammatory process.

This summary is divided into three sections: a very brief review of the known humoral and cellular abnormalities of neonatal PMN activity (1, 2); a summary of clinical and laboratory data demonstrating two (2) distinct mechanisms by which human PMN's move—*directed* migration or chemotaxis, and *nondirected* or random migration; and (3) characterization of the movement defect of neonatal PMN's and description of a recently applied method—membrane deformability—in our laboratory to the study of neonatal PMN's. The method has applicability to any PMN preparation, and thus appears to have significant utility in the study of neutrophil movement.

STUDIES OF NEUTROPHIL FUNCTION IN NEONATES—HUMORAL AND CELLULAR FACTORS

Humoral Factors

Opsonic activity of sera from term and premature human infants has been studied by a number of investigators. Although a wide range of methodologic differences exists, the overwhelming number of these studies demonstrates deficient opsonic activity of neonatal sera, being most marked in prematures. The nature of the opsonic deficiency is, at present, unclear although roles for a number of serum factors have been proposed. These include IgM (3), IgG (4), C3 (5), C5 (6), and proteins of the alternate pathway (7, 8).

Bactericidal activity against a variety of microorganisms, particularly Gram negatives, has been found deficient by a number of workers. The nature of these deficiencies appears to involve IgM and portions of the complement system (3, 9), although full understanding is not yet at hand.

Previous studies from this laboratory have demonstrated deficiencies in both the humoral and cellular components of the neonatal chemotactic response (10). Generation of chemotactic activity from neonatal sera incubated with preformed antigen-antibody complexes is significantly decreased in comparison with yields from similarly tested adult sera. The nature of the defect is not clear.

Cellular Factors

Conflicting data exist in phagocytosis. A number of investigators have found normal phagocytic activity in neonatal PMN's. Under certain experimental conditions, however, such as restricting the concentration of opsonins, neonatal phagocytes show significantly decreased phagocytic activity than adult PMN's (11, 12). *In vivo* support has been provided by Forman and Stiehm (4), who found that PMN's from six of nine term infants with various underlying clinical disorders were deficient in phagocytosis.

There have been many studies in bactericidal activities. All but a few have demonstrated no difference between bactericidal activities in neonatal and adult PMN's. The many methodologic variables make it difficult to be sure, however, on this subject.

In studies of metabolic activities, the problems are even more apparent than in the study of bactericidal activities. Among the conclusions that have been proposed by various investigators are (a) decreased HMP shunt activity following phagocytosis (13, 14); (b) increased O_2 consumption in resting neonatal PMN's, but normal increase in oxygen consumption and glucose utilization (15); (c) increased (15), decreased (16), and normal reduction of NBT dye (5). Rather than attempt to establish one of these studies as being correct to the exclusion of the others, it should be recognized that the differences are probably explained by variation in the conditions of the assays, particularly the time of the assays and the time of sampling of the NBT dye reduction. Bellanti and co-workers (16) suggested that activity of PMN glucose-6-phosphate dehydrogenase (G-6-PD) decays at a significantly greater rate in neonatal than in adult PMN's. They also found a decrease of G-6-PD and NBT reduction during the first 6 months of life, followed by a continued increase with age.

CHEMOTAXIS AND RANDOM MOBILITY—THEIR CLINICAL AND BIOLOGIC DIFFERENTIATION

Recently described disorders of neutrophil movement from our laboratory involve deficiencies of two types of neutrophil movement, i.e., directed migration (chemotaxis) and nondirected migration (random mobility). In the first of these disorders, the "lazy leukocyte syndrome" (17), two unrelated patients (a 4-year-old boy and a 3-year-old girl) were studied. Despite an entirely normal bone marrow examination, each child had a marked peripheral neutropenia with absolute PMN counts as low as 150 to 400 PMN's/cc. The patients were, however, unable to mobilize this apparently normal store of neutrophils to the peripheral blood stream as demonstrated by: stimulation of "marginal pool," or extra-marrow neutrophils through administration of epinephrine yielded no effective increase in circulating PMN; stimulation of marrow pool neutrophils by administration of endotoxin yielded no effective increase in circulating PMN; and *in vivo* inflammatory response as measured by the inflammatory cycle method (18) yielded no PMN. The nature of their defect was ultimately shown to involve a primary defect of cell movement involving both chemotaxis and random tube migration. By contrast, *in vitro* phagocytic and bactericidal activities of the PMN were normal. It thus appeared that a "cause and effect" relationship was established, i.e., the defect in cell movement was reflected by the abnormal epinephrine, endotoxin, and skin window responses, and the patients' symptoms were presumably related to their inability to mobilize PMN to the site of infection.

Upon the characterization of a second primary abnormality of PMN movement, however, these relationships seemed less clear (19). Two families were studied, in one family a brother and sister being involved and in the other an 11-year-old girl. All three patients had an unusual clinical course characterized by congenital ichthyosis and recurrent trichophyton rubrum infections. Neutrophil counts were relatively normal as were bone marrow examinations. PMN from the patients were normal in phagocytic and bactericidal activities but, as in the "lazy leukocyte syndrome," were deficient in chemotactic activity. Unlike the "lazy leukocyte syndrome," however, the measurement of random mobility was normal as was stimulation of neutrophils by epinephrine, endotoxin, or Rebuck window. The defect appeared to be familial as revealed by finding the same abnormalities of chemotaxis but *normal random mobility* in PMN from the fathers. These clinical observations suggested, therefore, that random mobility and chemotaxis might involve separate mechanisms or functions of neutrophil movement. The groups of experiments now summarized were undertaken to examine this hypothesis. Much of the previous confusion on this differentiation derives from the fact that the several methods used by investigators to measure "random" movement have not been measuring the same phenomena. The data now summarized show that "random migration," as assayed by the method of capillary tube movement, appears to measure a different PMN activity than random mobility as assayed by migration through a micropore filter. In these experiments human, peripheral blood PMN have been studied in three assay systems.

Chemotaxis has been studied by a previously described modification of the Boyden assay (18). Washed suspension of 5 $\times$ 10^6 PMN in medium 1066 with 10% heat-inactivated fetal calf serum was placed in the upper portion of a Sykes-Moore tissue culture chamber and separated from a source of chemotactically active material by a 3-μm pore size filter. The chemotactically active materials were generated by the addition of preformed antigen-antibody complexes to fresh, normal human serum. Following a 3-hr incubation period at 37°C, the filters were removed, stained, and the average number of PMN per high power field reaching the lowermost portion of the filter determined.

In the second assay, random migration by the filter method was studied by a modification of the method of Carruthers (20). The assays were performed in the same Sykes-Moore chambers as above, but the PMN's were prepared in concentrations of 5×10^6 PMN/cc and placed over an 8-μm, instead of a 3-μm, filter. Concentrations of buffer, plasma, or serum were identical on both sides of the filter. In other words, unlike the chemotactic assay, no gradient was present.

Random migration in *capillary tubes* was measured by a previously described modification of the method of Ketchel and Favour (18, 21). Washed plasma-free suspensions of 10^7 PMN/cc in 0.1% human albumin were placed in siliconized, microhematocrit tubes placed upon a microscope stage which was turned to the vertical position, thus placing the tubes in an upright position, like a sedimentation rate preparation. The distance migrated upward by the leading cells in the field after a 3-hr incubation period at room temperature was then measured with an ocular micrometer. The optics of the system were improved remarkably by placing the tubes in a chamber constructed out of capillary tubes sandwiched between two microscope slides. The chamber was filled with immersion oil and random migration tubes placed in the chamber. This modification permitted accurate observation of the cells within the tubes.

Effects of a variety of additive materials upon each of the three assays were then compared. The basic experimental protocol was as follows: normal PMN were incubated at 37°C for 30 min at constant rotation in the presence of a particular additive. The cells were then washed, resuspended as described, and tested in each of the three assays. Incubations in the following agents were compared.

Dinitrophenol in concentrations of 10^{-3}, 10^{-5}, and 10^{-9}M.
Potassium cyanide in concentrations of 10^{-3}, 10^{-5}, and 10^{-7}M.
Sodium fluoride in concentrations of 2×10^{-3}, 2×10^{-5}, and 10^{-7}M.
Iodoacetate in concentrations of 10^{-3}, 10^{-5}, and 10^{-9}M.
Mitomycin C at a concentration of 25 μg/ml.
Sodium EDTA at a concentration of 1 mg/ml.
Deoxyglucose in concentrations of 6×10^{-2}, 6×10^{-3} and 6×10^{-4}M.
Chemotactic factors generated as described for the chemotactic assay.

The results of these experiments are summarized in Table 1. A significant decrease following incubation in a particular additive is recorded only when the decrease exceeds by at least 2 SD the main value for that particular assay. Incubations with glycolytic inhibitors such as sodium fluoride or iodoacetate effected comparable decreases upon tube migration. By contrast, incubations with inhibitors of oxidative metabolism such as dinitrophenol or potassium cyanide had no effect on any of the three assays. PMN's which had been incubated in the presence of mitomycin C, sodium EDTA, deoxyglucose, or chemotactically active materials all showed markedly diminished chemotaxis and chamber migration but retained normal tube migration.

Thus, PMN's incubated in a wide variety of agents showed similar decreases of chemotaxis and random filter migration but retained normal random *tube* migration.

TABLE 1. *Comparative effects upon chemotaxis, random chamber migration, and random tube migration*

Agent	Chemotaxis	Chamber	Tube
Dinitrophenol	N	N	N
Potassium cyanide	N	N	N
Sodium fluoride	D	D	N
Iodoacetate	D	D	N
Mitomycin C	D	D	N
Sodium EDTA	D	D	N
Deoxyglucose	D	D	N
Chemotactic factors	D	D	N

N = Normal; D = Decreased by at least 2 SD from the mean value for each particular assay.

Several explanations merit consideration in the interpretation of this data. First, it might be argued that the capillary tube assay is simply less sensitive than either of the filter assays. This, however, can effectively be ruled out: (a) effects of a variety of agents, including temperature and sodium arsenite upon each of the three assays, are essentially identical; (b) PMN's which have been passaged through a Dow hollow fiber renal dialysis coil are rendered totally deficient in tube mobility yet retain significant chemotactic activity (22); and (c) several patients have been described whose PMN's show a *selective* defect in tube mobility with normal chemotaxis (23). Second, it might be argued that tube migration is simply an artifact which does not require living cells. This is easily ruled out. PMN's that have been killed by incubation in high concentrations of such agents as Wright's stain or EDTA lose all activity in each of the assays.

The interpretation that chamber migration and tube migration involve separable mechanisms of cell function is further supported by the deformability data summarized in the next section. Although a highly sensitive filter assay may enable differentiation of directed and nondirected movement (24), random filter movement may be masked by the chemotactic response (25). The need to perform both tube and filter assays of random mobility is indicated by the findings of normal tube mobility but abnormal random filter mobility in the Chediak-Higashi patients (26).

DEVELOPMENTAL ASPECTS OF PMN MOVEMENT AND THE SIGNIFICANCE OF MEMBRANE DEFORMABILITY

PMN's from neonates have been studied by the assay systems described above (10). The data have demonstrated highly significant differences in both humoral and cellular aspects of movement. Fresh sera from neonates when incubated with preformed antigen-antibody complexes yield significantly less chemotactic activity than generated from similarly treated adult sera toward control human PMN's. The nature of humoral deficiency(ies) or neonatal sera is presently unclear and will not be further discussed here, as the focus of this presentation is upon cellular events. PMN's from normal human neonates show significantly *decreased chemotaxis* but *normal* tube mobility.

Preliminary characterization of the movement defect of neonatal PMN's has been provided in our laboratory through the study of membrane deformability, as modified from the assay of Weed and co-workers (27).

Human PMN's have been prepared in suspension in a planer glass chamber and observed through a high-power light microscope with a long distance working objective (6.5 mm). Through the use of a micro-manipulator, individual PMN's have been directed to the orifice of small pore glass pipettes (internal diameter 3 to 5 μ). Upon application of carefully measured negative pressure to the pipette, the "deformability" of the PMN membrane is expressed as the amount of negative pressure required to draw the cell into the pipette. This assay is highly reproducible and has permitted the following observations: (a) PMN's treated with glycolytic inhibitors such as iodoacetate (10^{-3}M) or NaF (2×10^{-3}M) show significant *decreases* in deformability, i.e., become more rigid; (b) PMN's treated with trypsin also show decreased deformability; (c) treatment with cyclic 3,5-AMP has relatively little effect upon deformability, whereas treatment with ATP decreased deformability.

The studies thus demonstrate that membrane deformability of PMN's reflects metabolic activity of the cell; a general correlation appears between membrane deformability and chemotaxis, but not random mobility of PMN's, but differs in the effect of various nucleotides upon deformability and chemotaxis. The continued application of this assay appears extremely valuable in the characterization of PMN movement.

In order to further characterize the nature of neonatal PMN movement, membrane deformability has been studied. The "deformability" of the neonatal PMN was compared with that of adult PMN's. Neonatal PMN's showed markedly *decreased membrane deformability* over control PMN's—i.e., were much more rigid cells. The finding of a functional abnormality of the neonatal PMN membrane is unique and has major significance. Since neonatal PMN's are deficient in chemotaxis but normal in random mobility, membrane deformability may play a role in chemotaxis. This is supported by the observation that iodoacetate, NaF, and deoxyglucose, agents which decrease membrane deformability, also selectively inhibit chemotaxis. PMN membrane deformability is an active process. The deformability defect here may, therefore, reflect metabolic immaturity of the neonatal PMN.

REFERENCES

1. Miller, M. E.: Innate immunity. In Stiehm, E. R., and Fulginiti, V. A. (eds.): *Immunologic Disorder in Infants and Children.* W. B. Saunders & Co., Philadelphia. 1973.
2. Miller, M. E., and Stiehm, E. R.: Phagocytic, opsonic, and gamma globulin studies in newborns (medical progress). *Calif. Med.* 119:43, 1973.
3. Gitlin, D., Rosen, F. S., and Michael, J. G.: Transient 19S gamma-deficiency in the newborn infant and its significance. *Pediatrics* 31:197, 1963.
4. Forman, M. L., and Stiehm, E. R.: Impaired opsonic activity but normal phagocytosis in low-birth-weight infants. *N. Engl. J. Med.* 281:926, 1969.
5. McCracken, G. H., and Eichenwald, H. F.: Leukocyte function and the development of opsonic and complement activity in the neonate. *Am. J. Dis. Child.* 121:120, 1971.
6. Miller, M. E.: Demonstration and replacement of a functional defect of the fifth component of complement in newborn serum—A major tool in the therapy of neonatal septicemia (abstract). *Soc. Ped. Rec.* p. 31, 1971.
7. Koch, F., Schultze, H. E., and Schwick, G.: Komplementfaktoren and properdin beim gesunden saugling in ersten lebensjahr. *Klin. Wochenschrift.* 36:17, 1958.
8. Stossel, T. P., Alper, C. A., and Rosen, F. S.: Opsonic activity in the newborn: Role of properdin. *Pediatrics* 52:134, 1973.
9. Dossett, J. H., William, R. C., Jr., and Quie, P. G.: Studies on interaction of bacteria, serum factors and polymorphonuclear leukocytes in mothers and newborns. *Pediatrics* 44:49, 1969.
10. Miller, M. E.: Chemotactic function in the human neonate—Humoral and cellular aspects. *Pediatr. Res.* 5:487, 1971.
11. Miller, M. E.: Phagocytosis in the newborn infant—Humoral and cellular factors. *J. Pediatr.* 74:255, 1969.
12. Matoth, Y.: Phagocytic and ameboid activities of the leukocytes in the newborn infant. *Pediatrics* 9:748–754, 1952.
13. Coen, R., Grush, O., and Kauder, E.: Studies of bactericidal activity and metabolism of the leukocyte in full-term neonates. *J. Pediatr.* 75:400, 1969.
14. Donnell, G. N., Ng, W. G., Hodgman, J. E., et al.: Galactose metabolism in the newborn infant. *Pediatrics* 39:829, 1967.
15. Park, B. H., Holmes, B., and Good, R. A.: Metabolic activities in leukocytes of newborn infants. *J. Pediatr.* 76:237, 1970.
16. Bellanti, J. A., Cantz, B. E., Maybee, D. A., et al.: Defective phagocytosis by newborn leucocytes: A defect similar to that in chronic granulomatous disease? (abstract). *Pediatr. Res.* 3:376, 1969.
17. Miller, M. E., Oski, F. A., and Harris, M. B.: The lazy leukocyte syndrome. A new disorder of neutrophil function. *Lancet* 1:665, 1971.
18. Rebuck, J. W., and Crowley, J. H.: A method of studying leukocyte functions *in vitro. Ann. N. Y. Acad. Sci.* 59:757–805, 1955.
19. Miller, M. E., Koblenzer, P. J., and Schonauer, T.: A new familial defect of neutrophil movement. *J. Lab. Clin. Med.* 82:1–8, 1973.
20. Carruthers, B. M.: Leukocyte motility. I. Method of study, normal variation, effect of physical alterations in environment, and effect of iodoacetate. *Can. J. Physiol. Pharmacol.* 44:475, 1966.
21. Ketchel, M. M., and Favour, C. B.: The acceleration and inhibition of migration of human leucocytes *in vitro* by plasma protein fractions. *J. Exp. Med.* 101:647, 1955.
22. Henderson, L. W., Miller, M. E., Hamilton, R. W., and Norman, M.: Polymorph random mobility, dialysis leukopenia and the control of peripheral white blood cell levels. *Submitted for publication.*
23. Miller, M. E.: Leukocyte movement—*In vitro* and *in vivo* correlates. *J. Pediatr.* 83:1104, 1973.
24. Zigmond, S. H., and Hirsch, J. G.: Leukocyte locomotion and chemotaxis. New methods for evaluation, and demonstration of a cell-derived chemotactic factor. *J. Exp. Med.* 137:387, 1973.
25. Keller, H. V., and Sorkin, E.: Studies on chemotaxis. X. Inhibition of chemotaxis of neutrophil polymorphonuclear leucocytes. *Int. Arch. Allergy* 34:513, 1968.

26. Clark, R. A., and Kimball, H. R.: Defective granulocyte chemotaxis in the Chediak-Higashi syndrome. *J. Clin. Invest.* 50:2645, 1971.
27. Weed, R. I., La Celle, P. L., and Merrill, E. W.: Metabolic dependence of red cell membrane deformability. *J. Clin. Invest.* 48:795, 1969.

DISCUSSION

Becker: Talking about chemotaxis or spontaneous motility, one is referring to stimulated movement on the one hand, and unstimulated or apparently unstimulated movement on the other. You have, I think, demonstrated that there are at least two forms of unstimulated movement. As I made reference to in my presentation, one can find evidences of these two mechanisms of unstimulated movement in the Boyden chamber. The Boyden chamber, however, allows one of these forms of unstimulated movement, the cation dependent form, to manifest itself. From your results, it would appear that unstimulated movement in the Boyden chamber has a greater requirement for metabolic energy than that which is measured in your method using the capillary tube assay.

I think the work you have presented and the work that Dr. Gallin has quoted mean that in order to get a reasonably complete idea of the capacities of the neutrophil in regard to movement, one should run all three of these assays: that for stimulated movement as measured in one or another form of the Boyden chamber assay, and, in regard to the unstimulated movement, one should use both the Boyden chamber and the unstimulated movement of your capillary tube technique. The necessity for doing this is borne out by the reports of cases in which there are differences in the responses of cells to each form of these assays.

The second point that I want to make is that someone asked me whether I had tested the cells for the effect of deactivation in our unstimulated assay in the chemotaxis chamber, and I said no. But it was obvious from the hypothesis that I presented that these cells should show less unstimulated movement. In fact, this is precisely what you have demonstrated. And I think this is something that I definitely am going to have to follow up to really confirm and more firmly establish.

Miller: Thank you. I would agree with everything you said. I have modified my feeling about the filter assay, and now feel that the random filter assay is a useful clinical parameter. It is clear that random filter movement occurs even when chemotaxis is going on in the inner chamber. Certainly in the work Dr. Gallin presented, I think it is obvious that there are also clinical situations in which the random filter movement may show something that the capillary tube does not. I can only echo what you said. And I think the important thing with these assays is really to utilize the information from each of these parameters in attempting to arrive at meaningful hypotheses.

Ward: It is really remarkable that some of these inhibitors in these huge concentrations should absolutely shut off any pathway of energy production, and yet in the capillary tube technique permit movement in circumstances in which it would seem essential to have some energy expenditure. Do you have any explanation for this?

Miller: Not yet. I can only note that tube mobility does appear to be an energy-dependent process. First, temperature does decrease the capillary tube movement. Although we have not done correlative metabolic studies with running this at 4 degrees centigrade, it is likely that alterations in metabolic state have occurred. In addition, there is another set of data we have found with which perhaps somebody here can help me. If you take sodium arsenite and incubate these cells, they do show an appreciable drop in the capillary tube as well as the other two assays. That is the only metabolic inhibitor we have used to date in which we have found any effect. Strangely, the effect only appears when the cells are studied in the presence of plasma. As you will recall, the studies I reported were run in a plasma-free situation, and only when the sodium arsenite is put in plasma is that effect seen.

Becker: I think these results of yours are astonishing with respect to the lack of any apparent requirement for any form of metabolic energy. I think to really understand these results you would have to measure, say, ATP levels in your cell. It is not particularly difficult. And you would have to correlate this with your several assays.

Klebanoff: Would you review what is above and below the filter in the filter random motility test? Is it possible that the cells are stimulated by some chemotactic agent, but that there is no directional movement because of the absence of a gradient?

Miller: We have done the random filter migration in a variety of ways. You can do it, for example, by putting serum on either side of the filter in nongradient fashion. You can do it by putting the human albumin in buffer. Fetal calf serum, if it is put in, is put in on either side. As Dr. Becker suggested, you can certainly increase the random chamber migration by a number of factors which do not increase chemotaxis. There is, however, either an equivalent amount of material on either side, or nothing for chemotactic stimulus. The fetal calf serum, of course, is a problem of this field, and I was encouraged by what Baum and Hill said. Perhaps one has a way with a cytocentrifuge or some of the variations they have indicated to get rid of the fetal calf serum, which is always a problem in these assays.

Holmes-Gray: I notice you use a hematocrit tube for the tube assay. Does everyone use a tube with a heparin in it?

Miller: That touches upon how the cells really move in the tube. The issue really is whether this is glass adhesiveness and the cells are actually crawling up the side of the tube, or whether this is indeed a situation of cells moving in fluid up the tube. There are a number of conditions that have been used for the assay. We work in plasma-free, heparinized tubes in order to minimize the noncellular effects. However, this is an extremely important aspect which, I think, can be approached in a number of ways. One of the simplest approaches is by trying different diameter tubes, the idea being that one would get a different pattern of cell response as the tube diameter changed if it was, indeed, glass adhesiveness.

Hill: Have you tried the tube at different angles?

Miller: Yes, we have tried that, and you can turn the tube almost to the horizontal and not get any difference. If you look on the sides of the tube, it looks like the distribution of cells, in terms of how high they go, is approximately the same, which I would like to interpret as further evidence that it is not glass adhesiveness. There are data in the literature that say it is glass adhesiveness. Our observations, however, would suggest it isn't. Further, the patients of Paul Edelson showed normal nylon column adhesiveness of their neutrophils. If nylon and glass column adhesiveness measure the same neutrophil activity, that would also support the fact that cells which adhere normally to glass might not move normally in the capillary tube.

Alper: You showed that cells are incubated in EDTA and they cease to have random movement. Have you looked at those cells after rewashing and resuspension in physiologic buffer?

Miller: They are normal in the tube, but those cells show defects in the chamber EDTA.

Alper: I meant high concentrations of EDTA.

Miller: No, the high concentrations we have used are killing the cells.

Alper: But what happens if you resuspend them in physiologic buffer?

Miller: They don't work. We have done it both ways.

Ward: If you look at the capillary tube migration that is used in migration-inhibition assays, will this measure the same sort of thing as your capillary tube assay?

Miller: I don't know that. And I think the method Dr. Hill has used and modified from the method of McCall is really another parameter that ought to be included. If one really wants to comprehensively and genuinely find differences, I think there ought to be a comparison of that method with this method to see if it is doing the same thing.

Snyderman: I have gotten confused in terms of the glass-adhesiveness point. What exactly are the cells migrating on? I would have assumed they were migrating up the side of the glass inside the capillary tube. Are you saying this is not what happens?

Miller: Conceptually, if one thinks about random motility as a crawling-type movement, the idea would be they are migrating randomly in solution. Bryant and co-workers suggested that this was glass adhesiveness. In their system, run in serum, normal controls fell into two categories they called fast and slow reactors. Serum from the fast reactors resulted in a much greater degree of migration in the capillary tube. Assuming that serum was associated with and necessary for adhesion of polymorphs to glass, they postulated this was indeed glass adhesiveness. The evidence against that is the fact that we are using plasma-free, serum-free suspensions, and found no variation at all in terms of normal controls. In other words, we can't find the difference between one group of plasmas and another group of plasmas. The tubes are siliconized. Further, there is the clinical evidence of Edelson and co-workers of two patients who have an abnormal tube migration, yet whose PMN's adhere normally to nylon columns. If the nylon-glass column adherence is the same thing, that is a little support for the idea that this is not glass adhesiveness. But I don't know.

Snyderman: In terms of the time they migrate, how far do they move, let's say, in 1 hour or so?

Miller: In 1 hour you tend still to have fairly packed concentrations. We usually read these at about 3 hours. The data we get are comparable with what everybody else has gotten with this kind of assay. It is difficult to give you a linear distance because one of the problems with this kind of assay is you look in a single plane and you've got cells that are moving randomly—the distance out they go may not be a valid measurement at all. But we get about the same range as reported in the literature. If you carry it out to 24 hours, there is not an appreciable difference.

Frank: In terms of the glass adhesiveness, after the period of cell migration you might simply blow out the contents of the tube. Do the cells adhere to the tube walls or are they removed with the contents?

Miller: We haven't done that. That's a nice thought. Of course, if they were stuck, I wouldn't say that it is glass adhesiveness that has caused the movement.

Blaese: Is there any evidence for heterogeneity in the poly population, for example, just as people are talking about nonphagocytic monocytes? Could you be measuring random motility of bands or another subset of cells that are going up the side of the tube?

Miller: We have been very interested in that, and have looked (insofar as one can try) at different poly populations in terms of maturity. Obviously you can't get 100 percent of any of these. There is no real difference that can be seen. We have also studied a family with the Pelger-Huet anomaly with this assay, and their PMN's were perfectly normal. We have no evidence that there are subpopulations, but I don't think it is something that should be discarded.

Karnovsky: Dr. Ward mentioned the high inhibitor concentrations and the fact that there were sometimes no effects. But actually you had effects at extraordinarily low concentrations of fluoride, I think, down to 10^{-5} molar. That could hardly have been interference with energy metabolism where the standard concentration is about two times 10^{-2} molar. I am puzzled since I have never used any of these methods, and I have no critical ability to evaluate what is happening, except to wonder why there is all this excitement about looking at two possibly totally different phenomena. One might be described as crawling in little spaces, and one as swimming in an easy, lazy way, buffered by the hydrodynamic forces that are keeping the cells partially suspended. Would you like to explain to a simple chemist why we should be concerned about the differences between the capillary tube method and the method where you see random movement into these little pores?

Miller: I'll try to state at least why I feel it's important. The question of neutrophil homeostasis, how they get out of the bone marrow, how they get mobilized to appropriate body compartments during various inflammatory stimuli and various requirements of neutrophils obviously requires a mechanism of movement of these neutrophils. It appears that as clinical observations of neutrophil defects are growing, there are separable entities in terms of these types of movement. And it also appears that a variety of different intermediary factors, serum factors, etc., may affect one versus the other. I think our entire understanding of neutrophil interaction, both in terms of homeostasis, inflammatory response, and interaction with all of the cells in the immune system, may be significantly heightened by further understanding of these mechanisms.

Karnovsky: That is a nice explanation but my real dilemma is: Where are neutrophils ever in a situation comparable to that of your capillary tube situation, which is like that of those sensory-deprivation tanks that they put people in from time to time.

Miller: I don't know if that can be answered except to note that the entire field of *in vitro* assays of neutrophil function, even including killing, raises the same questions of correlation with *in vivo* situations. One can only try to accumulate evidence that is not only supportive, but reasonable, in terms of a cause-and-effect situation. That first entity I described, the lazy leukocyte syndrome, appeared very simple and straightforward. To date, of all the neutrophil movement defects that have been observed in our laboratory and other laboratories, that is really the only one that has had consistent, across-the-board, marked neutropenia, completely abnormal responses to the epinephrine and skin window. What has happened as further abnormalities have been observed is that the correlations have become increasingly complex.

Cohn: One of the questions I had was really whether the capillary tube test that you are using is artifactual. And I wonder if you have just looked at polys on a glass slide in a warm chamber and compared that type of random motion to what you would find in capillary tubes.

Miller: They look very similar, but I really haven't done them side by side.

Cohn: So concentrations of inhibitors which modify capillary tubes will also have a similar effect?

Miller: I haven't really carried out the whole range of studies: the effect of killing the cells—the killing, the temperature effect, the arsenite effect, plus that Dow filter study. For example, those neutrophils don't show normal random movement. But they do phagocytize. They chemotax fairly normally, and appear to kill normally. Thus that looks like a selective defect of cells that are not terribly afunctional, yet fail to move in the capillary tube.

Gallin: It was not quite clear in my mind what concentration of EDTA you used to get inhibition of random locomotion. Our group has studied the effects of four different chelators (oxylate, citrate, EDTA, and EGTA) on capillary tube random motility (Patten, E., Gallin, J. I., Clark, R. A., and Kimball, H. R.: Effects of cell concentration and various anticoagulants on neutrophil migration. *Blood* 41:711, 1973). We found inhibition of random movement with the relatively small concentration of these chelators routinely used for the anticoagulation of blood. However, we also found that the inhibition was reversed by addition of calcium and magnesium to the samples with magnesium restoring random movement better than calcium, but both divalent cations were required for an optimal response. I was wondering what are the "high concentrations" of chelators you used for your studies and have you studied the effects of a wide range of concentrations?

Miller: Where we have done the same relative tests, I found complete agreement with the results. The concentrations here are somewhat different in terms of how they affect the cells, because the particular assay we are using does have some differences. In other words, this is a pure poly suspension. The tubes may be different, and there may be a lot of factors that are different, which in terms of small dosage gives inhibition in one assay and not the other. I have not done, in specific answer to your question, a whole range of EDTA concentrations. I have just done normal kinds of anticoagulants.

Gallin: What were those?

Miller: This was 4×10^{-3} molar. You have, I know, observed somewhat different results. I think, however, our two assays have been performed under somewhat different conditions. If you go way up, in terms of effectively adding about as much EDTA as you can without failing to get it into solution, that is the kind of concentration I am talking about when I talk about killing cells. In other words, I am talking about a toxic concentration, the same thing as with Wright's stain. I have no experience with EGTA and the other reagents in these assays. Of interest, if we add serum to these preparations, we observe the same inhibition by EDTA as in your study.

Ward: I would like to state, along the lines of Dr. Cohn's question, that in our experience, if you take polys and submit them to concentrations of iodoacetate of 10^{-2} to 10^{-3} molar, it has a profound effect on these cells. They shrink; they become very small and spherical. And this is why I find it amazing that in the capillary tube technique they can still continue to function.

Miller: Under what conditions? Remember, this is a cell suspension, incubated for 30 minutes and washed. The iodoacetate is not present during the running of the assay.

Ward: We have washed them and then looked at them, and they still are profoundly altered.

Park: Have you tried your random capillary tube technique with monocyte or monocyte-rich preparations?

Miller: No.

The Phagocytic Cell in Host Resistance, edited
by Joseph A. Bellanti and Delbert H. Dayton.
Raven Press, New York © 1975.

Macrophages and the Development of Immunocompetence

R. Michael Blaese

Cellular Immunology Section, Metabolism Branch, National Cancer Institute, National Institutes of Health, Bethesda, Maryland 20014

The time of maturation of the T and B lymphoid cell systems is obviously of central importance in the expression of immunocompetence by the neonate. However, neonates of almost all species are relatively immunodeficient despite wide differences in physiologic maturity and thymic development at birth. We have investigated the role played by macrophages in the development of immunocompetence in three areas: (a) the production of antibody to a variety of antigens, (b) the development of resistance to infection with intracellular microorganisms, such as *Listeria* monocytogenes, and (c) the resistance to induction of specific immunologic tolerance. These studies have demonstrated that immaturity of the macrophage system may be a limiting step in the expression of immunocompetence to many antigenic stimuli during the neonatal period.

METHODS

Litters of Lewis rats of various ages were housed in individual cages with their mothers. Immunization with a variety of antigens with or without addition of various types of adult cells was given subcutaneously into the popliteal area of the left hind leg. The neonates were bled at various times following immunization-cell transfer, and individual serum antibody titers were determined by sensitive microhemolysis, microagglutination, or antigen-binding assays. Antibody-forming cells (AFC) in the spleens of some animals were determined by the agarose-slide modification of the Jerne technique.

RESULTS AND COMMENTS

Timing of Onset of Responsiveness

Neonatal rats of various ages were immunized with one of several antigens and the production of specific antibody was subsequently determined at intervals following immunization. It was found that neonatal rats develop the capacity to produce antibody to these different antigens in a distinct, stepwise sequence (Table 1).

Rats immunized within 18 hr of birth ultimately produced antibody only to

TABLE 1. *Onset of responsiveness to five antigens in neonatal rats*

Age at immunization (days)	*Brucella*[a]	SRBC[b]	BRBC[c]	KLH[d]	SSS_{III}[e]
NB	4.7 ± 0.4	0	0	0	0
1	5.3 ± 0.3	0	0	0	0
2	—	0	0	—	—
3	7.3 ± 0.0	2.9 ± 0.9	0	0	0
4	—	5.4 ± 0.4	0	—	—
7	—	—	0.6 ± 0.6	0	0
10–11	—	—	3.0 ± 0.0	7.7 ± 2	0
14–15	—	—	4.3 ± 0.9	10.4 ± 0.5	4/24
20–22	—	—	—	—	21/30
28	—	—	—	—	16/18

[a] Microagglutination titer ($\log_2$) ± 1 SE 8 days following immunization with 10^9 killed *Brucella* abortus organisms.
[b] Microhemolysin titer ($\log_2$) ± 1 SE 10 days following immunization with 10^8 SRBC.
[c] Microhemolysin titer ($\log_2$) ± 1 SE 10 days following immunization with 10^8 BRBC.
[d] Microagglutination titer ($\log_2$) ± 1 SE to KLH coupled with chromic chloride to Lewis rat RBC measured 14 days after immunization with 1 mg KLH.
[e] Number of responders at 8 days/total number immunized with 0.5 μg SSS_{III} as determined by a modified Farr assay capable of detecting ~30 pg ABC/0.025 ml.

one of the antigens tested, *Brucella* abortus organisms. By 3 days of age, all neonates had acquired the ability to respond to sheep RBC, but not to burro RBC or KLH. Antibody responses to these two antigens occurred only in animals at least 7 to 10 days of age at the time of immunization. Finally, antibody production to type III pneumococcal polysaccharide (SSS_{III}) was found only in rats at least 17 to 21 days of age at immunization.

It is unlikely that this stepwise onset of responsiveness can be explained simply by differences in the sensitivity of the antibody assays for the various antigens since identical techniques were used to detect antibody to antigens with widely differing response patterns. Serum responses were measured because of uncertainty as to the organ location of maximum antibody synthesis in the neonate. In fact, development of AFC (direct PFC) in the spleens of immunized neonates appeared to lag behind the detection of serum antibody to SRBC or BRBC, although the same sequence of appearance was present (Table 2).

The explanation for these findings is not readily apparent. Silverstein and colleagues (1) observed a similar sequential onset of immune responsiveness in the developing lamb fetus. In the lamb, antibody formation to bacteriophage $\phi\chi$ appeared during the first third of fetal life, followed by responsiveness to ferritin, hemocyanin, and ovalbumin. Following birth, responses developed to diphtheria toxoid, *S. typhosa,* and BCG.

Silverstein (2) has argued that these observations must support the germ-line

TABLE 2. *Appearance of antibody forming cells (PFC) in spleens of neonatal rats immunized with SRBC or BRBC*

Age at immunization (days)	PFC/10^7 spleen cells[a]	
	SRBC	BRBC
3	<1	<1
5	<1	<1
10	60	<1
15	175	39
adult	2,700	570

[a] Determined 5 days after (ip) immunization.

theory of the generation of antibody diversity, with the precise sequence of response development having evolved under some form of selective pressure. However, Arrenbrecht (3) concluded from studies of the onset of responses to DNP–KLH and DPN–BGG in mice that differences in the timing of onset of immunoresponsiveness were most likely due to random somatic mutation.

Macrophages and Neonatal Responses

The possibility that these observations may be due, at least in part, to factors unrelated to the generation of antigen-reactive lymphoid cells is suggested by the ability of accessory cells to markedly alter the response pattern observed in the neonate. Argyris (4) observed that neonatal mice would respond much more readily to immunization with SRBC if they had been given adult peritoneal exudate cells (PE) 2 days previously. In our studies, when newborn rats normally unresponsive to SRBC were given antigen mixed with macrophages obtained from adult rats with oil-induced PE, strong antibody responses resulted (Table 3).

Clearly, adult PE cells are capable of inducing antibody responses in these

TABLE 3. *Hemolysin response of newborn rats given antigen with or without adult cells of various types*

Immunization	SRBC hemolysins ($\log_2$)[a]
Saline	0.3 ± 0.3
10^8 SRBC	0.6 ± 0.6
15×10^6 adult PE cells[b]	0.3 ± 0.3
15×10^6 adult PE cells + 10^8 SRBC	8.2 ± 1.0 $p < 0.001$
15×10^6 adult thymocytes + SRBC	0.6 ± 0.4
3×10^6 adult PE lymphocytes + SRBC	0.5 ± 0.5
15×10^6 purified adult macrophages + SRBC	8.0 ± 1.3 $p < 0.001$

[a] Mean ± 1 SE.
[b] PE collected 4 days after ip injection of 10 ml mineral oil.

otherwise unresponsive neonates. However, the oil-induced PE used in these studies contained from 5 to 15% lymphocytes and 5 to 10% granulocytes and mast cells in addition to their 75 to 85% complement of macrophages. In order to prove that the macrophage was the essential cell in producing this neonatal response, a variety of controls were also performed (Table 3). Adult thymocytes given to the neonates in place of the PE cells were completely without effect in augmenting their antibody response. Also, column-purified peritoneal exudate lymphocytes (PEL), given in a number representing the equivalent of a 20% lymphocyte contamination of the whole PE, were also without effect in inducing an anti-SRBC response by the neonates. However, when macrophages purified by their adherence to plastic culture (5) vessels for 48 hr and containing less than 0.2% contaminating lymphocytes were used, again strong antibody production by the neonates was observed. As a final proof that the cells of the neonates themselves were producing the antibody under the influence of the adult macrophages rather than simply providing suitable *in vivo* culture medium for an adoptive transfer of responding cells, the neonates were irradiated before cell transfer and immunization. If the antibody production observed in the previous experiments was due to active production by the transferred cells, then prior irradiation of the host should not abolish this response. If, however, the cells of the neonatal host themselves were producing the antibody with the assistance of the adult macrophages, then irradiation should prevent this response. As shown in Table 4, irradiation of the neonatal rat before cell transfer completely

TABLE 4. *Response to irradiated neonates to cell transfer and immunization*

	SRBC hemolysins (log_2)
2-day-old rats + 10^8 SRBC	2.2 ± 1.0
2-day-old rats + SRBC + adult PE	11.5 ± 0.7 $p < 0.001$
2-day-old rats (750R) + SRBC + adult PE [a]	0

[a] Rats given 750R X-ray treatment 1 day before cell transfer and immunization.

abolished all subsequent antibody formation in response to SRBC given along with adult PE cells.

By a similar series of experiments, adult macrophages also were effective in inducing antibody formation in neonates immunized with BRBC and KLH. Therefore, maturation of the macrophages and the afferent limb of immunity would seem to be an essential and limiting step in the expression of immunocompetence by the neonate, at least as concerns antibody production to these three antigens.

Factors Controlling Macrophage Activation and Maturation

Looking back to Table 1, it is apparent that these neonatal rats are capable of responding to immunization with *Brucella* essentially at the time of birth. Is the antibody response to *Brucella* independent of macrophages, or is there something else special about this antigen that allows an earlier response by the neonate? That is, are *Brucella* organisms capable of inducing "premature" maturation or activation of the macrophages in the neonate so that more efficient antibody production results? To answer this question, SRBC were mixed in the same syringe with *Brucella* organisms and injected into newborn rats. Table 5 shows that, following this mixed immunization, the neonates produced a strong response to SRBC (and, not shown, to BRC and KLH as well). A variety of agents were found to be effective as replacements for adult macrophages in this experimental system. Included among these were endotoxin, pertussis vaccine, BCG, alum, silica, and poly A–poly U, each an effective adjuvant in adult animals as well.

TABLE 5. *Effect of macrophage-activating substances on the anti-SRBC response of newborn rats*

Immunization	SRBC hemolysins ($\log_2$)
10^8 SRBC	0
10^8 SRBC + 10^9 *Brucella* vaccine	10.2 ± 1.6
10^8 SRBC + 10^9 pertussis vaccine	8.1 ± 2.0
10^8 SRBC + alum	6.1 ± 1.7
10^8 SRBC + 0.025 γ *E. coli* endotoxin	6.7 ± 1
10^8 SRBC + 15 γ poly A:U	5.3 ± 1
10^9 *Brucella* vaccine	0.3 ± 0.3
0.025 γ *E. coli* endotoxin	0.2 ± 0.2

The ability of each of these materials to substitute for adult macrophages in inducing a response in the neonate could operate by several mechanisms. Endotoxin, in doses considerably higher than those used here, has been shown to bypass the need for T and B cell collaboration in the *in vitro* immune response of nude mouse spleen cells to SRBC (6, 7). Thus, a similar mechanism of direct B cell stimulation could possibly account for these observations in the neonatal rat. However, endotoxin as used *in vitro* to substitute for T cells has been shown to induce polyclonal production of antibody of many specificities (8), and in our experiments no evidence of such polyclonal activation was found.

As pointed out earlier, another potential mechanism in which these substances could substitute for adult macrophages is by activation of the "dormant" macrophages already present within the neonate. Two approaches were used to investigate this possibility. First, *Brucella* organisms were given to adult rats to see if their PE macrophages would then become more efficient in inducing an antibody response in the neonates. Suboptimal numbers of macrophages from these *Brucella*-stimulated adults were transferred along with SRBC to newborn rats. Table 6 shows that 10×10^6 macrophages from unstimulated adults were ineffective in inducing an anti-SRBC response in these neonates, whereas a similar number of macrophages from rats given *Brucella* organisms 1, 4, 7, and 13 days before macrophage harvest did induce neonatal responses. Thus, *Brucella* organisms are effective in increasing the level of activation of adult macrophages.

To determine the effect of these macrophage-activating substances directly in the neonate, another approach was taken. Resistance to infection with *Listeria* monocytogenes has been elegantly demonstrated by Mackaness (9) and his colleagues to be dependent upon the bacteriocidal properties of activated macrophages. Newborn rats were given *Brucella* organisms, endotoxin, or poly A–poly U and 2 days later infected with a lethal dose of *Listeria.* As Table 7 shows, newborns so treated are as effectively protected from the lethal effects of *Listeria* infection as they are by adult macrophages.

TABLE 6. *Effect of Brucella pretreatment on the activity of adult PE macrophages in inducing neonatal antibody responses*

Treatment[a]	Hemolysins (log_2)
SRBC	0
10 X 10^6 adult PE + SRBC	0.2
10 X 10^6 (24 hr BA) adult PE + SRBC	2.9
10 X 10^6 (4 day BA) adult PE + SRBC	3.5 $p < 0.01$
10 X 10^6 (7 day BA) adult PE + SRBC	2.7
10 X 10^6 (13 day BA) adult PE + SRBC	2.1

[a] Adult donors were given an intramuscular injection of 2 X 10^9 killed *Brucella* organisms 1 to 13 days prior to the collection of macrophages from peritoneum.

Thus, these substances are capable of activating macrophage function in both adult and neonatal rats, suggesting that at least part of their effects as immunolog-

TABLE 7. *Effect of various pretreatment on the survival of neonatal rats infected with Listeria monocytogenes*

Treatment	Survival at 10 days[a]
Saline	2/23
15 X 10^6 adult PE	15/21
Brucella vaccine	13/14
endotoxin	14/20
poly A–poly U[b]	8/10

[a] Number of survivors/total number in treatment group, no deaths occurred after 10 days following infection.
[b] 25 γ daily X 3 days.

ical adjuvants may operate by this mechanism. These data also suggest that exposure to the "sea of microorganisms" that constitute our environment may normally serve to induce and maintain activated macrophages within the body. In this regard, it is tempting to speculate that the delayed kinetics of the antibody response observed in germ-free animals by Bauer et al. (10) may reflect a relative lack of such a complement of activated macrophages in the germ-free state.

Activated Macrophages and Tolerance

In our studies of the timing of the onset of immune responses to various antigens it was noted that earlier responses to soluble antigens could be obtained by increasing the dose of antigen administered. Thus, although adult rats respond well to 0.1, 1, or 10 mg of KLH, 10-day-old rats failed to respond to 0.1 mg but did produce antibody when immunized with 1 mg soluble KLH. However, the neonates also failed to respond to 10 mg of KLH, suggesting that they may have become tolerant to the antigen given at that dose. The relative ease of tolerance induction during the neonatal period has been recognized since the pioneering work of Medawar and his colleagues, and it occurred to us that this phenomenon might also be partially attributable to immaturity of the macrophage-afferent limb of immune responsiveness. To test this hypothesis, neonatal rats were given 10 mg of KLH either alone or together with adult macrophages or *Brucella* vaccine. At 14 days of age, the rats were given an optimal immunization of 100 μg KLH emulsified in complete Freund's adjuvant and the subsequent antibody responses observed. Table 8 shows that neonates given 10 mg of soluble KLH alone did

TABLE 8. *Effect of macrophage maturation on the induction of specific immunologic tolerance in the neonate*

Pretreatment (4 days)	Immunization (14 days)	Titer 12[a] days	Titer 21[a] days
—	100 μg KLH–CFA	10.1	12
10 mg KLH	"	1.1	1.6
10 mg KLH + BA vaccine	"	4.3	8.6
10 mg KLH + adult macrophages	"	5.2	8.1

[a] Mean serum antibody titer ($\log_2$) 12 and 21 days after KLH-adjuvant challenge.

become tolerant as judged by failure to respond later to the KLH-adjuvant mixture. Neonates given the high dose of KLH in combination with adult macrophages or *Brucella* vaccine, however, were protected from tolerance induction and did respond to the KLH-adjuvant mixture given at 14 days.

These experiments strongly support the concept that immaturity of the macrophage is the limiting step in the expression of immunocompetence of the neonate to a variety of antigenic stimuli, including failure of antibody production to several antigens, susceptibility to infection with *Listeria* monocytogenes, and ease of tolerance induction. However, these studies on neonatal immune responses have disclosed that certainly other as yet undetermined factors are also involved in the development of immunocompetence. For example, the antibody response to SSS_{III}, which first appears in rats immunized at about 3 weeks of age, is totally uneffected by the addition of adult macrophages or macrophage-activating substances. Even immunization with whole formalinized pneumococcal vaccine rather than purified polysaccharide failed to alter the onset of responsiveness. Treatment of neonatal rats with antithymocyte sera in an attempt to reverse thymic suppressor cell activity results in a several-fold augmentation of the response to S_{III} but does not alter at all the age at which neonates become responsive to this antigen. Therefore, continued study of factors controlling the onset and expression of immunity in the neonatal period may offer new insights into the variety of interacting components which result in immunocompetence.

SUMMARY

Neonatal animals of almost all species are relatively immunodeficient despite wide differences in physiologic maturity and thymic development at birth. Neonatal Lewis rats are unresponsive to most antigens and are particularly susceptible to fatal infections with *Listeria* monocytogenes. Newborn rats given adult splenic lymphocytes or thymocytes remain immunodeficient, although neonates given adult PE macrophages become resistant to *Listeria* infection and produce antibody to several antigens. Neonates irradiated before macrophage transfer fail to produce antibody, indicating that the macrophage inoculum is actively inducing the neonate's lymphoid cells to produce the antibody found. The neonate's own macrophages can be activated by a variety of materials so that adult macrophages need not be given to accelerate the development of immunocompetence. *Brucella* vaccine, pertussis vaccine, endotoxin, BCG, alum, and poly A–U are all capable of promoting antibody synthesis in the neonate through macrophage activation, and these same agents also confer resistance to *Listeria* infection via this mechanism. The relative ease with which neonatal animals develop immunological tolerance is also a function of macrophage immaturity, and tolerance can be prevented by providing the neonates with adult macrophages or macrophage-activating substances. Thus, many aspects of the immunodeficiency of the neonate, including failure of antibody production, susceptibility to infection with facultative intracellular microorganisms, and ease of immunological tolerance induction, can be attributed to immaturity of the macrophage-afferent limb of immunity.

REFERENCES

1. Silverstein, A. M., Uhr, J. W., Kramer, K. L., and Lukes, R. J.: Fetal response to antigenic stimulus II. Antibody production by the fetal lamb. *J. Exp. Med.* 117:799, 1963.
2. Silverstein, A. M., and Prendergast, R. A.: Lymphogenesis immunogenesis, and the generation

of immunologic diversity. In Sterzl, J., and Ricka, D. (eds): *Developmental Aspects of Antibody Formation and Structure.* Academic Press, New York, p. 69, 1970.

3. Arrenbrecht, S.: Normal development of the thymus-dependent limb of humoral immune responses in mice. *Eur. J. Immunol.* 3:506, 1973.
4. Argyris, B. F.: Role of macrophages in immunological maturation. *J. Exp. Med.* 128:459, 1968.
5. Blaese, R. M., Oppenheim, J. J., Seeger, R. C., and Waldmann, T. A.: Lymphocyte-macrophage interaction in antigen induced *in vitro* lymphocyte transformation in patients with the Wiskott-Aldrich syndrome and other diseases with anergy. *Cell. Immunol.* 4:228, 1972.
6. Sjöberg, O., Anderson, J., and Möller, G.: Lypopolysaccharide can substitute for helper cells in the antibody response *in vitro. Eur. J. Immunol.* 2:326, 1972.
7. Watson, J., Trenkner, E., and Cohn, M.: The use of bacterial lipopolysaccharides to show that two signals are required for the induction of antibody synthesis. *J. Exp. Med.* 138:699, 1973.
8. Anderson, J., Sjöberg, O., and Möller, G.: Induction of immunoglobulin and antibody synthesis *in vitro* by lipopolysaccharides. *Eur. J. Immunol.* 2:349, 1972.
9. Mackaness, G. B.: The influence of immunologically committed lymphoid cells on macrophage activity *in vivo. J. Exp. Med.* 129:973, 1969.
10. Bauer, H., Paronetto, F., Burnes, W. A., and Einheber, A.: The enhancing effect of the microbial flora on macrophage function and the immune response. *J. Exp. Med.* 123:1013, 1965.

DISCUSSION

Ward: I would like to know how one can distinguish between macrophage effects and lymphocyte transfer effects in these experiments. How can you rule out that it is not the large lymphocytes conferring immunologic reactivity on the newborn rats?

Blaese: This is obviously a central issue in these experiments and we have tried a number of approaches to establish the responsible cell type. We induced immunologic tolerance to SRBC in the donors. Macrophages from these tolerant donors worked just as well as macrophages from nontolerant donors. We purified the lymphocytes from the peritoneal exudates and found that they were ineffective in inducing a response in the neonates. Culture purified macrophages were just as effective as the whole peritoneal exudate population. And finally, transfer of adult PE cells to previously irradiated neonates does not result in antibody production. Therefore, the cells of the neonates themselves are making the antibody and not the transferred adult cells.

Cohn: Have you given your neonatal animals the same mineral oil you use to stimulate your adults, and what happens to their reactivity?

Blaese: SRBC emulsified in the same oil that was used to induce the peritoneal exudate did not have an effect. Freund's adjuvant also did not have an effect. It turns out the oil itself is apparently an inhibitor. If you take *Brucella* vaccine and mix it with the oil, it abolishes the effect of the *Brucella.*

Cohn: Have you ever transferred neonatal macrophages to neonates?

Blaese: We have done this a little bit, and they don't work as well as adult cells. However, one of the problems in my hands is that everything I use to get hold of neonatal macrophages activates them so that they work better after such procedures. However, it has been published by Argyris that neonatal macrophages are less effective in the transfer system than adult macrophages.

Spitznagel: I notice you had used some pneumococcal polysaccharides. Have you tried these with any of the subsequent experimental designs which you have shown here? In other words, have you any information as to the relationship between the macrophage and B cell antigens?

Blaese: As I mentioned in the last couple of paragraphs of the chapter, we have tried most of these antigens with macrophages, and pneumococcal polysaccharide is a very curious antigen. Nothing we can do to it changes the time of response. Injecting it with *Brucella* vaccine or injecting it with macrophages has no effect. Because T suppressor cells have been shown to be important in modulating the response to SSS III, we thought newborns might have such active T suppressor cells. Therefore we treated the neonates with antilymphocyte serum. When they finally make antibody, they produce several logs higher titer, but they don't make it earlier in life. Obviously there are other factors involved. Even giving the whole pneumococcus instead of the polysaccharide didn't make any difference.

Bellanti: I noticed there was a greater effect on the adoptive transfer of adult macrophages than on the *Brucella* response. There seemed to be a maximum response at 4 days, followed by a gradual falling off. Do you think this represents a state of activation of these cells?

Blaese: Yes. We have done the experiment five times and it seems to work consistently.

Cohn: Have you tried to follow the fate of your adopted transferred macrophages in these neonates?

Blaese: No.

Cohn: I wonder if they are functional in phagocytic activity, or do they have to be viable?

Blaese: They have to be viable. If they have been killed with heat or freezing and thawing, they do not work even if you have incubated them with the antigen before they are killed. They have to be viable at the time of transfer. We haven't traced them as yet, but we are planning such experiments.

Holmes-Gray: When you did the hybridization of the strain that will not transfer, you went F_1 to parent, or parent to F_1?

Blaese: We went both ways. And it doesn't work either way. As shown by Shevack and Rosenthal, in the guinea pig the parent-F_1 combination does allow lymphocyte transformation *in vitro,* but in my system it does not work. Each of the controls will work. F_1's will work with F_1's and parents work with parents, but when you cross them, it doesn't.

Sbarra: I don't remember the data on the guinea pig, but isn't it correct that the magnitude of the response in the F_1 is less?

Blaese: I think it is.

Kirkpatrick: I am curious about breaking tolerance with the macrophages. This indicates the animal's lymphocytes are intact. If you are able to break tolerance with the macrophages from adults. . . .

Blaese: I hesitate to say "break tolerance." I think preventing the induction of tolerance is quite a different matter.

Kirkpatrick: In the experiment you did, were the antigen and the macrophages given at the same time?

Blaese: Yes, they were mixed together.

Kirkpatrick: Have you looked at the chronology of this at all?

Blaese: We haven't done it with macrophages, but we have with *Brucella* vaccine. If you give *Brucella* a couple of days before you give the tolergenic dose, you not only prevent tolerance but you also detect a primary response to the KLH.

Kirkpatrick: Could it be the antigen is sequestered in the cell population in such a way that it doesn't tolerize? I guess that's your point, that it is not available to tolerize the newborn recipient. That's an awful lot of KLH to be taken up by those cells.

Blaese: I don't think it is taken up by the cells in the sense that it's sequestered. I think it is inducing an immune response when macrophages are present.

Johnston: The newborn macrophage would seem to constitute something of an experiment of nature. It says to me, at any rate, that the macrophage really is a necessary cell in "processing" or at least as an intermediate cell. Do you have any idea why? Does the neonatal macrophage eat less well? Does it spit out something less well? Or is it producing something that is not as well formed as the product of a mature macrophage? A corollary of that is: Are neonatal macrophages harder to activate by lymphokines?

Blaese: That is an excellent question. But I really don't have very much data on which to base a comment. I do think that they don't "eat" as well. And I think perhaps how well macrophages "eat" depends on their environment. There have been experiments in germ-free animals showing that the kinetics of antibody response in a germ-free situation is often delayed and suppressed. You can visualize germ-free animals having less endotoxin and therefore having a lower degree of activation of their macrophages and thus producing antibody less well. Clearly, many of the materials, such as *Brucella* and endotoxin, can activate the listeriocidal activity of the neonatal macrophage as well as allow "premature" antibody responses. Since macrophage membrane associated antigen has been shown to be particularly important for the induction of an antibody response, it seems reasonable that these activating materials must somehow affect the neonatal macrophage membrane. But if this does in fact happen and by what mechanism remains to be explored.

Spitznagel: Is there any difference in macrophage turnover or production in neonates compared with more adult animals?

Blaese: I don't know of any information.

Cohn: I don't think anybody has looked at it carefully. In fact, the amount of information on macrophage production rates in bone marrow and in tissues is essentially nonexistent. I think one has to be a little careful in considering whether this necessarily represents processing in a certain sense of the word. Macrophages have an effect here, but exactly what it is is unclear.

Blaese: I agree with that completely. "Processing" is a very vague concept at best. However, the fact that just any old macrophage will not work in this system, but only those matched with the recipient at the major histocompatibility locus, suggests that the macrophage must be able to get to some special place to do its thing. Perhaps it must interact with a specific histocompatibility receptor on the lymphocyte.

Cohn: That presumably relates to the necessity for viable cells in the system. That is one way of looking at it also.

Blaese: The fact that parental strain cells which would not be rejected by the F_1 still don't work suggests that the interaction requires something more than viability.

Bellanti: Doesn't the later onset of stimulability by soluble antigens and the better inducibility by particulate antigens suggest that there might be some role for the macrophage in inducing an immune response?

Blaese: Yes, it is interesting if you look at the requirement for macrophages in inducing immune responses in the intact adult animal, that soluble antigens like guinea pig gammaglobulin are the ones in which you can demonstrate the most pronounced macrophage dependence, whereas more large or more particulate antigens like KLH give equivalent responses whether mixed with macrophages or given alone. It is only when neonates are used as the test animals that the macrophage dependence of these other antigens becomes so readily apparent. This difference can be most easily explained by the presence in the adults of macrophages capable of avidly collecting large and particulate antigens so that, in effect, they are being given essentially macrophage associated antigens.

Park: Have you tried RNA extract on macrophages?

Blaese: Not for several years. When we started some of these experiments in mice, we tried it without much success.

Park: Have you tried the Jerne's plaque technique?

Blaese: Yes, there is one table showing the effect of the technique, and with burro red cells and sheep red cells you get the same sort of sequence. We chose to look at serum antibody responses because we didn't know where the antibody was going to be made in the neonate. We couldn't assume assaying the spleen would tell us what was happening in the intact animal. If you look at plaque formation, it lags behind our ability to detect serum antibody. I think it is about 10 days of age before you can detect plaque-forming cells in the spleens of the sheep red cell immunized rats, whereas we could detect a response earlier in the serum.

Snyderman: Have you ever looked for IgE type antibody in the animals that don't have the circulating hemolysin, or what I presume is IgG or IgM antibody?

Blaese: We are getting set up to do those kinds of experiments, but we haven't had a chance to look at IgE responses yet.

The Phagocytic Cell in Host Resistance, edited
by Joseph A. Bellanti and Delbert H. Dayton.
Raven Press, New York © 1975.

Biochemical Changes in Human Polymorphonuclear Leukocytes during Maturation

Joseph A. Bellanti, Brigette E. Cantz, Mei C. Yang, Horst von Thadden, and Robert J. Schlegel [1]

Departments of Pediatrics and Microbiology, Georgetown University School of Medicine, Washington, D.C. 20007, and the Department of Pediatrics, Charles R. Drew Postgraduate Medical School, Los Angeles, California 90059 [1]

Although it has been known for several years that the young infant is unusually susceptible to a wide variety of bacterial pathogens, the picture up until recently has been unclear with respect to the specific immunologic basis. In recent years major advances have occurred in our understanding of the immunologic responses of the young host, and it has become increasingly clear that at present a number of maturational deficiencies are seen in the young infant which may predispose him to infection (1). Thus, deficiencies in immunoglobulin M, in the complement system, and in specific opsonization have been demonstrated.

During the course of our studies in chronic granulomatous disease (CGD), an X-linked disorder of phagocytic function (2), we were impressed with the numerous parallels between the responses to infection of afflicted patients and those occurring in the neonatal infant. For example, in both there is a predilection to infections caused by *Staphylococcus aureus* and Gram-negative bacilli *(Klebsiella enterobacter, Escherichia coli, Serratia marcescens).* Moreover, infections both in the newborn infant and in patients with CGD are usually severe, are characterized by insidious clinical manifestations and poor responses to antibiotic therapy, and are frequently associated with similar tissue lesions consisting of granulomatous infiltrations of mononuclear cells with few polymorphonuclear leukocytes.

These analogies suggested that CGD might serve as a model (3) to better understand the phagocytic responses of the young infant. Several specific enzyme deficiencies of the hexose monophosphate pathway have been demonstrated in the X-linked form of CGD, including an NADH oxidase deficiency (4), and an unusual lability of leukocyte G-6-PD (2) and a glutathione peroxidase deficiency (5) in the autosomal recessive form. The present studies were performed to extend our observations in CGD to the leukocytes of normal infants and children. It will be shown that an increase in NBT dye reduction and leukocyte G-6-PD occurs in the leukocytes of infants and children during maturation.

MATERIALS AND METHODS

Subjects

The study group consisted of 122 infants and children and 24 adults. At Georgetown University Hospital Medical Center 23 newborn infants were studied immediately following delivery. The infants were all full-term (larger than 2,500 g) and were in apparent good health; neither the infants nor their mothers had received medications at the time of birth other than anesthesia. An additional 99 older infants and children and 24 adults also in good health were included in the study in order to measure changes in leukocyte function at different ages.

Blood Specimens and Preparation of Leukocyte Suspensions

Venous blood suspensions were obtained from the umbilical cord in the newborn infants and from peripheral veins in the older subjects.

Methods used for the preparation of relatively rich suspensions of granulocytes were those described by Baehner and Nathan (6) with minor modification. Leukocytes were harvested from 10 to 30 ml heparinized blood by adding sufficient 10% dextran in 0.15 M NaCl to each specimen in order to obtain a final concentration of 1% dextran. Following sedimentation for 45 min, the leukocyte-rich plasma was removed and two volumes of 0.87% ammonium chloride were added to the plasma to remove any residual erythrocytes. Following centrifugation at 100 × *g* for 5 to 10 min, the supernatant fluids were withdrawn and the cells washed twice with Krebs-Henseleit-bicarbonate buffer, pH 7.4 containing 200 mg/100 ml of glucose. Differential counts of these fluids revealed values consistently in excess of 90% polymorphonuclear leukocytes.

Quantitative Nitroblue Tetrazolium Test

The quantitative nitroblue tetrazolium test (NBT) was performed by the method of Baehner and Nathan (6), results being expressed as the change in optical density (Δ OD) between resting and phagocytosing values for 2.5×10^6 cells for 15 min at 37°C.

Leukocyte Enzyme Determinations

Cell homogenates were prepared from frozen cell suspensions. Homogenization was accomplished by untrasonication (2). Immediately after cell disruption the homogenates were centrifuged at 4°C for 15 min at 20,000 × *g*, the supernatants were analyzed for protein content, and enzymatic assays were performed as described previously (2).

Leukocyte G-6-PD and 6-phosphogluconic dehydrogenase (6-PGD) activities were performed by slight modification of the spectrophotometric method of Richterich (7). Activity was determined by measuring the initial rate of reduction of NADP at 25°C. The increase of absorbance at 340 nm was recorded on a Gilford spectrophotometer at 1-min intervals for 5 to 10 min. The reaction mixture used for assay contained: 0.214 mM NADP, 0.86 mM D-glucose-6-phosphate (or 6-phosphogluconic acid), 10 mM $MgSO_4$ and 50 mM triethanolamine-5 mM EDTA buffer pH 7.5, and 0.1 ml of leukocyte homogenate supernatant in a final volume of 1.3 ml. Since in the crude leukocyte homogenate both G-6-PD and 6-PGD were present, the difference of the reduction rate of NADP between the reaction mixture containing D-G-6-P and 6-PG and the reaction mixture containing only 6-PG was used to calculate G-6-PD activity. The results of enzyme activities were expressed as nanomoles of NADP reduced per minute per milligram of protein at 25°C.

G-6-PD Lability Experiments

Experiments were performed to measure the lability of G-6-PD activity during serial incubation periods at 37°C according to methods described previously (2). Leukocyte homogenates, prepared from leukocytes frozen at −70°C were tested in the presence of 6 μM NADP plus 25 mM 2-mercaptoethanol (2-ME) at 0, 30, 60, and 120 min of incubation at 37°C.

RESULTS

The results of the quantitative NBT dye reduction tests are shown in Table 1 and Fig. 1. The mean Δ OD ± SE values in the newborn period were 0.127 ± 0.011 and then fell during the first 6 months to a value of 0.090 ± 0.008. Following that there was a gradual increase in dye reduction during infancy, reaching adult values of 0.206 ± 0.025. The mean values for infants up to 12 to 18 months of age were significantly lower than adult values. After this age, the results were not significantly different.

The results of changes in leukocyte G-6-PD activity with maturation are shown in Table 1 and Fig. 2. The mean ± SE value activity in the newborn period was found to be 78.2 ± 10.4 μM/mg and then fell in the first year of life followed by a gradual increase, reaching adult values by 4 to 10 years.

The results of changes in leukocyte 6-PGD are shown in Table 1 and Fig. 3. The mean ± SE value in the newborn period was found to be higher than all other age groups with a value of 82.2 ± 7.6. However, no changes in activity in 6-PGD were detected at other ages.

The results of experiments measuring thermal stability of G-6-PD in leukocytes at varying ages are shown in Fig. 4. It can be seen that a lability of leukocyte G-6-PD was detected in the leukocytes of the newborn and the young infant. With maturation, there was a gradual increase in stability of the enzyme.

TABLE 1. *Changes in leukocyte NBT dye reduction G-6-PD and 6-PGD activities with maturation*

Age	Newborn	1–6 months	6–12 months	12–18 months	1.5–4 years	4–10 years	10–14 years	Adults years
	(23)	(13)	(21)	(18)	(20)	(19)	(8)	(18)
NBT (mean Δ OD) ± SE	0.127 ± 0.011	0.090 ± 0.008	0.098 ± 0.008	0.123 ± 0.011	0.148 ± 0.013	0.139 ± 0.007	0.175 ± 0.024	0.206 ± 0.025
	(9)	(8)	(10)	(14)	(17)	(14)	(6)	(24)
G-6-PD (μM/mg Prot.) mean ± SE	78.2 ± 10.4	21.2 ± 5.5	7.8 ± 0.7	44.6 ± 11.2	52.3 ± 10.6	98.1 ± 12.5	147.7 ± 17.3	141 ± 3.6
6-PGD (μM/mg Prot.)	82.2 ± 7.6	~ 39.0 ± 3.0	44.1 ± 3.6	50.6 ± 2.4	44.4 ± 2.9	45.5 ± 2.6	43.7 ± 2.8	34.6 ± 1.5

Numbers in parentheses are number tested in each age category.

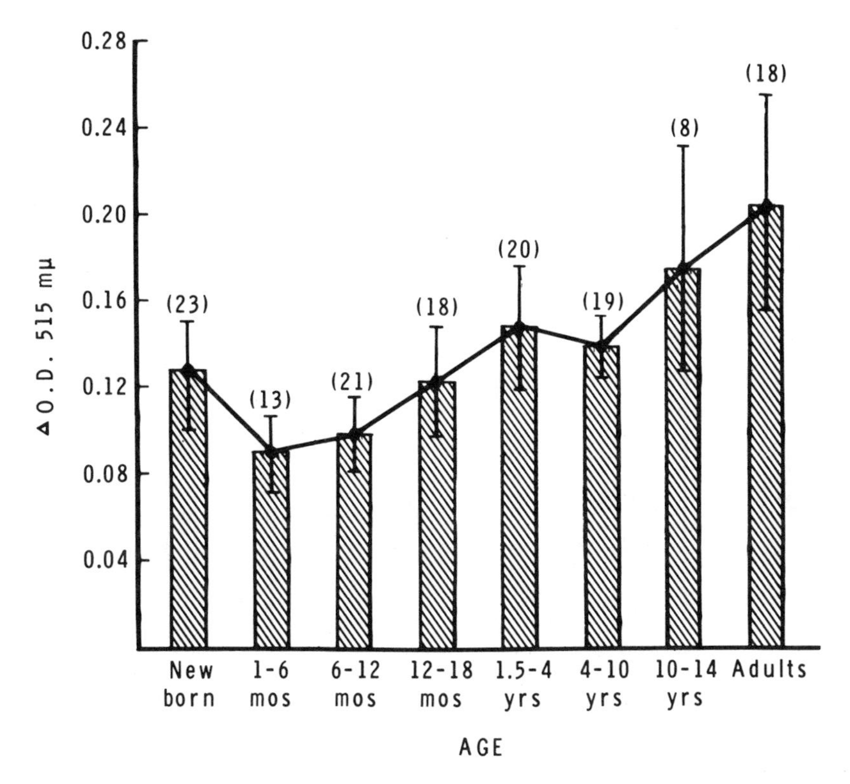

FIG. 1. Results of quantitative NBT dye reduction (mean Δ OD ± SE) by leukocytes at different ages.

DISCUSSION

The metabolic findings in the leukocytes of infants resemble those found in CGD although the molecular basis may, and probably does, differ in the two situations. Nevertheless, it seems likely that these features bear the same functional consequences for the phagocytic act in both circumstances. The points of similarity include a diminished capacity to reduce NBT dye by leukocytes during phagocytosis and evidence of an abnormally labile G-6-PD activity under conditions of storage and heating.

We have previously reported a diminished G-6-PD activity in the red cells and polymorphonuclear leukocytes of patients with CGD (2). In that situation the diminished G-6-PD activity appeared to represent a phenomenon due to an abnormal lability of the enzyme within these cell types. Furthermore, it was found that the lability was more marked in leukocytes than in erythrocytes. It was postulated by us that the findings were consistent with either a variant G-6-PD protein or an enhanced degradative system, with the preponderance of data favoring the latter hypothesis. The diminished G-6-PD found in the present

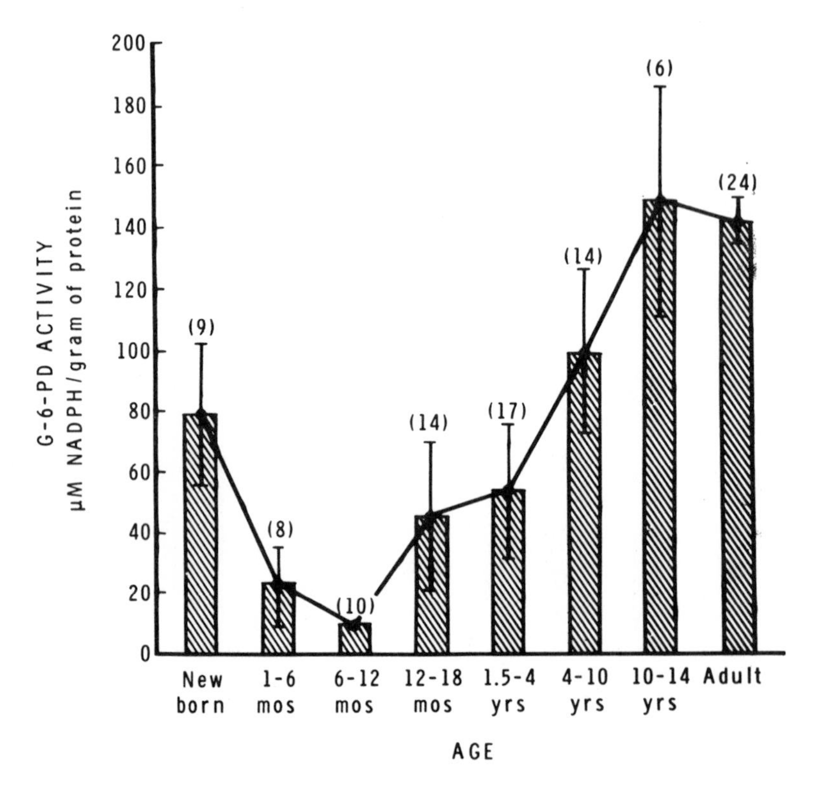

FIG. 2. Leukocyte G-6-PD activity (mean μM/mg ± SE) at different ages.

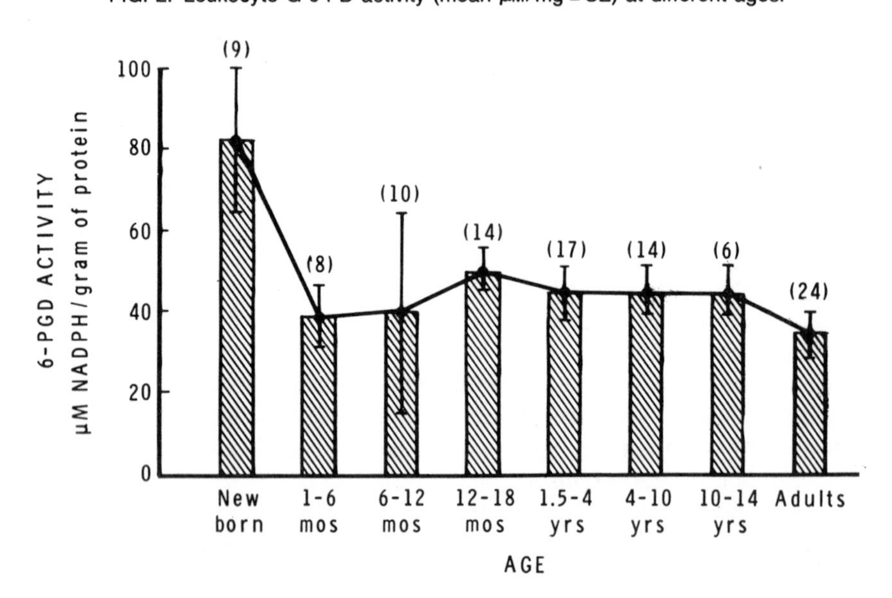

FIG. 3. Leukocyte 6-PGD activity (mean μM/mg ± SE) at different ages.

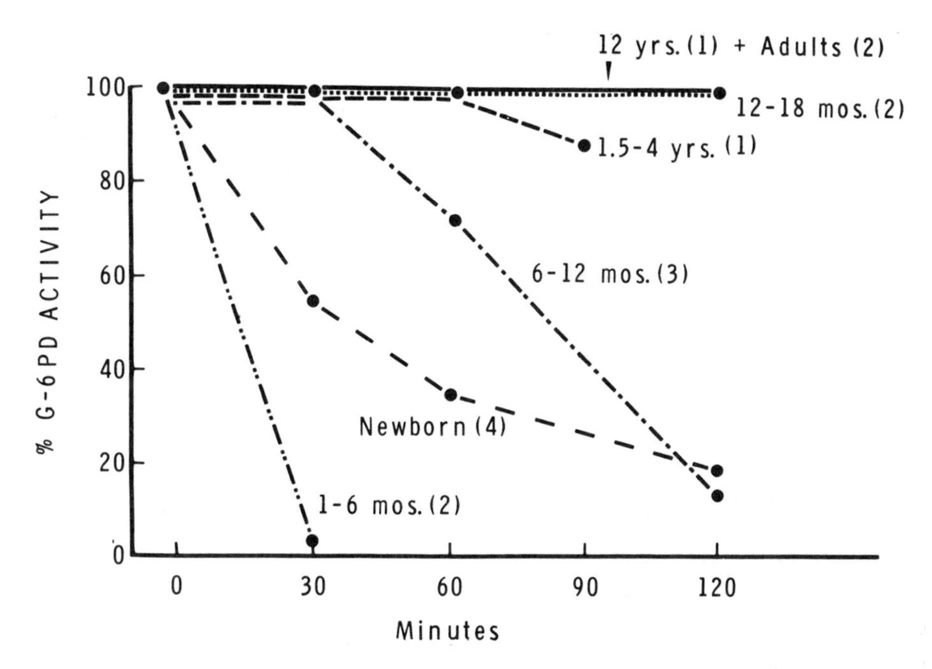

FIG. 4. Thermal stability (37°C) of leukocyte G-6-PD at different ages. Homogenate + mercapto-ethanol + NADP.

experiments in young infants may result from different molecular bases. It may be a consequence of an enhanced rate of degradation by systems extrinsic to the G-6-PD protein itself or may represent a consequence of an immature form of the enzyme. The present data do not allow any definitive conclusions in this regard. However, because 6-PGD activity was found to be normal in the leukocytes of the infants, the diminished activity does not appear to reside in the coenzyme systems governing G-6-PD: both are NADP-dependent systems.

It has been pointed out that the hexose-monophosphate pathway provides a significant proportion of the total energy requirements for phagocytosis, increasing its output from approximately 5% of that involved in total cellular energy supply to approximately 40% during phagocytosis (3). The reduction of NBT dye may constitute an indirect measure of HMP activity during phagocytosis. The present findings demonstrate a relative diminution in NBT dye reduction during phagocytosis in the leukocytes of newborn infants relative to those of the adult, which may have some bearing on the increased susceptibility of young infants to serious infections.

The findings of the present studies are at variance with those of Park et al. (8), who demonstrated increased metabolic activity in the leukocytes of the newborn infant. The conditions under which the experiments were performed may in part explain these differences. The test as originally described by Baehner and Nathan called for reading the NBT test after 15 min of phagocytosis of latex particles in order to take advantage of the linear portion of the reduction curve. The studies of Park et al. (8) were performed after 30 min of incubation.

It has been demonstrated that a correlation exists between NBT dye reduction, HMP activity, and bactericidal activity of polymorphonuclear leukocytes. A diminished capacity to reduce NBT dye has been demonstrated in CGD (6). In the present studies a diminished capacity to reduce NBT dye in the leukocytes of young infants was demonstrated and a maturation of this function occurs with age. These low values of NBT dye reduction point up the need for equating this function with age in using this test for diagnostic purposes, particularly in the small infant.

The present studies also suggest that CGD may serve as a valuable model with which to understand an important aspect of the immature immune responses to infectious disease. The many parallels with regard to the type of organisms, tissue responses, and sites of infection in the two situations are found to reside in a similar functional disturbance of neutrophils of patients with CGD and in the young infant. Although the molecular bases of the two probably differ, it is tempting to speculate that they follow a similar common pathway from the disturbed leukocyte function on the one hand to the immature function of the immune responses in the other.

Finally, it has been repeatedly found in collected studies of serious bacterial infections of infants, such as sepsis, pneumonia, and meningitis, that a preponderance of male infants exists over female. We have suggested elsewhere (9) that this finding is explicable, at least in part, in terms of the altered G-6-PD function of the polymorphonuclear leukocytes. It might be expected that in the female the benefits of heterozygosity as a result of her 2 X chromosomes would result in an increased biologic fitness. Such a mechanism has been proposed in numerous situations of genetico-polymorphism, i.e., the increased resistance to malaria found with sickle cell hemoglobin and also in the case of other G-6-PD variants in which attention has heretofore been focused on functional abnormalities of red cells manifested by hemolysis.

Additional factors contributing to the enhanced susceptibility of the newborn to serious bacterial infection may be elucidated by functional analysis of other facets in the matrix of immunity. Identification of additional defects in phagocytic responses, particularly those concerned with initial recognition and chemotaxis, may be expected to shed further light on the mechanism of the immature responses of the young infant (1).

ACKNOWLEDGMENTS

These studies were supported in part by the U.S. Army Medical Research and Development Command under research contract DA-49-193-MD-2633 and National Institutes of Health Training Grant HD-00261 from the National Institute of Child Health and Human Development.

REFERENCES

1. Miller, M. E., and Stiehm, E. R.: Phagocytic, opsonic and immunoglobulin studies in newborns. *Calif. Med.* 119:43, 1973.
2. Bellanti, J. A., Cantz, B. E., and Schlegel, R. J.: Accelerated decay of glucose-6-phosphate dehydrogenase activity in chronic granulomatous disease. *Pediatr. Res.* 4:405, 1970.
3. Karnovsky, M. L.: Chronic granulomatous disease—Pieces of a cellular and molecular puzzle. *Fed. Proc.* 32:1527, 1973.
4. Baehner, R. L., and Karnovsky, M. L.: Deficiency of reduced nicotinamideadenine dinucleotide oxidase in chronic granulomatous disease. *Science* 162:1277, 1968.
5. Holmes, B., Park, B. H., Malawista, S. E., Quie, P. G., Nelson, D. L., and Good, R. A.: Chronic granulomatous disease in females. A deficiency of leukocyte glutathione peroxidase. *N. Engl. J. Med.* 283:217, 1970.
6. Baehner, R. L., and Nathan, D. G.: Quantitative nitroblue tetrazolium test in chronic granulomatous disease. *N. Engl. J. Med.* 278:971, 1968.
7. Richterich, R.: *Clinical Chemistry, Theory and Practice.* S. Karger, Basel, 1969.

7a. Erickson, R. P., Stites, D. P., Fudenberg, H. H., and Epstein, C. J. Altered levels of glucose-6-phosphate dehydrogenase stabilizing factors in X-linked chronic granulomatous disease. *J. Lab. Clin. Med.* 80:644, 1972.

8. Park, B. H., Holmes, B., and Good, R. A.: Metabolic activities in leukocytes of newborn infants. *J. Pediatr.* 76:237, 1970.
9. Schlegel, R. J., and Bellanti, J. A.: Increased susceptibility of males to infection. *Lancet* 2:826, 1969.

DISCUSSION

Karnovsky: The formazan deposition that you showed looked as if it's all over the cytoplasm; is that right?

Bellanti: Yes.

Karnovsky: So that agrees with your remark toward the end of your talk?

Bellanti: Correct.

Karnovsky: What substrate does one put in? Just glucose? Or are these whole cells incubated in glucose? Or were the cells first lightly fixed and then exposed to G-6-P or something like that?

Bellanti: For the histochemical test, this particular technique is performed with a few drops of blood.

Karnovsky: And then they were stimulated?

Bellanti: One-half were stimulated with endotoxin. The rest were resting cells and were unstimulated.

Karnovsky: Do you think that stimulation causes any artifactual entry of the NBT?

Bellanti: I'm sure it doesn't.

Klebanoff: The test is a modification of the Gifford and Malawista procedure described by Ochs and Igo (*J. Pediatr.* 83:77, 1973) in which a drop of blood is placed on a slide coated with endotoxin and the white cells are allowed to settle and stick to the surface of the slide. The white cells are then incubated with NBT and about 90 to 95 percent become NBT-positive. In the absence of endotoxin, approximately 30 to 40 percent of the cells become positive even in the absence of phagocytosis, due to activation by the spreading procedure.

Karnovsky: That would relate to the endotoxin-induced respiratory stimulation that Cohn and Morse, I think, saw originally, and others have seen with other substances that are surfactants?

Bellanti: Correct.

Karnovsky: This would be really quite different from the picture Dave Nathan saw in phagocytosis where, if I remember correctly, all the reduction of the dye was actually in the phagosome.

Bellanti: This is precisely the point. Some of the discrepant results may reflect a difference in methodology.

Karnovsky: The second point I wanted to make is that I think the analogy you draw between the newborn and young children and the CGD is interesting, but the key piece of information now, I think, could be obtained very readily by Dr. Root's technique. I think he said he needed one million cells to get a good reading by his scopoletin technique. The key thing is that one wants to know whether there is any point to pushing the analogy only in terms of establishing whether or not the cells are deficient in peroxide production. And, I think, agreement has more or less broken out that CGD is, at the molecular level, described simply as a deficiency of peroxide production; we can temporarily ignore what the source of the peroxide might be. If that is the key thing, then I think it would be very important to take a look at these newborn cells and 6-month-old baby cells before one says that the analogy is appropriate to pursue.

Bellanti: Yes. We look on disorders of altered peroxide production as a final common pathway of perhaps a number of deficiencies of any of a number of enzymes in the shunt, in much the same way we see other diseases in pediatrics, such as adrenogenital syndrome with a failure of steroid. There are a number of enzymatic deficiencies in the 17-hydroxylase, the 11-hydroxylase, the 3-beta-hydroxylase, all contributing to the production of a product, e.g., hydrocortisone, but the final common pathway is the same; the end-point is the same. We would suggest that there are a number of deficiencies that could contribute to phagocytic dysfunction, both in CGD as well as in the maturational deficiencies of the young infant.

Karnovsky: Except we don't know whether there is a deficiency in the newborn, and afterward, in production of peroxide. I think that should be the jumping-off ground. I say it apologetically, because it is easy to say it in retrospective terms, but that is the key thing that we should know first.

Baehner: The other point that might be raised is the purity of the preparations used in performing the G-6-PD and 6-PGD assays. Was there an attempt to separate polys away from lymphocytes?

Bellanti: We used essentially your method of dextran sedimentation.

Baehner: So you have a heterogeneous population of cells. As you know, one could draw similar parallel plots for the proportion of polys and lymphocytes in the blood throughout the first 8 to 12 years of life. During the first 24 to 48 hours, the newborn peripheral blood contains a predominance of polymorphs. Thereafter lymphocytes predominate for the next 4 to 8 years. I wonder if the differences in enzyme activity you see with age of the child could be explained by the relative proportion of lymphocytes contaminating your polymorph preparation.

Bellanti: I think that is a good point. I will have to go back to the original data to check it out. We used essentially your method and obtained a purity of approximately 90 to 95 percent polys in all our preparations.

Baehner: I was speaking in particular about the enzyme assay.

Bellanti: The same method of purification was used.

Holmes-Gray: Whatever abnormality you might be looking at which might account for susceptibility to infection, it seems to me that it must be a very profound one. Certainly in the case of G-6-PD, wasn't it 5 percent G-6-PD that is enough to give a normal function?

Baehner: Yes.

Holmes-Gray: Five percent of normal is enough to make a normal, functioning poly in terms of its bactericidal capacity. And you certainly have not reached that level.

Bellanti: We don't know. The confusion is the point we made about lability and the interpretation we were dealing with a variant enzyme. We are in complete agreement that G-6-PD deficiency does not lead to recurrent infections unless the enzyme is practically absent, as in the cases you described. The question of lability is another matter, because the G-6-PD can approach zero activity depending on the stability of that enzyme within the cell. We are not talking about a variant enzyme, but a normal enzyme which has an enhanced rate of degradation.

Klebanoff: You would have to say, then, that in CGD, G-6-PD in every neutrophil is completely nonfunctional.

Bellanti: Not unless there is lyonization. This would be in 50 percent of cells, as Windhorst's calculations have shown.

Klebanoff: Does the lability of G-6-PD in normal newborn cells suggest that G-6-PD is nonfunctional here as well?

Bellanti: I am not sure I understand your question.

Klebanoff: The newborn G-6-PD is labile to heat at 37 degrees.

Bellanti: But not to the same extent. There is an enhanced degradation of the G-6-PD enzyme. And if you compare a normal homogenate and G-6-PD homogenates, it, too, has an enhanced degradation. There is something that is causing an increased degradation.

Sbarra: When you were showing your maturation of the enzyme, your basis was on milligrams of protein.

Bellanti: That is correct.

Sbarra: Do you know what the ratio of protein to cell is as maturation proceeds? It would seem to me that you would have to know this in order to be able to really say that you are getting maturation.

Bellanti: The cell populations were adjusted to concentrations of 2.5×10^6 milliliter, and then also a protein was done on that and the activity expressed as an activity per milligram of protein.

Sbarra: But that is not enough. You have to do it the other way, too. Unless you can show the protein-to-cell ratio is the same throughout. . . .

Bellanti: That is the assumption we made, but I think that is a good point. We haven't made that calculation.

Ward: Is the red cell G-6-PD labile, too?

Bellanti: Yes, in the original cases we described, it was labile.

Holmes: I wonder if we could speak to another issue. Has anyone done skin windows in newborns during the first 24 hours?

Miller: There are conflicting results. There haven't been many studies. The first series suggested there was an eosinophilia which occurred at about 2 hours, much more than one sees in the usual situation. Subsequent studies didn't show the eosinophilia in as many patients, and the explanation was that the patients with eosinophilia were a subgroup that actually would turn out to have allergic disease.

The Phagocytic Cell in Host Resistance, edited
by Joseph A. Bellanti and Delbert H. Dayton.
Raven Press, New York © 1975.

The Phagocytic Cell in Host Resistance: A Perspective Summation

James G. Hirsch

Rockefeller University, New York, New York 10021

The theme for my summary is the title of the volume, namely, the phagocytic cell in host resistance. I will give you my view of the "state of the art" on this topic. I shall not review the individual chapters, and obviously I won't be able to cover the topic in any kind of encyclopedic fashion.

As a guide for my discussion of the subject, I have taken something from Metchnikoff (1), which I have been doing for most of my career. In a book summarizing work he had done on the role of phagocytic cells in host defense, work done in the 1870's and 1880's, he pointed out very clearly that overall host resistance function of the phagocytic defense system was dependent on a number of steps. And the steps that he quoted are almost the same as the following:

1. Production of adequate numbers of phagocytic cells in the bone marrow.
2. Delivery of marrow phagocytes to the blood stream.
3. Margination and emigration of blood phagocytes into the tissues.
4. Mechanisms for establishing contact between phagocytic cells and the invading microbes.
5. Phagocytosis.
6. Morphologic events that follow phagocytosis.
7. Metabolic events that follow phagocytosis.
8. Killing of the engulfed microbes.

Metchnikoff followed Step 5 directly with killing. I have inserted, as a result of more recent work, postphagocytic morphologic and metabolic events, which are both concerned with the killing process. Metchnikoff emphasized the fact that a deficiency anywhere along the line would result in overall suppression of host resistance to infection. That certainly is still the case.

In this volume we have been forced to neglect many of these steps. Consideration, for example, of new information on marrow production and storage would be more than enough for a separate volume. Therefore, I will go through the list of steps and comment briefly on those not covered in this volume, as well as discuss those steps we did consider in detail.

We now have reasonably good information on life histories of the two types of phagocytic cells. They are both produced in the bone marrow. In the case of the polymorph, detailed knowledge is available on production in the bone marrow. There are two phases of the production process in the bone marrow. The first phase is the proliferative phase, which takes about 6 days and involves four or five cell divisions. It involves quite a remarkable change in cell morphology at each of these cell divisions to produce the well-known sequence of blast to progranulocyte to myelocyte to metamyelocyte forms. The second phase of production in the marrow is the maturation phase, which also requires 6 or 7 days during which the cells acquire the morphologic features of the mature cell. And it is also during this maturation phase in the bone marrow that polymorphs acquire their functional capacity. Immature cells are generally nonfunctional. There is a large storage compartment of mature neutrophils in the bone marrow.

In the case of monocytes, we know less detail about the bone marrow production, but it seems clear that these cells are also produced almost entirely in the bone marrow. There does not appear to be a large storage compartment of monocytes in the marrow, but rather they are delivered into the blood stream soon after their maturation.

Both mononuclear and polymorphonuclear leukocytes, when delivered to the blood, spend a relatively short time in the blood stream. The blood serves mainly as a means for transporting them from the site of their production in bone marrow to the site of their action in tissues. In the case of the polymorph, the half-time in the blood is of the order of 6 to 7 hr. The monocyte spends more time in the blood, something like a day.

The mechanisms that allow exit from the blood stream, margination and emigration, have been known for a long time and have been observed repeatedly, but we still don't have any solid information on determinants of these two processes. The cells emigrate in most instances by crawling between capillary endothelial cells. Still unanswered are questions about what causes the cells to stick to the capillary walls, and how they manage to crawl between endothelial cells and through the underlying basement membrane to reach the tissue spaces.

This brings up a topic that was discussed here, the deformability of phagocytic cells in relation to age of the cells. Metchnikoff also pondered this question. One of the characteristics that was noticed early about phagocytic cells was their unusual capacity to crawl through very tiny openings. This characteristic was studied in Metchnikoff's day by slicing ivory tusks very thinly, the equivalent then of Millipore filters, I suppose, and seeing whether the cells would or would not crawl through them. Many of the observations made were similar in many regards to those made in modern days.

Metchnikoff wondered, as have many others, about the reason for the polymorphous nucleus in the neutrophil. Why, in terms of evolution, should a cell develop a crazy nucleus such as that? In the course of his studies on cells crawling through tiny openings, Metchnikoff noted that if they got hung up, they got hung up on the nucleus. The cell cytoplasm, in most instances, could be stretched out into very tiny strands indeed, but the nucleus was much less deformable. Thus he developed the hypothesis that the polymorphous nucleus was simply an adaptation that facilitated crawling through the tiny openings. The studies on deformability that have been done in Rochester and Los Angeles recently measure overall cell deformability due to both nuclear and cytoplasmic factors. It would be nice to have these studies pursued further with a little more precise definition of what is determining their response to the test, sucking of cells into these tiny capillaries.

The next topic is contact between invading microorganisms and phagocytic cells. This is, of course, the first step in the business end of their function. It is well to keep in mind that contact can be established by one of two means. Either Mohammed goes to the mountain, or the mountain comes to Mohammed. If invading microorganisms gain entry into lymphatic or blood circulation, then their removal is very largely a function of the fixed clearance systems in these vascular systems. In that case the bacteria or invading particles move to the phagocytic cells, which are arranged in a baffle system, sometimes called the reticuloendothelial system, primarily in lymph nodes, liver, and spleen. Circulating phagocytic cells are inefficient in terms of clearing organisms in the circulation, because both the microbes and the cells are moving passively in the same stream.

The second mechanism of contact applies primarily to organisms lodged in tissues, and in this instance phagocytic cells from the blood stream or from adjacent tissue move to the site of challenge in order to come into contact with the microorganisms. The physiologic functions of the cell that are very important in this particular aspect of the picture are, of course, locomotion and chemotaxis. There are a large number of very interesting chapters in this volume on cell movement and chemotaxis. I must say, in all candor, that I found several of them somewhat difficult to interpret. Let me make a few suggestions in relation to our thinking about these processes, so we don't muddy the waters further. First of all, we ought to define our terms and use them precisely. There are really three phenomena involved, motility, locomotion, and chemotaxis. Motility or movement means anything that is moving. Locomotion means moving from one place to another. And the two are not synonymous. A macrophage that is sitting tightly on glass and not moving from here to there at all, not locomoting, nevertheless can be a highly motile cell. Chemotaxis in the classical sense—and I think we should preserve the classical sense of the use of the word—means directed locomotion as opposed to random locomotion. Chemotaxis does not mean collection of cells at a site in tissues, on a Millipore, or on a glass slide.

Chemotaxis and locomotion have been studied for more than 100 years. The history of studies on these two processes is replete with difficulties related to techniques used for their study. In fact, this subject, techniques used for chemotaxis and locomotion, was the subject of Henry Harris's thesis when he was a student at Oxford. He published an extensive review in 1954 (2), in which he went into great detail on possible artifacts that influence capillary tube systems or sticking-to-glass systems, or many of the other systems that were used at the time. Anybody who is studying chemotaxis and locomotion should certainly read Harris's review so he will be aware of some of these difficulties. Some of the difficulties are hard or impossible to surmount. Chemotaxis is not easy to study.

The use of the Millipore filter or one of its modifications in the Boyden chamber has certainly been very important in stimulating activity in this area because it makes measurement quite easy. We are all aware of the fact that technical factors such as the nature of the filter or the size of the pores influence behavior of cells in the Boyden chamber. However, there are some features to the Millipore system that I think are not kept in mind as much as they should be. It has been demonstrated that after cells crawl through a Millipore, with time they may fall off the bottom. They don't necessarily adhere to the bottom. So, depending on the particular type of Millipore and the duration of incubation and other factors, it may not be adequate simply to count the number of cells on the bottom of the filter. I would urge you to consider the technique developed by Sally Zigmond (3), in which she looks at the locomotion through a Millipore filter by observing the front of cells moving into the filter. One can measure the distance from the top to the front of cells moving into the filter very readily with the micrometer on the fine focus knob of the microscope. It is a very simple observation to make, much easier in fact than counting cells on the bottom surface. If one does this, one can study the process as a rate process. In a sense, looking at the number of cells on the bottom of the filter is equivalent to measuring an enzymatic reaction by measuring the amount of end product 1 hr after the reaction starts, whereas following the rate at which the cells penetrate, as influenced by varying conditions, is more analogous to a kinetic study of an enzymatic reaction in which rate, especially early in the process, is the parameter used in the study. In addition, the Zigmond technique permits one to examine locomotion in cells such as lymphocytes, which do not adhere well.

The Zigmond adaptation of the Millipore method is an excellent technique for estimating rate of cell locomotion. One should keep in mind that rate of cell locomotion influences directly, in a very impressive way, the number of cells that reach the far side. Here again, one must be wary of concluding that a change in rate or in number of cells in the Millipore system is a chemotactic change. The change in the rate can be a result of stimulated random locomotion as well as of directed locomotion, the true reflection of chemotaxis. It can be exceedingly difficult to distinguish between these two. The standard method that Steven Boyden introduced in his original paper (4) was simply to put the putative chemotactic substance in the top as well as in the bottom and see whether or not the stimulation persisted. Even this is not a sure-fire measure. Many substances in high concentration actually inhibit locomotion, and at lower concentrations stimulate or direct locomotion, so that the effects of a gradient in the filter may be quite different from the effects of an equal amount of a given substance on the top and on the bottom.

The capillary tube method has been used very widely, and probably with good purpose in terms of crawling up the sides. Cells do diffuse in a passive sort of way, the same as molecules or particles or anything else diffuses. If one packs cells into a capillary tube and they are not stuck to each other, they will slowly diffuse and climb up the tube. The capillary tube "migration" is not necessarily a valid measure of locomotion. It can be a passive process. And passive processes of this kind can be influenced by a number of factors—eddies in capillary tubes, whether or not cells are aggregated, influences of added substances on cell stickiness.

In a similar vein substances that affect sticking of cells, whether to one another or to Millipore filters or to glass, may introduce changes that can be misinterpreted as changes in movement. This is particularly so in the case of the so-called skin window. What you see when you examine a skin window is the cells that have stuck to the slide, and these may or may not reflect accurately the cells that have migrated into the tissue or tissue fluid adjacent to the slide. Similarly in biopsies of tissues, an accumulation of cells does not necessarily indicate a chemotactic influence. Such an accumulation may be a reflection of random locomotion and immobilization at the site.

One of the best ways of checking out a result on locomotion or chemotaxis is to look directly at cells under the microscope. It is easy to see locomotion in thin preparations. It is easy to see chemotaxis in thin preparations. I would therefore recommend direct observations of this type for confirmation of the indirect results obtained with capillaries or with filters.

The next step in phagocytic function is phagocytosis, a topic that was barely covered in this volume. There is, again, a lot of new information. Phagocytosis can be divided into two quite distinct steps, the attachment phase and the ingestion phase. The attachment of particles to phagocytic cell surfaces involves receptors, and two of these receptors have been recognized: the receptor for the F_c end of the immunoglobulin molecule, and the C3 receptor. Almost certainly there are other receptors on the phagocyte surface that have not been recognized. For example, there are many instances of attachment and phagocytosis of certain types of particles in the complete absence of serum factors of any kind. This is true of many rough strains of bacteria, certain parasites, and certain inanimate particles.

The ingestion process itself seems fairly straightforward in terms of the overall mechanism, but the real factors that determine the process at the subcellular level are completely unknown.

We did have considerable discussion of complement. The complement sequence has been beautifully worked out, and there seems to be fairly good agreement that $C3_a$ and $C5_a$ play an important role in chemotaxis, and that $C3_b$ plays an important role in opsonization, although some opinion was expressed that the latter was not clearly established.

After phagocytosis, the morphologic and biochemical events that follow are very important ones. The morphologic event of note is degranulation, with delivery of contents to the phagocytic vacuole. The new information available on this topic relates to the fact that with certain microorganisms, such as mycobacteria (5) or toxoplasma (6), the microorganism apparently has the capacity to block or inhibit degranulation. Modern methods enable us to look at host-parasite interactions at the subcellular level. Further studies at this level may well add considerably to our understanding of pathogenesis of infectious diseases, especially in those instances of so-called intracellular parasitism.

The metabolic events that follow phagocytosis have been reviewed by Karnovsky *(This Volume):* increase in glycolysis, a change in oxygen uptake, a marked increase in shunt. Their real importance is in relation to the last step in phagocyte function, the function of the cell to kill invading microorganisms.

My last topic will be the state of knowledge on intraphagocytic killing (Klebanoff, *This Volume*). I will divide the killing systems into two, the Klebanoff system and all others. The numerous studies done on the myeloperoxidase-mediated antibacterial system (the Klebanoff system) in recent years point strongly toward its probably important role in intraphagocytic killing of microbes. The final pathway of this killing, the cellular substance that does the microbes in, has not been definitely established: it may be an "active" peroxide, hypochlorite, or superoxide, or something else.

It has been stated that the peroxidase-mediated system might also, under some circumstances, exhibit toxicity for mammalian cells, and that has now been demonstrated (7). I would remind you that, from the point of view of host defense, specificity of the system for microorganisms is to be desired. Phagocytes are to some extent expendable troops, but we would just as soon not sacrifice our own cells at the time of killing microorganisms, and obviously this does not happen. Macrophages and polymorphs that have killed microorganisms in their cytoplasms do survive, as far as we know, for their ordinary life span. Therefore, in the final killing pathway I would anticipate we will find something highly specific in terms of antibacterial action, something with little or no effect on the host cell. And, if we are thinking of effects on membranes, we should keep this in mind.

Important as the Klebanoff system is, there is good evidence that there are other important systems as well. Dr. Klebanoff has used the terms "back-up systems" and "overkill capacity," and I think those are perfectly good terms. The fact that the other systems may be playing important roles in certain situations is illustrated by three facts. First, it is generally agreed that congenital myeloperoxidase absence has a relatively mild effect in terms of altering host resistance. In this situation the compensatory hypertrophy, if you want to use the term, of some of the other systems apparently takes place. A second instance in which systems unrelated to myeloperoxidase seem to function very effectively is in the case of certain macrophages which clearly kill ingested microorganisms as efficiently as do polymorphs, maybe even more efficiently in some situations, and, as far as we can detect, do not contain myeloperoxidase. And thirdly in this regard, as was pointed out by John Spitznagel and colleagues some time ago, in certain species of animals, chickens, for example, the neutrophils do not contain any demonstrable myeloperoxidase. Maybe there is a different kind of enzyme that is simply not recognized by the test. I don't know if it has been looked for chemically as well as histochemically.

The susceptibility of various species of microorganisms to the various killing systems, I would certainly agree, has not been adequately investigated.

The background of knowledge that has accumulated in the last 15 years on physiology, biochemistry, and morphology of phagocytic cells has led to the subsequent recognition of a number of congenital anomalies in which certain of these functions or activities are abnormal. Chronic granulomatous disease (CGD) of childhood is one example. The CGD story seems to be very well worked out, and there is general agreement that deficient generation of intracellular hydrogen peroxide is the hallmark of the condition. There seems now to be fair agreement between the Minnesota group and the Boston group about levels of NADH oxidase in CGD. I am not sure whether the final level of suppression should be interpreted to be significant or insignificant. It remains to be determined what is the primary genetically determined deficiency in this disease, and, in fact, whether it is the same deficiency in all forms of the disease that are now recognized. Certainly the end product (peroxide) is deficient, but it may not be the same enzyme that is absent if this end product arises in several different ways.

Chediak-Higashi is an abnormality of the morphologic rather than the metabolic type in which the giant azurophil granules result in maldistribution of azurophil constituents to phagocytic vacuoles. In this disorder the polymorph carries all of its eggs in one basket, so to speak. There are associated with the Chediak-Higashi anomaly a number of other impaired functions, such as inadequate mobilization and impaired response to chemotaxis or impaired locomotion. Some of these impaired functions may actually be a secondary consequence of the large granules. It is conceivable that giant granules which are relatively nondeformable may impede movement of the Chediak-Higashi cells through very small openings, interfering with delivery *in vivo* or with migration through Millipores *in vitro.*

There are many other congenital disorders of other parts of the sequence of steps we discussed above: cyclic neutropenia in relation to production of the cells, or some complement deficiencies, for example, deficiency of C3, which has a marked effect on host resistance, apparently acting at multiple sites with impaired opsonization and defective mobilization.

Almost certainly there are many other congenital anomalies to be recognized. Of note is the fact that we have recognized very few anomalies in the mononuclear phagocytic system. As far as I know, the abnormality of mononuclear phagocytes in CGD is the only one that is clearly established in this regard.

It is really amazing to survey the advances in the fields of phagocytic cells and host resistance in the last 15 years. Almost all of the modern information on leukocyte production and kinetics, all of the modern information on metabolism of these cells, the nature of the granules, the degranulation process, macrophage activation, the story of complement sequence, the bypass pathway, the whole lymphokine story, CGD, and other inherited disorders—all of these are new in the last 15 years. The advances have been very rapid and many indeed. Despite the fact that these advances have been so impressive, there remains much that we still really don't understand at all, and I would close by asking you to bear this fact in mind. Let me mention just a few areas where our knowledge is deficient, where we need some elementary work to get on the track.

One of these is in the field of regulation of marrow production and release. This is an extraordinarily precise regulatory mechanism acting on a very complex series of events, and we are only beginning to get adequate information on means of regulation. I would predict that in the next 15 years this would be a beautifully worked out story.

Locomotion has been observed and described, as ameboid locomotion, since the 1850's. It was studied thoroughly back in the good old days in terms of environmental influences on locomotion. But we still have no good concept of how the cell gets from here to there, the mechanism of locomotion. It is a completely virgin field.

Chemotaxis, again, has been observed for well over 100 years. It appears that the cells have a sensory system of some sort by which they detect gradients in their environment and, as a result, change their locomotion from random to directed. There have been many studies, old and recent, on agents that exert chemotactic effects, but no information is available on the mechanism by which the cell detects the chemotactic gradient and responds to it in such an impressive manner.

As mentioned earlier, margination and emigration from the blood stream also have been observed widely, but nobody has a very good idea of why the cells stick when they stick, what the impetus is for crawling between the capillaries, or how the polymorph penetrates not only the interendothelial space but also the basement membrane.

Finally, in many of the most crucial processes in normal phagocytic cell function, the important event is membrane fusion. The final act of the phagocytic process is membrane fusion. The determinant of degranulation is membrane fusion. And in both of these instances it is a type of membrane fusion that does not occur under normal circumstances, that is, without the phagocytic stimulus. Normal cells do not fuse with their own membranes if they come into contact, or with membranes of their brothers. Studies on the determinants of membrane fusion, membrane-to-membrane interaction, is an exciting field for the future.

REFERENCES

1. Metchnikoff, E.: *Lectures on the Comparative Pathology of Inflammation,* Kegan Paul, Trench, Truber and Co., London, 1893.
2. Harris, H.: Role of chemotaxis in inflammation, *Physiol. Rev.* 34:529, 1954.
3. Zigmond, S. H., and Hirsch, J. G.: Leukocyte locomotion and chemotaxis, *J. Exp. Med.* 137:387, 1973.
4. Boyden, S.: Chemotactic effect of mixtures of antibody and antigen on polymorphonuclear leukocytes, *J. Exp. Med.* 115:453, 1962.
5. Armstrong, J. A., and Hart, P. D.: Response of cultured macrophages to mycobacterium tuberculosis, with observations on fusions of liposomes with phagosomes, *J. Exp. Med.* 134:713, 1971.
6. Jones, T. C., and Hirsch, J. G.: The interaction between toxoplasma gondii and mammalian cells, *J. Exp. Med.* 136:1173, 1972.
7. Edelson, P. J., and Cohn, Z. A.: Peroxidase mediated mammalian cell cytotoxicity. *J. Exp. Med.* 138:318, 1973.

INDEX

A

B

C

N

O

T

U

V

W

X–Z